BETTER
ENGLISH
in 30
MINUTES A DAY

BETTER ENGLISH *in* 30 MINUTES A DAY

CONSTANCE IMMEL • FLORENCE SACKS
EDIE SCHWAGER • DIANNA CAMPBELL

BARNES
&NOBLE
BOOKS
NEW YORK

CONTENTS

Better Grammar In 30 Minutes a Day

By
Constance Immel and Florence Sacks

Preface

Better Grammar In 30 Minutes a Day is a workbook for people who have something to say but have difficulty saying it in standard English. We believe that the clearly worded definitions and examples, together with a variety of exercises, can help those in writing courses, in English-as-a-second-language classes, and in writing laboratories and tutor-assisted classes. We also believe that anyone can use this book on their own to brush up on rusty grammar skills.

To help people write clear, error-free sentences, the book features:

• Thorough coverage of key areas of grammar.
• Clear explanations with a minimum of grammatical terms.
• An abundant variety of exercises.
• An answer key at the end of the book to encourage readers to work at their own pace and check their answers as they go.

We think that people learn best when they are actively engaged in the learning process. Therefore, we keep the explanatory material short, but we provide extensive examples and exercises that demonstrate the principle. Thus, readers are never faced with long, complicated explanations that are difficult to understand.

Many of the exercises are in paragraph form or contain sentences all on one topic. The topics are on subjects that should be of interest to anyone.

It is our hope that by using *Better Grammar In 30 Minutes a Day,* people will become competent writers by building their skills and confidence.

Constance Immel
Florence Sacks

Better Grammar

Chapter 9 Punctuation and Capitalization 175

Chapter 10 Usage 191

Better Grammar

Better Grammar

Contents

Chapter 1

Nouns and Pronouns

1.1 Identifying Nouns

If you were asked to give some examples of **nouns,** you probably would respond with words like astronaut, Mars, or spaceship. You would be right, because a noun does name a person, a place, or a thing, but a noun can also refer to an idea such as truth or an activity such as orbiting. A noun, then, names a person, a place, a thing, an idea, or an activity.

If you are not sure whether a word is a noun, put the word the in front of it. If the word is a noun, in most cases, the phrase will make sense. In addition to the, some other common noun markers are a, an, these, those, that, and this. A **noun marker** is an adjective that points to the noun that follows it: a car, the Washington Monument, that routine.

Common and Proper Nouns

All of the examples in the previous paragraph except the Washington Monument are **common nouns**, which refer to people, places, things, ideas, or activities in general terms. Common nouns are usually not capitalized except at the beginning of a sentence.

Better Grammar

However, when we refer to the name of a specific person, place, or thing, we use proper nouns, which always begin with capital letters. In general we do not capitalize the names of ideas or activities. Using "the" as a noun test will not always help you identify proper nouns, but remembering that they are capitalized will help you pick them out.

Common Nouns	Proper Nouns
bridge	Vincent Thomas Bridge
woman	Yvonne Burke
street	Freshman Drive
college	Metropolitan Community College

Exercise 1.1

Using the noun test, identify the underlined words.

A. If the word is a noun, write N above the word.
B. If it is not a noun, write X above the word.

N   X

Example: The <u>clouds</u> gathered <u>before</u> the storm.

1. The traffic <u>on</u> the <u>highway</u> stopped.

2. <u>Rain</u> fell <u>last</u> night.

3. Some <u>drivers</u> were <u>cautious</u>.

4. The <u>surface</u> of the <u>road</u> was slick.

5. John's <u>Buick</u> had good <u>brakes</u>.

Do not be confused by other words in addition to the noun marker that may be in front of the noun. These words that describe or limit the noun are also called **adjectives.** For example:

Noun Marker	Adj.	Noun	Noun Marker	Adj.	Noun
the	car	keys	this	new	typewriter

Adjectives answer questions such as <u>which</u> or <u>how many</u> in reference to a noun.

Adj.   N

Example: let the car keys   Which keys?   The <u>car</u> keys.

Exercise 1.2

Using the noun test, identify all the nouns in these sentences. Write N above each noun.

N   N   N

Example: Angela ate a large apple and a cheese sandwich.

Notice that the word <u>cheese</u> is not a noun in this sentence as it is in the sentence: <u>Joe likes cheese</u>. Angela is not eating plain cheese without any bread; she is eating a sandwich. <u>Cheese</u> tells us what kind of sandwich she is eating.

1. Mr. Cuadros gave us two free tickets to the basketball game.

2. Would you like a bowl of chicken soup and a fresh fruit salad?

3. I bought a digital watch for thirty dollars at Kmart.

4. Lori wore a new green wool dress to her job interview.

5. The young doctor had a pleasant smile and a reassuring manner.

•••

1.2 Singular and Plural Nouns

•••

Use a **singular noun** when you are referring to only one person, place, thing, idea, or activity, and a **plural noun** when you are referring to more than one.

Noun Markers for the Singular

These words indicate that a singular word usually follows:

one	each
a	every
an	a single

Note: The noun marker **a** is followed by a word beginning with a consonant, and the noun marker **an** is followed by a word beginning with a vowel or a silent **h**.

Examples: a shoe   a home   an orange   an honor

Plural nouns present a special problem: Writing the singular form instead of the plural can change the meaning of your sentence. Study these basic rules for spelling the plural forms of nouns.

1. Most nouns form the plural by adding the letter **s**.

bed, beds   pen, pens   pipe, pipes

Exercise 1.3

Write the plural forms of these nouns.

1. dog _____   6. word _____
2. date _____   7. sentence _____
3. trick _____   8. paragraph _____
4. test _____   9. operator _____
5. sale _____   10. student _____

2. Words that end in y, preceded by a vowel (**a, e, i, o, u**) usually add **s** to form the plural. Words that end in **y**, preceded by a consonant, form the plural by changing the **y** to **i** and adding **es.**

city, cities   duty, duties   But note: bay, bays

Exercise 1.4

Write the plural forms of these nouns.

1. sky _____   6. turkey _____
2. day _____   7. county _____
3. lady _____   8. candy _____
4. penalty _____ 9. army _____
5. key _____   10. battery _____

3. Words that end in **sh, s, ch, x,** and **z** form the plural by adding **es.**

wish, wishes   church, churches,   buzz, buzzes

Exercise 1.5

Write the plural forms of these nouns.

1. brush _____   6. glass _____
2. watch _____   7. box _____
3. bus _____   8. mess _____
4. waltz _____   9. rash _____
5. tax _____   10. stitch _____

4. Nouns that end in **f, ff,** or **fe** usually add **s.** Certain nouns change the ending to **ve** and then add **s.** Consult your dictionary to be sure.

knife, knives loaf, loaves calf, calves
thief, thieves roof, roofs belief, beliefs
proof, proofs cliff, cliffs staff, staffs

Exercise 1.6

Write the plural forms of these nouns.

1. self _____   6. life _____
2. half _____   7. thief _____
3. hoof _____   8. wolf _____
4. shelf _____   9. cliff _____
5. proof _____   10. wife _____

5. Most nouns ending in **o** form the plural by adding **s.** Here are six commonly used words, however, that are exceptions: echo, hero, potato, tomato, torpedo, and veto. To these words, add **es**.

echo, echoes   hero, heroes   potato, potatoes

Exercise 1.7

Write the plural forms of these nouns.

1. soprano _____
2. veto _____
3. tomato _____
4. potato _____
5. piano _____

6. radio _____
7. zero _____
8. ratio _____
9. hero _____
10. domino _____

6. Some nouns do not add **s** or **es** to form the plural. These nouns change their spelling.

woman, women   foot, feet   tooth, teeth
goose, geese   child, children   mouse, mice

Exercise 1.8

Fill in each blank with the plural form of the noun in parentheses.

1. The children loved to play with the three white _____ (mouse).

2. We should have our _____ (tooth) examined twice a year.

3. Many _____ (woman) watch Monday-night football on television.

4. All of the _____ (child) in his family have gone to college.

5. There are five _____ (man) on the basketball court.

Noun Markers for the Plural

These words indicate that a plural word usually follows:

all	two (or more)	many	several	one of (the)
a lot of (the)		both	few	some
each of (the)			most	

••

1.3 Possessives
••

Making Nouns Possessive

In addition to nouns changing their forms to indicate the plural, nouns can change their forms to show ownership or a belonging-to relationship. To signal this relationship, we change the form of the noun by adding an apostrophe and the letter **s** or in some cases just the apostrophe.

Rules for Writing Possessive Nouns

1. Add an apostrophe and an **s** to words that do not end in **s**.

the girl	the men	Linda
the girl's scarf	the men's coats	Linda's pen

2. Add *only* an apostrophe to words that end in **s**.

the girls	the monkeys	Mr. Harris
the girls' scarves	the monkeys' tails	Mr. Harris' house

3. Add an apostrophe and an **s** to the final word in a compound noun.

   my father-in-law's business   somebody else's mistake

4. Add an apostrophe and an **s** to the second noun when two nouns are used to show common ownership.

   John and Gina's mother   Smith and Lopez's market

5. Generally the possessive form is not used with nonliving things.

   the table leg   the magazine cover

The following groups of words show a belonging-to relationship.

   the trophy that belongs to the swimming team
   the papers that belong to the students

But if you were writing about the trophy or the papers, you probably would use the possessive form of the noun.

   The swimming *team's* trophy is on display.
   The English teacher returned the *students'* papers.

Exercise 1.9

Rewrite the underlined words in the possessive form.

Example: The <u>claws of the cats</u> are sharp.   the cats' claws

1. The <u>names of the cats</u> are Ginny and Max. _____

2. They listen to the <u>commands of their owners</u>. _____

3. They like to sleep in the <u>crib of the baby</u>. _____

4. The <u>mother of the baby</u> chases them out of the crib. _____

5. Sometimes Max tries to eat the <u>food that belongs to Ginny.</u> _____

Special Forms of the Possessive

Relationships other than possession are also shown by using the apostrophe and the letter **s.** Here are some examples:

time: today's class   yesterday's visit
measure: money's worth   two dollars' worth

Exercise 1.10

Put the apostrophe in each underlined noun to make it a possessive form.

1. Rain caused a cancellation of <u>Saturdays</u> game.

2. Jenny will be paid for two <u>weeks</u> vacation.

3. We will have a party on New <u>Years</u> Eve.

4. The employees have completed a good <u>days</u> work.

5. Where can you buy a <u>pennys</u> worth of candy?

Plurals and Possessives

Not every word ending in **s** requires an apostrophe. Most words ending in **s** are not possessive; many of them are noun plurals. The following exercise will give you practice using the plural and possessive forms of nouns. If necessary, review the rules given in this chapter on forming noun plurals and possessives.

Exercise 1.11

Add apostrophes to the possessive forms of the nouns in the following sentences. Some of the nouns are plural but not possessive and do not require apostrophes.

1. The Larsons visited friends in St. Paul.

2. Their friends house is near a lake.

3. On May 2, the refugees boat landed.

4. The refugees had only a few supplies with them.

5. Those dictionaries belong to the students.

6. I returned the students books to them.

7. Many customers were dissatisfied with the product.

8. Did the company refund the customers money?

9. When my car was being repaired, I used my parents car.

10. Many parents of the athletes attended the banquet.

● ●
1.4 Personal Pronouns
● ●

Pronouns are words that take the place of nouns and noun phrases. **Subject** and **object pronouns** act as the subject or object of a verb just as nouns do. The use of pronouns avoids the unnecessary repetition of nouns. Although pronouns perform the same functions in sentences as nouns do, you do not make the same changes in their forms. Do not add **s** for the plural and do not add an apostrophe in the possessive.

11

Person, Number, Gender

Personal pronouns show person, number, and gender. **Person** indicates the person speaking, the person spoken to, or the person or thing spoken about. See Chapter 3 for more on the use of pronouns.

First person shows the person speaking.

I mailed the letter.
We walked to the store.

Second person shows the person spoken to.

Did you mail the letter?
You are both invited to the party.

Third person shows the person or thing spoken about.

She shopped all day.
He wrapped and mailed the package.
It should arrive soon.
They enjoyed the play.

Avoiding Shifts in Person

Try to avoid unnecessary shifts from one person to another. These can confuse the reader. When writing about a person, choose one pronoun and stay with that pronoun.

The most common shift is to the pronoun you.

Incorrect: Most students can pass the tests my geology teacher gives if you study.

Correct: Most students can pass the tests my geology teacher gives if they study.

The noun <u>students</u> refers to third person; therefore, write <u>they</u> (third person) instead of <u>you</u> (second person). The pronoun should be in the same person as the noun it stands for.

Incorrect: When <u>I</u> shop for food, <u>I</u> check the price of each item that <u>I</u> put in the shopping cart. That way <u>you</u> know how much the bill will be when <u>you</u> get to the cashier.

Correct: The second sentence should read: That way <u>I</u> know how much the bill will be when <u>I</u> get to the cashier.

In the incorrect example, the writer has shifted from <u>I</u> (first person) to <u>you</u> (second person).

Exercise 1.12

Some of the following sentences contain shifts in person. Identify each error by drawing a line under the pronoun; then write the correct form above the word. You may have to change the form of the verb.

he or she

Example: When a person goes for a job interview, <u>you</u> should be well groomed.

1. I enjoy eating out instead of cooking at home. Living in Seattle, you have a choice of many different kinds of restaurants. My favorite restaurant is a Japanese one near my home. It is small and very popular, so you usually have to wait for a table.

13

2. If a person wants to learn to play a musical instrument well, you will have to develop self-discipline. The serious music student, for example, must be willing to give up watching two or three hours of television a day, and, instead, spend your time practicing.

3. During the past year or two, the price of food has risen sharply. Every time I go to the market, you can see increases in several items. Not so long ago, your twenty dollars bought quite a few bags of groceries, but now I can carry twenty dollars' worth of food home in one bag.

4. I received a camera for a graduation present last year. It worked fine at first, but after a few months, you could tell that something was wrong with it. The pictures were so blurry that you couldn't recognize the people in them. The repairperson at the camera shop wanted too much money to repair it, so I stopped using it. You would be wasting your money to buy film for that lemon.

5. My brother likes his job as a lifeguard at the beach. You don't have to wear a coat and tie to work, and you are out in the fresh air all day. A lifeguard has an

important job. You don't just watch pretty girls; you are responsible for the lives of all those people who come to enjoy the ocean.

Number indicates whether pronouns are singular or plural. Singular means one person or thing. Plural means more than one person or thing. Pronouns do not add **s** or **es** to form the plural.

Singular forms are used to refer to *one* person, thing, or idea.

I live in an apartment.
Don, have *you* met Carole?
She sent *it* to *her* mother.

Plural forms are used to refer to *more than one* person, thing, or idea.

Don't lose *them* again.
Three of *you* are tied for first place.
We have never met *their* son.

Third person pronouns have masculine, feminine, and neuter **gender.**

Third Person Pronouns

	MASCULINE		*FEMININE*		*NEUTER*	
	Singular	**Plural**	**Singular**	**Plural**	**Singular**	**Plural**
Subject	he	they	she	they	it	they
Object	him	them	her	them	it	them
Possessive	his	their	her	their	its	their

15

Possessive Pronouns—Short Forms (Use with Nouns)

Possessive pronouns are used to show possession or ownership.

Example: I washed <u>my</u> car.

In this sentence, I own the car; therefore, it is <u>my</u> car.

Person	Singular	Plural
First	my	our
Second	your	your
Third	his, her, its	their

In questions, use the pronoun **whose**.

Never add apostrophes to possessive pronouns.

Possessive Pronouns—Long Forms (Use without Nouns)

Person	Singular	Plural
First	mine	our
Second	yours	yours
Third	his, hers	theirs

The long form of the possessive pronoun replaces the noun. completely. We use the long form when the sentence follows another in which the noun is clearly stated.

Example: I washed my car. You didn't wash <u>yours</u>.

In these sentences, the reader should have no trouble understanding that <u>yours</u> replaces <u>your car</u> since the noun <u>car</u> is stated in the previous sentence.

Exercise 1.13

Rewrite the following pairs of sentences. Repeat the first sentence, but change the second one so that the underlined noun is not repeated. Use the long form of the possessive pronoun in place of the noun.

Example: This my pen. Your <u>pen</u> is in your pocket.

You write: This is my pen. <u>Yours</u> is in your pocket.

1. We like your car. The Palkas like their <u>car</u> too.

   _____

2. Professor Wong teaches his classes in the morning. Professor Levy teaches her <u>classes</u> in the afternoon.

   _____

3. Jerry carries his calculator in his pocket. Anna and Marlon carry their <u>calculators</u> in their briefcases.

   _____

4. Aaron helps Rosa with her problems. No one helps Aaron with his <u>problems</u>.

   _____

5. Your notebook is here on the desk. My <u>notebook</u> is in the car.

   _____

Better Grammar

The Pronoun Who

When used as the object of a verb or a preposition, the pronoun who has a special form—whom.

Examples: Whom do they recommend?
For whom did the city council vote?

Informal English accepts who rather than whom, except after a preposition. In conversation, most people would say, "Who do they recommend?"

Also, remember the possessive form whose is used before a noun. Do not confuse it with the contraction who's, which replaces who is.

Contractions

In conversation and informal writing, the pronoun is often joined together with the verb that follows it. This is called a **contraction.** The two words are joined together with an apostrophe that takes the place of any missing letter.

Example: I am = I'm   you are = you're   it is = it's

Do not confuse the spelling of the possessive pronoun your with the contraction you're, or its with the contraction it's.

Exercise 1.14

Correct the spelling errors in the underlined pronoun forms.

1. Your moving to Oregon in a new van.   _____

2. Their parked in a no-parking zone.   _____

3. Whose going to the restaurant with us?   _____

4. Its too late to register for this class.   _____

5. <u>Their</u> playing my favorite song on the _____
radio.

6. Joanne gave Marsha her house key _____
because Marsha lost <u>her's</u>.

7. The Indians are leading in their division, _____
and the Braves are leading in <u>theirs'</u>.

8. My dog has learned to give me <u>it's</u> paw _____

when I say, "Give me <u>you're</u> paw." _____

9. <u>Who's</u> dictionary may I borrow? _____

10. <u>Your</u> going to pass this test on the first try. _____

1.5 Reflexive Pronouns

Pronouns that end in **-self** and **-selves** are called **reflexive** pronouns.

Reflexive Pronouns

Singular
I ← – myself
you ← – – – – – – – – – – – – – – – – – – yourself
he ← – – – – – – – – – – – – – – – – – – himself
she ← – – – – – – – – – – – – – – – – – herself
it ← – – – – – – – – – – – – – – – – – – itself

Plural
we ← – – – – – – – – – – – – – – – – – ourselves
you ← – – – – – – – – – – – – – – – – – yourselves
they ← – – – – – – – – – – – – – – – – themselves

Do not write <u>hisself</u>, <u>themself</u>, or <u>theirselves</u>. These words are nonstandard English.

Better Grammar

The reflexive pronoun is used in two ways:

a. I cut <u>myself</u>.

In sentence a, <u>myself</u> is used to refer back to <u>I</u>.

b. The president <u>himself</u> shook my father's hand.

In sentence b, <u>himself</u> is used to emphasize the person named, the president.

Do not misuse reflexive pronouns by using them instead of personal pronouns in this way:

c. Gerry and <u>myself</u> went for a walk.

You would not write: <u>Myself</u> went for a walk. Use the subject form of the pronoun, I: Gerry and <u>I</u> went for a walk.

d. The Harts took Stan and <u>myself</u> sailing.

You say: The Harts took <u>me</u> sailing, not <u>myself</u>. Use the object form of the pronoun, <u>me</u>: The Harts took Stan and <u>me</u> sailing. You can avoid making this error by using a reflexive pronoun only when it refers to another word in the sentence. Sentences c and d have no words for <u>myself</u> to refer back to.

Exercise 1.15

If the use of the underlined reflexive pronoun is correct, write C on the line. If the use is not correct, write the correct pronoun.

1. He <u>himself</u> did all the work. _____

2. Laura and <u>myself</u> are science fiction fans. _____

3. We treated <u>ourselves</u> to large banana splits. _____

4. Give the plans to Mr. Zapata and <u>myself</u>. _____

5. They consider <u>themselves</u> experts. _____

Here is a chart of the pronouns you have studied in this chapter. Use it to help you remember the different kinds of pronouns we use in sentences.

Person	Subject Pronouns		Object Pronouns		Possessive Prounouns (With Nouns)		*-s* Form Possessive Pronouns (Without Nouns)	
	Singular	Plural	Singular	Plural	Singular	Plural	Singular	Plural
First	I	we	me	us	my	our	mine	ours
Second	you	you	you	you	your	your	yours	yours
Third	he	they	him	them	his	their	his	theirs
	she	they	her	them	her	their	hers	theirs
	it	they	it	them	its	their		

Chapter 2

Verbs

2.1 Present and Past Tenses: Regular Verbs

Every sentence must have a **verb** to describe the action of the subject. Since the subject and the verb are the two most important parts of a sentence, learning to recognize verbs is essential to your progress in becoming a better writer. Let's review <u>three characteristics of verbs</u> that help to identify them.

1. The verb tells what the subject does, did, or will do (action), is, was, or will be (linking).

Example: Reggie caught the fly ball.
What did Reggie do?
He caught. Therefore, <u>caught</u> is the verb.

2. The verb changes its form to show time (tense).

Example: Reggie catches the fly ball. (The time is the present.)

23

Reggie caught the fly ball. (The time is the past.)
Reggie will catch the fly ball. (The time is the future.)

3. The verb changes its form in the third person singular, present tense to agree with the subject.

Example: I catch the fly ball. (first person)
She/He catch<u>es</u> the fly ball. (third person)

There are two kinds of verbs: **action verbs** and **linking verbs.**

Action Verbs

Most verbs tell what the subject (someone or something) does, did, or will do. These **action verbs** are usually easy to identify, especially when the action is a familiar one, such as *swim, talk, buy, chew, study,* or *explode.*

Linking Verbs

Other verbs show a relationship between the subject and a completer that follows the subject. The completer usually describes or renames the subject, and the **linking verb** links the subject to this completer.

Subject	Linking Verb	Completer
Mr. Lopez	is	my Spanish teacher.
He	seems	tired.
Tacos	taste	good.

The linking verb used most frequently is some form of the verb *be (am, is are, was, were).* Some other linking verbs are *seem, grow, look, sound, taste,* and *appear.*

Exercise 2.1

In the following sentences, underline the verbs and write them on the lines at the right.

1. The train stops for only a few moments   _____
at Oakhurst.

   The train stopped for only a few moments   _____
at Oakhurst.

2. Gene hurries to get on the train already   _____
in motion.

   Gene hurried to get on the train already   _____
in motion.

3. He trips over a woman's suitcase in the   _____
aisle.

   He tripped over a woman's suitcase in the   _____
aisle.

4. Gene and the woman glare at each other.   _____

   Gene and the woman glared at each other.   _____

5. In his seat at last, he watches the dawn   _____
through the smeary windows of the train.

   In his seat at last, he watched the dawn   _____
through the smeary windows of the train.

The verbs in Exercise 2.1 form the past tense by adding **-d** or **-ed** to the base form. Most verbs follow this pattern. These are called **regular verbs.**

Verbs change their forms to indicate the time the action takes place. We call this sign of time **tense.** The **present tense** is used in commands and suggestions and to indicate habitual action or continuing ability.

Better Grammar

Examples: Command: Deliver this message immediately.
Suggestion: Discourage them from coming if
you can.
Habitual action: He paints beautifully.

Present progressive tense indicates that something is taking place right now and may continue to occur for a while. The words now and right now often indicate the use of the present progressive tense.

Examples: I am driving carefully.
He is chopping the onions now.

The **past tense** is used in sentences about action that happened before the present time. Say "Yesterday" at the beginning of the sentence to remind you to use the past tense.

Examples: Yesterday he chopped the onions for tonight's
dinner.

Here is a chart showing the pattern of the regular verbs in the present and the past tenses.

Model Verb—Walk

	Present Tense			Past Tense	
Person	**Singular**	**Plural**	**Person**	**Singular**	**Plural**
1st	I walk	we walk	1st	I walked	we walked
2nd	you walk	you walk	2nd	you walked	you walked
3rd	he walks	they walk	3rd	he walked	they walked
	she walks	they walk		she walked	they walked
	it walks	they walk		it walked	they walked

26

Exercise 2.2

Underline the verb in each of the following sentences. Write the present tense form of each verb on the line at the right.

1. Momoko planned a ski vacation in the mountains. _____

2. She worked extra hours at her job. _____

3. She saved half of her paycheck every week. _____

4. Momoko opened a special bank account. _____

5. She watched her money grow very slowly. _____

6. She waited for the first heavy snowfall. _____

7. She listened to the weather forecast every day. _____

8. Finally, the weather changed. _____

9. It snowed for three days and nights. _____

10. Momoko removed her money from the bank happily. _____

2.2 Present and Past Tenses: Irregular Verbs

Most verbs are regular verbs. We add **-d** or **-ed** to them to form the past tense. Verbs that do not add **-d** or **-ed** to form the past tense are called **irregular verbs.** Use your dictionary to find the past tense of irregular verbs or consult the chart of irregular verbs that follows.

Better Grammar

Here is a chart listing some of the most commonly used irregular verbs.

Present (base form) Use with I, you, we, they, and plural nouns.	Present + -s (-es) Use with he, she, it, and singular nouns.	Past Use with all pronouns and nouns.	Past Participle Use with auxiliary verbs (has, had, have).	Present Participle Use with auxiliary verbs (is, am, are, was, were).
am, are	is	was, were	been	being
beat	beats	beat	beaten	beating
begin	begins	began	begun	beginning
bite	bites	bit	bitten	biting
blow	blows	blew	blown	blowing
break	breaks	broke	broken	breaking
bring	brings	brought	brought	bringing
burst	bursts	burst	burst	bursting
buy	buys	bought	bought	buying
choose	chooses	chose	chosen	choosing
come	comes	came	come	coming
dig	digs	dug	dug	digging
do	does	did	done	doing
draw	draws	drew	drawn	drawing
drink	drinks	drank	drunk	drinking
drive	drives	drove	driven	driving
eat	eats	ate	eaten	eating
fall	falls	fell	fallen	falling
fight	fights	fought	fought	fighting
find	finds	found	found	finding
fly	flies	flew	flown	flying
forget	forgets	forgot	forgotten	forgetting
freeze	freezes	froze	frozen	freezing
give	gives	gave	given	giving
go	goes	went	gone	going
grow	grows	grew	grown	growing
hang	hangs	hung	hung	hanging
have	has	had	had	having
hear	hears	heard	heard	hearing

hide	hides	hid	hidden	hiding
hold	holds	held	held	holding
know	knows	knew	known	knowing
lay	lays	laid	laid	laying
lie	lies	lay	lain	lying
lose	loses	lost	lost	losing
make	makes	made	made	making
ride	rides	rode	ridden	riding
ring	rings	rang	rung	ringing
rise	rises	rose	risen	rising
run	runs	ran	run	running
say	says	said	said	saying
see	sees	saw	seen	seeing
set	sets	set	set	setting
shake	shakes	shook	shaken	shaking
shine	shines	shone	shone	shining
sing	sings	sang	sung	singing
sink	sinks	sank	sunk	sinking
sit	sits	sat	sat	sitting
sleep	sleeps	slept	slept	sleeping
slide	slides	slid	slid	sliding
speak	speaks	spoke	spoken	speaking
spin	spins	spun	spun	spinning
stand	stands	stood	stood	standing
steal	steals	stole	stolen	stealing
stick	sticks	stuck	stuck	sticking
strike	strikes	struck	struck	striking
swear	swears	swore	sworn	swearing
swim	swims	swam	swum	swimming
swing	swings	swung	swung	swinging
take	takes	took	taken	taking
teach	teaches	taught	taught	teaching
tear	tears	tore	torn	tearing
throw	throws	threw	thrown	throwing
wake	wakes	waked	waked	waking
wear	wears	wore	worn	wearing
win	wins	won	won	winning
write	writes	wrote	written	writing

Better Grammar

Exercise 2.3

All of the verbs in the following sentences are present tense forms of irregular verbs. Underline each verb. Then write the past tense form of each verb on the line at the right.

Example: The convention <u>begins</u> on Thursday.   began

1. Jugglers meet once a year at an international convention.   _____

2. They come from all age groups and many occupations.   _____

3. Each one gives a demonstration of his or her specialty.   _____

4. Everyone makes his or her presentation unique.   _____

5. These artists throw just about everything from cigar boxes to gold lamb beanbags up in the air.   _____

6. Some ride unicycles during their performances.   _____

7. One man even eats parts of an apple and a cucumber in his act.   _____

8. Jugglers have their names in the *Guinness Book of World Records.*   _____

9. Rastelli, an Italian juggler, still holds the record: ten balls or eight plates in motion at once.   _____

10. Amateur or professional, jugglers keep things on the move.   _____

2.3 Principal Forms of Verbs

When you change the spelling of a verb, you are changing the form of the verb. All verbs have five principal forms.

1. The **present or base form** is the verb without any changes in spelling. It is used with the pronouns I, you, we, and they and with plural nouns.

Examples: walk   see

2. The **present +s form** is spelled by adding an **-s** or **-es** to the base form. It is used with singular nouns and with the pronouns he, she, and it.

Examples: walks   sees

3. The **past form** is spelled by adding **-d** or **-ed** to a regular verb. Irregular verbs change the base form spelling in different ways. They should be memorized. The past form is used with all pronouns and nouns.

Examples: walked   saw

4. The **past participle** is spelled the same as the past form in regular verbs. Irregular verbs that change the spelling should be memorized. The past participle is used with a form of the auxiliary verb *have.*

Examples: has walked   has seen

31

Better Grammar

5. The **present participle** is spelled by adding **-ing** to the base form of the verb. It is used with a form of the auxiliary verb *be*.

   Examples: am walking   am seeing

All VERBS form the PRESENT PARTICIPLE by adding **-ing** to the PRESENT form:

Present	*Present Participle*	*Present*	*Present Participle*
walk	walking	try	trying

Some verbs, however, require a spelling change:

A. Drop a final, unpronounced **e** before adding a suffix beginning with a vowel.

   Examples: like, liking   use, using   come, coming
   dine, dining

B. Double a final single consonant before a suffix beginning with a vowel: (1) if the consonant ends a stressed syllable or a word of one syllable, and (2) if the consonant is preceded by a single vowel.

   Examples: run, running   hop, hopping
   begin, beginning   drag, dragging

Exercise 2.4

Add **-ing** to these words.

1. let_____   4. occur _____

2. jump _____   5. drip _____

3. hit_____   6. wrap _____

7. return _____   9. scream _____

8. swim _____   10. get _____

Exercise 2.5

Write the principal forms of the following regular verbs. Use your dictionary.

Present (base form) Use with I, you, we, they, and plural nouns.	Present + -s Use with he, she, it, and singular nouns.	Past Use with all pronouns and nouns.	Past Participle Use with auxiliary verbs (has, had, have).	Present Participle Use with auxiliary verbs (is, am, are, was, were).

Example:

walk	walks	walked	walked	walking
1. stop				
2. carry				
3. watch				
4. try				
5. hope				

Better Grammar

Principle Forms of Irregular Verbs

Unlike regular verbs, irregular verbs do not form their past and past participles by adding **-d** or **-ed** to the present form. Instead, they use some other change in form or they don't change at all:

begin-began-begun   go-went-gone   set-set-set

Exercise 2.6

Write the principal forms of the following irregular verbs.

Present (base form) Use with I, you, we, they, and plural nouns.	Present + -s Use with he, she, it, and singular nouns.	Past Use with all pronouns and nouns.	Past Participle Use with auxiliary verbs (has, had, have).	Present Participle Use with auxiliary verbs (is, am, are, was, were).

Example:

see _____ sees _____ saw _____ seen _____ seeing

1. am, are _____ _____ _____ _____
2. freeze _____ _____ _____ _____
3. run _____ _____ _____ _____
4. choose _____ _____ _____ _____
5. shake _____ _____ _____ _____

2.4 Auxiliary Verbs

An **auxiliary verb** is often added to the main verb to form the verb in a sentence. The present participle and the past participle forms are *not* used alone as the verb in a sentence. They are preceded by an auxiliary verb.

> **Example:** Do not write: Thomas <u>taking</u> his brother to the park.
>
> Do write: Thomas <u>is</u> <u>taking</u> his brother to the park.

Note: When the verb phrase is underlined in this book, one line will indicate the auxiliary verb and two lines, the main verb. Example: <u>will</u> <u>be</u> <u>speaking</u>

The auxiliary verb has two main uses. First, the auxiliary verb indicates shades of meaning that cannot be expressed by a main verb alone.

> He <u>might</u> <u>go</u> to college.   He <u>can</u> <u>go</u> to college.
>
> He <u>should</u> <u>go</u> to college.   <u>Would</u> he <u>go</u> to college?

Second, the auxiliary verb indicates tense—the time the action of the verb takes place.

> He <u>is</u> <u>going</u> to college.   He <u>will</u> <u>go</u> to college.
>
> He <u>has</u> <u>gone</u> to college.   He <u>does</u> <u>go</u> to college.

Note that in a question, the subject separates the auxiliary verb and the main verb.

> <u>Will</u> he <u>go</u> to college?

Auxiliary verbs are commonly divided into two groups.

Better Grammar

Group 1: The following words are used with main verbs, but they are *not* used as verbs alone except in answer to a question. They *signal* the approach of a main verb.

can	may	shall	will	must
could	might	should	would	ought (to)

Exercise 2.7

Underline the auxiliary verb once and the main verb twice. There may be more than one auxiliary verb.

Example: I would like to place an order.

1. Do you shop at home?
2. You might have received a mail-order catalog from time to time.
3. Many people have found these catalogs convenient.
4. Years ago, farm families could send for clothes and household needs.
5. Today, urban shoppers can order a variety of goods from specialty stores.

Group 2: The following verbs may be used as auxiliary verbs or as main verbs. When they serve as auxiliaries, another form of a verb is used as the main verb of the verb phrase.

be	am	have	do
being	is, are	has	does
been	was, were	had	did

36

Remember

1. A sentence must always have a main verb, but it may or may not have an auxiliary verb.

2. If the sentence has an auxiliary verb, it is always placed in front of the main verb.

3. In a question, the subject separates the auxiliary verb and the main verb.

Exercise 2.8

In the following sentences, underline the auxiliary verb or verbs once and the main verb twice. Do not underline the contraction for *not (n't)*.

Example: I <u>did</u>n't <u>understand</u> the question.

1. Many injured athletes have been helped by a new instrument called an arthroscope.

2. With the arthroscope, doctors can see inside the knee.

3. The doctor can examine bones and tissues.

4. The surgery may be done within an hour.

5. Without the arthroscope, a doctor must cut open the knee.

Summary

1. Present and past participles must be accompanied by an auxiliary verb.

2. Present and past participles cannot function alone as the verbs of a sentence.

Better Grammar

3. *Be, have,* and *do* sometimes function as auxiliary verbs.

I <u>have</u> <u>finished</u> my homework. I <u>didn't</u> <u>speak</u> to him.

I <u>was</u> <u>eating</u>.

4. *Be, have,* and *do* often function alone in a sentence as main verbs.

I <u>have</u> a penny. I <u>do</u> my homework. I <u>was</u> an only child.

Exercise 2.9

Fill in the correct form of the main verb in parentheses to complete the sentence. Consult the chart of irregular verbs or your dictionary.

1. (run) Since his father's death, Nick <u>has</u> _____ the family business.

2. (sing) Our college chorus <u>has</u> _____ at the Music Center before.

3. (see) We <u>have</u> _____ that movie twice.

4. (hear) <u>Have</u> you _____ the results of the election yet?

5. (break) Lee <u>has</u> _____ his promise again.

6. (know) How long <u>have</u> you _____ Liang Wong?

7. (fly) The pilot <u>had</u> _____ helicopters over Vietnam before he came to the United States.

8. (bring) The letter carrier <u>has</u> _____ the mail early today.

9. (eat) We <u>had</u> never _____ at that restaurant before we tried it last week.

10. (say) What <u>has</u> Vince _____ about his trip to Japan?

Adverbs

An **adverb** is a modifier that adds further information about verbs, adjectives, and other adverbs. The following adverbs, in addition to others, frequently appear between auxiliary verbs and main verbs. These words are not auxiliary verbs. Do not underline them as verbs.

never	always	often	sometimes
not	still	seldom	completely
just	ever	frequently	

Examples: Television <u>will</u> **never completely** <u>replace</u> the radio.

The football game <u>has</u> **just** <u>ended</u>.

Contractions

In conversation and informal writing, two words are often joined together with an apostrophe that takes the place of any missing letters. The contraction for *not (n't)* may be added to many auxiliaries, for example:

haven't   doesn't   aren't   can't   isn't   won't

Note: *n't* is not an auxiliary verb; do not underline it as one.

Examples: We <u>had</u>n't <u>seen</u> them for years.

The mechanic <u>could</u>n't <u>repair</u> the car in one day.

Exercise 2.10

In the following sentences, underline the auxiliary verb or verbs once and the main verb twice. Put parentheses around any adverbs or contractions.

Example: Cassandra <u>does</u>(n't) <u>smoke</u> cigarettes any
longer.

1. Dr. Dimaio isn't in her office today.

2. You should always practice your scales.

3. My boss must certainly give me a raise.

4. Tim may travel to New Orleans next month.

5. Could you close the window for me?

• •
2.5 Future Tense
• •

The **future tense** is used for sentences about something that will happen in the future. The future tense is formed by using the auxiliary verbs <u>will</u> or <u>would</u> and the base form of the main verb. Here is a chart showing the pattern of all verbs in the future tense.

Model Verb—Walk

Person	Singular	Person	Plural
1st	I will walk	1st	we will walk
2nd	you will walk	2nd	you will walk
3rd	he will walk	3rd	they will walk
	she will walk		they will walk
	it will walk		they will walk

Although it is correct to express future action by using the present progressive tense (**I am going** to graduate in June.), use only the future tense (**I will graduate** in June.) when you are writing the exercises in this lesson.

Exercise 2.11

Complete the following sentences by using the future tense of the verb in the parentheses.

1. (want) Tomorrow Tom _____ your car.

2. (earn) Tomorrow I _____ my first paycheck.

3. (begin) Next week Linda _____ her new ,job.

4. (stay) From now on Jan _____ home in the evenings.

5. (ask) I hope he _____ me for a date this afternoon.

Will and Would

Will points to the future from the present. **know/will**
Would points to the future from the past. **knew/would**

a. You <u>know</u> that you <u>will</u> do well in this class.

In sentence a, "you know" <u>now</u> (in the present) that "you will do well" in the <u>future</u>.

b. You <u>knew</u> that you <u>would</u> do well in this class.

In sentence b, "you knew" <u>then</u> (in the past) that "you would do well" in the <u>future</u>.

Exercise 2.12

In the following sentences, fill in <u>will</u> or <u>would</u> to indicate the future.

1. Herb knows that he _____ win someday.

2. Herb knew that he _____ win someday.

3. Wu arrives early so he _____ get the best seats.

4. Wu arrived early so he _____ get the best seats.

5. He says that he _____ hire a band.

6. He said that he _____ hire a band.

2.6 Perfect Tenses

In the lesson on auxiliary verbs, you used the perfect tenses in some of the verbs that you identified or wrote. The name **perfect tenses** gives no clue to the uses of these tenses. Study the following examples to learn how to use the perfect tenses.

A. The present perfect tense is formed by using the auxiliary verb **have** in the present tense plus the past participle of the main verb.

Model Verb—Run

Person	Singular	Person	Plural
1st	I have run	1st	we have run
2nd	you have run	2nd	you have run
3rd	he has run	3rd	they have run
	she has run		they have run
	it has run		they have run

Use the present perfect tense to show that an action began in the past and has continued until now, or that an action has just happened. It is often used to show that an action occurred at an indefinite time in the past. Adverbs such as *just* and *already* are commonly included.

Exercise 2.13

Fill in the present perfect tense of the verb given in the parentheses. Use the chart of irregular verbs or your dictionary.

Example: Mike <u>has</u> <u>seen</u> all the home games of the Dallas Cowboys this season.

1. (predict)   The weatherman _____ just _____ snow for the weekend.

---

2. (keep) We _____ _____ the puppies in our backyard for two months.

3. (plan) What kind of food _____ you _____ to serve this evening?

4. (bring) The students _____ _____ their dictionaries to class for the past two sessions.

5. (buy) They _____ _____ their groceries at the same store for many years.

B. The **past perfect tense** is formed by using the auxiliary verb **had** plus the past participle of the main verb.

Model Verb—Run

Person	Singular	Person	Plural
1st	I had run	1st	we had run
2nd	you had run	2nd	you had run
3rd	he had run	3rd	they had run
	she had run		they had run
	it had run		they had run

Use the past perfect tense to show that one action happened before another action in the past. Use it only when you are writing in the past tense.

Exercise 2.14

Fill in the past perfect tense of the verb given in parentheses. Use the chart of irregular verbs or your dictionary.

Example: After we <u>had</u> <u>seen</u> the play, we went to a restaurant for dessert.

1. (show) The nurse _____ _____ me how to diaper the baby before she left.

2. (promise) Darrell _____ _____ to love her when they got married.

3. (have) Antonio _____ _____ an excellent job in New Orleans before he moved to Houston.

4. (run) The dog _____ _____ after the cat until the cat climbed a tree.

5. (choose) We _____ _____ this book before we looked at the others.

C. The **future perfect tense** is formed by using the auxiliary verbs **will have** plus the past participle of the main verb.

Model Verb—Run

Person	Singular	Person	Plural
1st	I will have run	1st	we will have run
2nd	you will have run	2nd	you will have run
3rd	he will have run	3rd	they will have run
	she will have run		they will have run
	it will have run		they will have run

Use the future perfect tense to show that something will happen in the future by a specific time.

Exercise 2.15

Fill in the future perfect tense of the verb given in parentheses. Use the chart of irregular verbs or your dictionary.

Example: By the time her trip is over, Anita <u>will</u> <u>have</u> <u>seen</u> every state in the United States.

1. (learn) By this time next week, you _____ _____ _____ how to drive a car.

2. (pay) By this time next year, Paul _____ _____ _____ for the car.

3. (live) By next June they _____ _____ _____ in that house for twenty years.

4. (go) By September I _____ _____ _____ to college for two years.

5. (speak) By election day the candidate _____ _____ _____ at ninety meetings.

• •
2.7 Tense Shift Problems
• •

Do *not* shift tenses in the middle of a sentence, a paragraph, or an essay unless you have a reason to do so. If you begin writing in the present tense, don't shift to the past. If you begin in the past, don't shift to the present.

Incorrect:	Kite flying *is* a good way to meet people. They *were* curious when they *saw* my kite up there. They *wonder* why I *waste* my time with a kite.	Shifts from present to past tense and back to present tense.
Correct:	Kite flying *is* a good way to meet people. They *are* curious when they *see* my kite up there. They *wonder* why I *waste* my time with a kite.	All the verbs are in the present tense.
Correct:	Kite flying *was* a good way to meet people. They *were* curious when they *saw* my kite up there. They *wondered* why I *wasted* my time with a kite.	All the verbs are in the past tense.

Exercise 2.16

Some of the following sentences contain shifts in tense. Identify each error by drawing a line under the incorrect verb. Write the correct form above the word.

stepped
Example: The rain began when we <u>step</u> off the bus.

1. Last Tuesday night I went to the library because I had a

test in history on Wednesday morning. It is too noisy at

home to study. My brother is playing the stereo, my mother

was vacuuming, and my little sister and her friend are

chasing each other around the house. How am I supposed to concentrate with all that commotion?

2. My friend Greg loves peanut butter. Every morning he spread peanut butter on his toast or waffles. He snacked on peanut butter cups at school, and, of course, he ate peanut butter sandwiches for lunch every day. Nowadays he bakes his own peanut butter cookies because his mother had refused to make them anymore. Greg was a hopeless case; he even covers a slice of chocolate cake with peanut butter.

3. My wife and I bought a golden retriever puppy last year. We made the mistake on the first few nights of allowing the puppy to sleep on a rug by our bed because he misses his brothers and sisters. Later when we made a bed for him in the laundry room, he howls and scratches on the door for several hours every night. After a while the neighbors call on the telephone to complain about the noise. We thought that he will never give up. The puppy finally learned to sleep by himself, and the neighbors start speaking to us again.

Chapter 3
The Sentence

3.1 Subjects and Verbs

The **subject** of a sentence is the person or the thing the **verb** is asking or telling about. The subject may be a **noun** or a **pronoun.** Every sentence must have at least one subject and one verb and express a complete thought.

> **Example:** The tourists <u>have</u> <u>returned</u> home. Subject = tourists.

To find the subject ask, "Who <u>have</u> <u>returned</u> home?" The answer, "The tourists," is the subject.

Finding Subjects and Verbs

1. First, find the verb. Underline the auxiliary verb once and the main verb twice.

   Fish <u>swim</u>.   They <u>can</u> <u>play</u>.

---

2. Then, find the noun or pronoun subject by asking <u>who</u> or <u>what</u> with the verb, Circle the subject.

What <u>swim</u>? (Fish) <u>swim</u>.   Who <u>can</u> <u>play</u>? (They) <u>can</u> <u>play</u>.

The answer gives you the noun or pronoun subject circled previously.

3. If the sentence asks a question, put the sentence in the form of a statement to help you find the subject and the verb.

<u>Are</u> the children <u>playing</u>? Change to: The children <u>are</u>

<u>playing</u>.

Then ask: Who are playing? The answer gives you the subject. The (children) <u>are</u> <u>playing</u>.

4. Remember that every sentence must have at least <u>one</u> subject and <u>one</u> verb.

Exercise 3.1

Underline the auxiliary verb once and the main verb twice. Circle the subject. The last sentence has more than one subject and verb.

Example: <u>Has</u> the (letter) <u>arrived</u> yet?

1. Does a Scotsman wear anything under his kilt?

2. Americans can satisfy their curiosity without a trip to the Highland Games in Scotland.

3. Similar festivals are held in the United States each year.

4. The numerous events include many tests of strength, such as contests for shot putters, hammer throwers, and caber (pole) tossers.

50

5. During the caber toss, the contestants are throwing 100-pound, eighteen-foot poles with remarkable balance and accuracy.

Commands and Requests

Each sentence must have at least one subject and one verb, but the verb can stand alone in a sentence without a stated subject in a **command** or **request.**

The subject in such a sentence is **"you, understood."** In other words, it is understood that the subject is "you."

Example:
V   S   V
Look! = (You) look!

V   S   V
Hurry! = (You) hurry!

Exercise 3.2

Fill in the blanks with verbs that command or request.

1. _____ to the party tomorrow.

2. _____ your name here.

3. _____ the door.

4. _____ me here after class.

5. _____ a glass of punch.

3.2 Prepositional Phrases

Not many sentences have subjects and verbs as easy to recognize as those in the sentences you have been working with.

Better Grammar

We usually add words to the subject and the verb to give more information about them. Sometimes we use one word, sometimes a group of words. A group of words introduced by a preposition and known as a **prepositional phrase** is often used to expand the subject and the verb.

Prepositions are the short words that show position, relationship, or direction. For example, if you were trying to give the location of your pencil, you might say: The pencil is on the desk. Or, the pencil is under the desk. The prepositions are <u>on</u> and <u>under</u>. The prepositional phrases are <u>on the desk</u> and <u>under the desk</u>.

Each prepositional phrase contains at least two words: a **preposition** (P) and an object (O). The **object** (O) is always a noun or a pronoun.

S   P   O

Example: Lloyd <u>enjoys</u> a glass of root beer.

Some prepositional phrases contain adjectives that come between the preposition and the object. These words describe the object.

S   P   Adj   Adj   O

Example: Lloyd <u>enjoys</u> a glass of cool, foamy beer.

Commonly Used Prepositions

Position	Direction	Relationship
about	at	as
above	beyond	because of
across	down	but
after	from	by
against	in	except
along	into	for
before	on	like
during	to	of
near	toward	since
until	up	with

In this chapter bracket ([]) all prepositional phrases in sentences to help locate the subjects and verbs of the sentences. The main reason for learning to recognize prepositional phrases is to help find the subject and the verb of a sentence. One common mistake in identifying the subject of a sentence is confusing it with a noun used as the object of the preposition. Any word that is part of the prepositional phrase *cannot* be the subject of the sentence.

Exercise 3.3

Bracket all the prepositional phrases in the following sentences. Use the chart to help you identify the prepositions.

Example: Many young Americans work [in Washington, D.C.]

53

1. Since 1789 young Americans between the ages of fourteen and eighteen have served as congressional pages in our nation's capital.

2. Some work during vacation while others leave their families and friends to live in Washington, D.C., for a year, continuing high school classes at Page School in the Library of Congress.

3. A page delivers mail, answers telephone calls, and runs errands for members of Congress from 9 a.m. to 5 p.m.

4. Not all legislators approve of the present system. One senator believes that the pages' work is demeaning and that they should be at home with their parents.

5. Most pages would not agree, for despite the pressures of a busy schedule, they enjoy their work and the excitement of national political life.

Prepositions of Two or More Words

These prepositions are made up of two or more words as in the sentence: I made the cake according to those directions.

according to	in addition to	in spite of
along with	in case of	on account of
because of	in front of	on top of
by means of	in the middle of	out of
contrary to	in place of	together with
for the sake of	instead of	with reference to

Exercise 3.4

Bracket all the prepositional phrases in the following sentences. Use the lists given earlier to help you identify the prepositions.

Example: [In the middle of the night,] the telephone rang.

1. The rack on top of the car will hold our skis and several pieces of luggage.
2. Instead of a salad, Kevin prefers soup with his dinner.
3. The man in front of me complained about the long wait in line.
4. After two innings, the baseball game at Yankee Stadium was called because of rain.
5. The mayor, together with several council members, participated in a panel discussion on the city's transit problems.

3.3 Direct Objects of Action Verbs

Some action verbs may be followed by a **direct object** to complete the meaning of the sentence. To find the direct object of the verb, place <u>what</u> or <u>whom</u> after the subject and the verb.

Finding the Direct Object of the Verb

1. Gail's bicycle needs a new tire.

         S   V

2. Ask: "Gail's bicycle needs what?"

            S   V   O

3. The answer is: "Gail's bicycle needs a new tire."

4. Therefore, the noun <u>tire</u> is the object.

Exercise 3.5

A. Place brackets around the prepositional phrases.

B. Write the word that is the direct object of the verb on the line at the right. If there is no object, leave the space blank.

Direct Object

           S

Example: <u>Do</u> ⟨you⟩ <u>want</u> some coffee [for lunch]?   <u>coffee</u>

1. My uncle plays for the Dodgers.   _____

2. The children asked many questions today.   _____

3. Did you order food from the dell?   _____

4. Marilyn sang in the choir last year.   _____

5. Can Steve play the guitar?   _____

• •
3.4 Linking Verbs
• •

Action verbs tell what the subject does, did, or will do.

Linking verbs do *not* tell what the subject does. Linking verbs are verbs of being. They include all forms of the verb <u>be</u>—am, is, are, was, were, been, and <u>being</u>—and other verbs such as <u>seem, feel, become</u>, and <u>appear</u>, which can be substituted for forms of <u>be</u>. Linking verbs link the subject with another word in the sentence that is called the **completer.**

1. The verb links the subject to a noun completer that *renames* the subject.

56

S   NC

Examples: Judi is a *dancer.*

S   NC

Mr. Bradley is our football *coach.*

2. The verb links the subject to an adjective completer that *describes* the subject.

  S AC   S   AC

Examples: Judi is *graceful.* Mr. Bradley is *enthusiastic.*

Linking Verbs

| appear | become | grow | remain | taste |
| be | feel | look | seem | turn |

In the following examples, S = subject and C = completer.

   S C
1. The velvet <u>feels</u> soft.

   S C
2. <u>Has</u> this milk <u>turned</u> sour?

     S   C
3. Nevertheless, she <u>will</u> <u>remain</u> our president.

 S   C
4. Darrell <u>had</u> <u>become</u> a pole vaulter in college.

         S   C
5. On the surface, the coach's decision <u>seemed</u> reasonable.

Better Grammar

Some of these linking verbs can also be used as action verbs. When used as action verbs, they may be followed by direct objects. They may also be used as action verbs without direct objects. Study these examples:

Linking Verbs	Action Verbs
S LV C	S V O
a. The corn grows tall.	d. The farmer grows corn.
S LV	S V
b. The cake tasted	e. Marla tasted the
C	O
delicious.	cheesecake.
S LV	S——————S
c. The patient appeared	f. Richard and Elizabeth
C	V
better.	appeared in a play together.

In sentences d and e, the action verbs are followed by direct objects. In sentence f, the action verb is not followed by a direct object. Remember that these verbs are linking verbs only when they are followed by a word or phrase that renames or describes the subject of the sentence, as in sentences a, b, and c.

Exercise 3.6

Circle the subject, underline the auxiliary and the main verbs, and label the completer in each of the following sentences.

                 S   LV   C

Examples: The (mango) is a tropical fruit.

S   LV   C

This (mango) <u>looks</u> ripe.

1. My daughter is a first-year student at Jackson Community College.

2. Everyone seemed happy about the election results.

3. The traffic light is finally turning green.

4. Marie and Kevin have just become partners.

5. Can you be the moderator of our next discussion?

3.5 Pronouns Used as Subjects and Objects

Subject Pronouns

Subject pronouns are used primarily as the subjects of sentences or clauses. They also are used after all forms of the verb <u>be</u> in formal writing.

Example: It is <u>I</u>. (In conversation, most people would say, "It's me.")

Subject Pronouns

Person	Singular	Plural
First	I	we
Second	you	you
Third	he, she, it	they

Exercise 3.7

Referring to the forms in the box above, underline the subject pronouns in the following sentences.

Example: <u>They</u> enjoy bowling because <u>it</u> is good exercise.

1. He removed the tire because it was flat.
2. Have you seen Pat since she returned from Chicago?
3. As parents, you will be interested in this program we are proposing.
4. They read the instructions carefully.
5. Every Saturday I play tennis.

Object Pronouns

Object pronouns have two main uses: as objects of verbs and as objects of prepositions. As the objects of verbs, they usually follow the verbs.

V   Noun Object

The outfielder caught the *ball.*

V   Pronoun Object

The outfielder caught *it.*

Object pronouns can also be objects of prepositions, words such as <u>in</u>, <u>to</u>, <u>with</u>, and <u>for</u>:

Prep. Noun Object

Shana gave a party for *Donna.*

Prep. Pronoun Object

Shana gave a party for *her.*

Objects always follow the preposition:

to <u>me</u>   with <u>you</u>   in <u>it</u>   for <u>us</u>   without <u>them</u>

Object Pronouns

Person	Singular	Plural
First	me	us
Second	you	you
Third	him, her, it	them

Exercise 3.8

Referring to the forms in the box, underline the object pronouns in the following sentences.

Example: The coach gave the awards to <u>him</u>.

1. The stereo is too loud; turn it down.
2. Eduardo met us at Disney World.
3. Terry will wait for her.
4. Did Todd tell you about them?
5. The news pleased me.

3.6 Compound Subjects, Verbs, and Objects

Until now, most of the sentences in this book have contained simple subjects and simple verbs. Many sentences, however, have **compound subjects** and **compound verbs.** A compound subject is made up of two or more subjects joined by coordinating connectives, such as <u>and</u> or <u>or</u>. A compound verb is made up of two or more verbs joined by coordinating connectives, such as <u>and</u> or <u>or</u>.

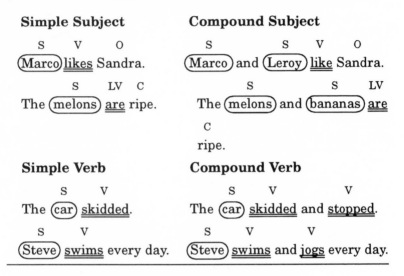

Simple Subject	Compound Subject

S   V   O

(Marco) <u>likes</u> Sandra.

S   S   V   O

(Marco) and (Leroy) <u>like</u> Sandra.

S   LV C

The (melons) <u>are</u> ripe.

S   S   LV

The (melons) and (bananas) <u>are</u>

C

ripe.

Simple Verb   **Compound Verb**

S   V

The (car) <u>skidded</u>.

S   V   V

The (car) <u>skidded</u> and <u>stopped</u>.

S   V

(Steve) <u>swims</u> every day.

S   V   V

(Steve) <u>swims</u> and <u>jogs</u> every day.

Objects and completers can also be compound.

Compound Object

S   V   O   O   O

(She) <u>brought</u> fresh beans, squash, and tomatoes from her garden.

Compound Completer

S LV   C   C

(He) <u>is</u> an actor and a musician.

      S   LV C   C   C

The (colors) of her dress <u>are</u> red, white and blue.

Pronouns in Compound Subjects and Objects

Compound subjects and objects can be a problem when they include pronouns. For example, what pronouns would you place in these blanks?

1. Bob and _____ (me, I) went to the game Friday.

2. We waited for Tom and _____ (he, him) after class.

<u>I</u> is correct in sentence 1 because <u>I</u> is the subject of the verb. <u>Him</u> is correct in sentence 2 because <u>him</u> is the object of the preposition <u>for</u>.

When you are in doubt about the form of a pronoun in sentences like these, leave out the noun subject or the noun object and the connective and read the sentence with the pronoun by itself.

1. Bob and <u>I</u> went to the game Friday. (You read, "<u>I</u> went to the game Friday" because you wouldn't say, "<u>Me</u> went to the game Friday.")

2. We waited for Tom and <u>him</u> after class. (You read, "We waited for <u>him</u> after class" because you wouldn't say, "We waited for <u>he</u> after class.")

Sometimes you might have to change the sentence slightly:

Bob and _____ (me, I) have been friends for years. Change to: <u>I</u> have been <u>Bob's friend</u> for years.

Exercise 3.9

Underline the correct pronoun.

Example: My brother and (I, me) want to buy a condominium together.

1. We want to find one that has a bedroom for (he, him) and one for me.

2. (He, Him) and (I, me) have been sharing one bedroom for a long time.

3. There has never been any trouble between (we, us).

4. The real estate agent asked whether my brother and (I, me) need two bathrooms.

5. My brother said that (he, him) and (I, me) need two bedrooms and two bathrooms.

• •
3.7 Contractions
• •

You learned that the contraction for *not (n't)* may be added to many auxiliary verbs (do not = don't; does not = doesn't). Contractions may also be formed by combining pronoun subjects and verbs. In writing contractions, do not omit the apostrophe. Note in the following examples that the apostrophe replaces the letter or the letters that have been omitted.

Omitting Letters in a Verb

Examples: She is my sister. She's my sister.

She will have to explain. She'll have to explain.

In each of these examples, a pronoun (she) and a verb (is, will) have been combined. The apostrophe takes the place of the letter i in is and the letters wi in will. She is = she's; she will = she'll.

Omitting the i in Here is and There is

Contractions may also be formed by combining there with is and here with is.

Examples: There is John now. There's John now.

Here is your book. Here's your book.

In both cases the apostrophe takes the place of the letter i in is. Note: There are and here are are never contracted. Furthermore, when a sentence begins with the words here is or there is, the noun that follows the verb is the subject.

Exercise 3.10

Supply the contractions for these words.

1. she will	she'll	6. I am	_____
2. they have	_____	7. we have	_____
3. he had	_____	8. here is	_____
4. he is	_____	9. it is	_____
5. I will	_____	10. we are	_____

• •
3.8 Sentence Patterns
• •

There are four basic sentence patterns.

Better Grammar

Pattern 1. Subject-Verb (S-V) Sentences following this pattern may have only a subject and a verb:

S	V	S	V	S	AV	V

a. People <u>travel</u>.   b. Planes <u>landed</u>.   c. They <u>had</u> <u>arrived</u>.

This pattern, of course, can have compound subjects and/or verbs:

S	S	V	S	V

d. Elaine and Allen <u>sang</u>.   e. The audience <u>clapped</u> and

V

<u>whistled</u>.

Modifiers, however, are frequently included in the sentence:

Adj   S   AV   V   Adj   S   V

f. A heavy rain <u>is</u> <u>falling</u>.   g. The cold wind <u>blew</u>

——— Adv ———

in the mountains.

S   V   Adv

h. That roof <u>leaks</u> badly.

Pattern 2. Subject-Verb-Object (S-V-O) In addition to the subject and verb, Pattern 2 requires a direct object. The verb, as in Pattern 1, is an action verb, and the object may be single or compound.

S   AV   V   O   S   V   O

a. The waiter <u>has</u> <u>forgotten</u> the water.   b. He <u>served</u> pizza,

O   O   S   S   AV   V   O

salad, and gelato.   c. Chris and Mike <u>are</u> <u>drinking</u> wine.

Pattern 3. Subject-Linking Verb-Noun Completer (S-LV-NC) In this pattern, a linking verb connects the subject and the noun completer. The completer may be single or compound.

S   S   LV   NC   S

a. The Millers and the Burns <u>were</u> neighbors. b. Ed Burn

AV   LV   NC   S   AV   LV   NC

<u>has</u> <u>become</u> the governor. c. They <u>will</u> <u>remain</u> friends.

Pattern 4. Subject-Linking Verb-Adjective Completer (S-LV-AC) The first three sentence patterns require only nouns and verbs. In this pattern, the verb links an adjective to the subject. The adjective completer may be single or compound.

S   AV LV   AC   AC

a. The weather <u>has</u> <u>turned</u> warm and sunny. b. The

S   LV   AC   S   LV   AC

pitcher <u>looks</u> confident. c. That decision <u>seemed</u> fair.

Exercise 3.11

Complete the sentences by filling in the appropriate subjects, verbs, direct objects, noun completers, and adjective completers. Identify the sentence patterns on the lines at the right.

Sentence Pattern

Example: Traffic was <u>heavy.</u>　　　　　<u> S-LV-AC </u>

1. Our conference was a/an _____.　　_____

2. I have lost the _____.　　_____

3. _____ growl.　　_____

4. Troy likes _____.　　_____

67

Better Grammar

5. The child _____ and _____.   _____

6. That lesson seems _____.   _____

7. _____ and _____ are dancing. _____

8. Marie has become a/an _____.   _____

9. Mr. McBride bought a/an _____.   _____

10. This T-shirt is _____, _____, _____

    and _____.

Chapter 4

Expanding the Sentence

4.1 Adding Details with Adjectives

• •

The sentences you completed for the exercises in the first three chapters are just a beginning. Readers usually ask more of the writer—more color, more variety, more information—in short, more specific details. Adjectives added to nouns, and adverbs added to verbs give the reader additional information by further describing and qualifying the nouns and verbs.

Adjectives

An **adjective** makes a noun or pronoun specific or concrete by limiting and describing it.

       N   N   Adj   Adj   N
a. Zoos   protect   species.   Some   new   zoos   protect

       Adj   N
endangered species.

    N   N   Adj   N   Adj

b. Zoos breed animals. Far-sighted zoos breed rare and

   Adj   N
exotic animals

    N   N   Adj   N   Adj   Adj

c. Zoos need support. All zoos need continued public

   N
support.

Kinds of Adjectives

Possessive Pronouns and Possessive Nouns The possessive form of the pronoun is called an adjective because it
describes and qualifies nouns: his book, my book. The possessive form of a noun is also called an adjective. Your reader
knows exactly what house you are talking about when you
write Gene's house or the Martins' house. The possessive
nouns are modifying the noun "house" and are, therefore,
adjectives.

Exercise 4.1

Bracket all possessive pronouns and possessive nouns.

Example: The bike [riders'] protests were loud when they
        heard that [their] lanes of traffic would be
        closed.

1. New York City's chief engineer maintains its highways
   and bridges.

2. His main job is to keep the city's bridges from decaying
   and collapsing.

3. Today's larger trucks have ruined many of America's roads and bridges.

4. In addition, although salt is used successfully to melt snow, the salt's acidity has destroyed our highways.

5. The chief engineer's judgments about repairs affect many people's lives.

Noun Markers Noun markers indicate that a noun will follow.

Noun Markers

a	that	all	either	more
an	these	any	every	most
the	this	both	few	much
some	those	each	many	neither

Some of these words seem to point to
the noun: <u>that</u> truck.

Others limit the noun: <u>few</u> people.

Numbers All numbers are adjectives. They modify and qualify the noun by telling how many.

Examples: <u>five</u> apples   <u>fifty</u> dollars   <u>twenty-four</u> hours

Descriptive Adjectives The adjectives above do not actually describe nouns. To give the reader a mental picture of something, the writer chooses adjectives that describe the qualities or characteristics of it.

Adj   N

Six clowns entertained the <u>excited</u> children under the top of

---

71

Better Grammar

Adj   Adj   Adj   N
the enormous white canvas tent.

          Adj   Adj   N   Adj
A clown with curly orange hair kept falling off a small

Adj   N
red tricycle.

Position of Adjectives

1. The adjective usually appears in front of the noun:

Adj   N   Adj   N   Adj   N
spring vacation   freshman class   term paper

2. But the adjective can follow the noun it modifies:

             N   Adj   Adj
The woman's answer was polite but guarded.

These adjectives are completers following the linking verb was.

Adj   N   Adj   Adj
The winning team, laughing and shouting, ran off the field.

These present participles are adjectives modifying the noun team. Notice that two of them, laughing and shouting, follow the noun.

Special Forms of Adjectives

1. Sometimes present and past participles are used as adjectives:

Adj	N	Adj	N	Adj	N
excited	fans	winning	pass	opening	game

Adj	N
defeated	team

2. When a noun precedes another noun, the first noun is used as an adjective to describe or limit the second noun:

Adj	N	Adj	N	Adj	N
canvas	tent	circus	tent	plastic	cushions

Adj	N
cotton	candy

3. Prepositional phrases are also used as adjectives.

   $$\text{N} \qquad \text{Adj}$$

   Toshiro sent five letters of application.

   Of application specifies the kind of letters that Toshiro sent; therefore, the phrase is an adjective.

Exercise 4.2

In the following sentences, bracket all the participles and nouns used as adjectives.

Example: Alex spent an [exciting] time at the [opening pro-football] game.

---

1. In his box seat, Alex watched a closely fought battle.
2. The turning point came for the home team during the last few minutes of the game.
3. Everyone praised the winning pass of the rookie quarterback and the clever tactics of the head coach.
4. The excited fans roared as the place kicker sent the ball through the uprights of the goal post for the extra point.
5. The winning team, laughing and shouting, ran off the football field.

How to Choose Adjectives

When writers choose adjectives to create a picture for the reader, they are asking themselves questions about their subjects.

1. What kind?

   Example: <u>dancing</u> lessons   "Dancing" tells what kind of lessons.

2. How many?

   Example: <u>ten</u> lessons   "Ten" tells how many lessons.

3. Which one?

   Example: the <u>last</u> lesson   "Last" tells which one.

4. Whose?

   Example: <u>Judy's</u> lesson   "Judy's" tells whose.

Questions like these can help writers to add details to a sentence.

Exercise 4.3

Bracket all the adjectives in the following paragraph.

It is [a] [beautiful], [sunny] day in [a] [popular] [theme] park in [the] United States. Mr. and Mrs. Tomita, on their first trip to this country, listen attentively to a tour guide's claim that thirty-five thousand adults and children visit the park every day. Most visitors to this magical place are attracted by an amazing variety of shows, rides, exhibits, and restaurants. Both Mr. and Mrs. Tomita, however, are impressed by the clean surroundings. They are staying at the vacationland's hotel where all the rooms have immaculately clean blue plastic furniture, green and beige walls, and beds covered with purple-green spreads. The hotel's parking lot, with its carefully planted vegetation, is also sparkling clean. The smallest scrap of litter is sucked underground and rushed via pipes to a fabulous trash compactor. Even the friendly birds do their part by picking some bread crumbs off the restaurant's patio at the hotel. Mr. and Mrs. Tomita know that they will enjoy themselves in this spotless American tourist attraction.

Punctuating Adjectives Before a Noun

Use commas to separate two or more adjectives that modify the same noun if they are not linked by a coordinating connective such as <u>and</u> or <u>but</u>.

Examples: a. The irritated candidate spoke in a loud, indignant voice.

b. The reporter's harsh and probing questions annoyed the candidate. (no comma needed)

Exercise 4.4

Insert commas as needed in the following sentences.

1. Bradley and Carol tried to talk to the instructor in the cluttered noisy office he shared with two other people.
2. Twenty-five airline passengers were rescued from the frigid ice-covered Potomac River.
3. Driving a battered rusty old Volkswagen is more fun than driving a luxurious shiny new Cadillac.
4. Walt admired the graceful elegant and stately style of the dancer.
5. Mary insisted on wearing the old-fashioned clumsy worn-out slippers around the house.

Study Chapter 8 for additional material on this use of the comma.

Comparison of Adjectives

Adjectives have three forms: positive (base form), comparative, and superlative. Most adjectives change their form for use in comparisons. For example, **soft, softer, softest** show differences in degree.

Comparative Degree

a. Walt is <u>strong</u>.

b. Dan is <u>stronger</u> than Walt.

The first sentence simply tells us about one quality of Walt: his strength. The second sentence compares Walt's strength to Dan's strength. <u>Stronger</u> is the **comparative** form of the adjective <u>strong</u>.

Superlative Degree

a. Pete is <u>the strongest</u> of all.

b. He <u>the strongest</u> wrestler on the team.

<u>Strongest</u> is the **superlative** form of the adjective <u>strong</u>. Superlative forms are often followed by prepositional phrases as shown in the examples just given.

Forming Comparatives and Superlatives

1. Add **-er** to adjectives of one syllable.

Add **-est** to adjectives of one syllable.

	Positive	Comparative	Superlative
	rich	richer	richest
	sweet	sweeter	sweetest
	tall	taller	tallest
Exceptions:	good	better	best
	bad	worse	worst

Better Grammar

2. Place the words more or most before adjectives of two or more syllables.

brilliant	more brilliant	most brilliant
dangerous	more dangerous	most dangerous
exciting	more exciting	most exciting

Exception: To form the comparative of two-syllable adjectives ending in **-y,** change the **-y** to **-i** and add **-er.** To form the superlative add **-est.**

happy	happier	happiest
lovely	lovelier	loveliest
lazy	lazier	laziest

Use the comparative form to compare two or more persons, places, ideas, or things.

Use the superlative form to compare more than two persons, places, ideas, or things.

Example: Marion is the tallest player on our team.

Less and Least Less and least may be substituted for more and most to show a lesser degree in a comparison.

Comparative (followed by *than*)	**Superlative** (followed by *of* or other prepositions)
less dangerous	least dangerous
less comfortable	least comfortable

Exercise 4.5

Fill in the blanks with words that show a lesser degree of comparison.

1. The speaker was _____ interesting than I had expected.

2. Highway 10 is the _____ dangerous way of all through the mountains.

3. That house is _____ expensive than the one we looked at this morning.

4. I am the _____ creative member of our family.

5. The baby seems _____ sleepy than she was an hour ago.

Exercise 4.6

Change the adjective in parentheses into the comparative or superlative degree. The first sentence is completed as an example.

1. Buying a computer for home or business may be the

   <u>most important</u> purchase you will make in the next ten
   (important, superlative)

   years.

2. The computer you choose for the home will soon be

   _____ to use than the telephone.
   (easy, comparative)

3. It will enable you to have a _____ method of
   (good, comparative)

   controlling the family budget.

4. You should be sure to buy a computer that can be

   upgraded to a _____ , _____ model
                        (big, comparative)   (powerful, comparative)

   sometime in the future.

5. The data-processing computer has become the

   _____ addition to the business world.
   (recent, superlative)

6. Some computerized information systems offer busi-

   nesses _____ productivity.
           (great, comparative)

7. They even promise _____ use of energy.
                     (efficient, comparative)

8. The use of computers encourages _____
                                  (simple, comparative)

   business procedures.

9. The _____ computer systems are powerful
      (large, superlative)

   enough to process company payrolls.

10. The computer you buy for home or business should be

    the _____ quality at the _____
        (good, superlative)   (low, superlative)

    price.

4.2 Adding Details with Adverbs

Another kind of modifier is an adverb. Adverbs add further information about verbs, adjectives, and other adverbs. Study the following tests for an adverb.

Tests for Adverbs

1. Ask the question, When?

   Example: I ran five miles <u>yesterday</u>.
   The word <u>yesterday</u> tells *when* I ran five miles.

2. Ask the question, How?

   Example: I ran five miles <u>slowly</u>.
   The word <u>slowly</u> tells *how* I ran five miles.

3. Ask the question, Where?

   Example: I ran five miles <u>around the track</u>.
   The words <u>around the track</u> tell *where* I ran five miles.

4. Ask the question, Why?

   Example: I ran five miles <u>for my health</u>.
   The words <u>for my health</u> tell *why* I ran five miles.

From these examples, you can see that an adverb can be a single word *(yesterday)* or a phrase *(around the track)*. To determine if a word or group of words is an adverb, ask *when, where, how,* or *why.* Adverbs answer these questions.

Function of Adverbs

Adverbs are usually added to a basic sentence to give the reader more information.

Example: She arrived.   basic sentence
She arrived <u>early</u>.   tells <u>when</u> she arrived
She arrived <u>suddenly</u>.   tells <u>how</u> she arrived
She arrived <u>at my door</u>. tells <u>where</u> she arrived
She arrived <u>to stay</u>   tells <u>why</u> she arrived
<u>with me</u>.

Basic Pattern 1 sentences need added information to make them more interesting to your reader. Adverbs add interest and information.

Note: A few words that are usually nouns sometimes function as adverbs.

They tell where he walked: He walked <u>home</u>.
They tell how far: He walked a <u>mile</u>.
They tell when: He walked <u>yesterday</u>.

The adverb tells **the time** the action happened, **the place** it happened, **the manner** in which it happened, and **the purpose** of the action.

Position of Adverbs

The position of an adverb in a sentence is flexible; that is, it can be moved around in a sentence. The position of the adverb <u>occasionally</u> is correct in all the sentences in the following example:

Example: <u>Occasionally</u> she eats in the cafeteria.
She <u>occasionally</u> eats in the cafeteria.
She eats <u>occasionally</u> in the cafeteria.
She eats in the cafeteria <u>occasionally</u>.

Exercise 4.7

In the following sentences, write in one-word or preposi-
tional-phrase adverbs of your choice on the lines. The
sentences form a paragraph.

Example: Kimiko had been planning her vacation

<u>for six months</u>.
(when)

1. Kimiko   arrived   _____   after   a   long
(when)

   flight _____.
   (where)

2. The   pilot   landed   the   plane   _____   and
(how)

   _____.
   (how)

3. All   the   passengers   _____   applauded
(where)

   _____ .
   (how)

4. Kimiko   walked   _____ toward   the   exit   door
(how)

   _____.
   (why)

5. She was thrilled to be _____ after so many years.
(where)

Comparison of Adverbs

Adverbs, like adjectives, have degrees of comparison: the positive, the comparative, the superlative.

Forming Comparatives and Superlatives

1. To form the comparative of adverbs of one syllable, add **-r** or **-er.** To form the superlative, add **-st** or **-est.**

Positive	Comparative	Superlative
late	later	latest
fast	faster	fastest

2. A few adverbs of one syllable are exceptions to rule 1. To form the comparative and superlative of these words, change the spelling of the adverb. Consult your dictionary.

Positive	Comparative	Superlative
far	farther	farthest (physical distance)
far	further	furthest (mental degree)
well	better	best

3. To form the comparative of adverbs of more than one syllable, place <u>more</u> before the adverb. To form the superlative, place <u>most</u> before the adverb.

Positive	Comparative	Superlative
beautifully	more beautifully	most beautifully
carefully	more carefully	most carefully

Exception: badly   worse   worst

Use the comparative form when comparing two actions. Use the superlative form when comparing three or more actions.

Example: I had thought that Jan skated <u>more gracefully</u> than Marie. But then I saw Adele skate after the other two girls. Adele skated <u>most gracefully</u> of all.

Exercise 4.8

Change each adverb in parentheses into the comparative or superlative degree. The first is completed as an example.

1. Marty Porter, a night school student and the mother of three children under the age of ten, had decided <u>most reluctantly</u> to give up her full-time job.
(reluctantly, superlative)

2. She found herself performing these three demanding roles _____ than her own high standards
(efficiently, comparative)
required.

3. The inability to organize her activities was not the problem; she planned each day _____ than the
(systematically, comparative)
last.

4. The company she worked for, however, _____
(definitely, superlative)
did not want to lose a valuable employee like Mrs. Porter.

5. Her supervisor arranged a flexible schedule that allowed her to fulfill _____ her obligations at
(easily, comparative)
home, at school, and at work.

4.3 Adding Details with Verbal Phrases

Verbal phrases can be indispensable additions to a basic sentence because they greatly increase the possibilities for expanding it.

Example: Carla waited.

> Breathless and exhausted, Carla waited to hear the choreographer's opinion of her audition.
> Anxious to hear the choreographer's opinion of her dancing, Carla waited, forgetting her exhaustion.

Verbals are formed from verbs and introduce verbal phrases. They usually include a noun and/or a prepositional phrase. They are used as nouns, adjectives, and adverbs in sentences.

1. to choose a pet   The verbal is to choose, formed from to plus the present form of the verb.

2. chosen for its intelligence   The verbal is chosen, the past participle.

3. choosing a Seeing Eye dog   The verbal is choosing, the present participle.

Pay special attention to the first type of verbal phrase (to choose a pet) because it looks like a prepositional phrase. Read the information below carefully.

Note

The word *to* is used to introduce both verbal phrases and prepositional phrases. TO + A VERB = A VERBAL PHRASE

Example: to travel

TO + A NOUN AND ITS MODIFIERS =

A PREPOSITIONAL PHRASE

Example: to the moon

Exercise 4.9

A. In the following sentences, bracket all verbal and prepositional phrases.

B. Underline the auxiliary verb once and the main verb twice.

C. Circle the subjects.

Example: Many years ago (Chief Billy Bowlegs) [leading 200 of his Seminole tribe,] <u>hid</u> [in the Florida Everglades.]

1. Today 1,500 Seminole Indians live on the reservation built on 120,000 acres of swamp in the Florida Everglades.

2. A group of these Indians, living near Tampa, has defied the law.

3. In addition to a shrine and a museum, the Seminoles have built a drive-thru smoke shop there.

4. The Indians have been selling cigarettes without charging sales tax.

5. From the first, state and local law enforcers did not like these Indians to sell cigarettes.

Punctuation

At the beginning of a sentence, use a comma after an introductory verbal phrase.

Examples: Standing at the end of the line, I had little hope of getting a ticket.

Discouraged by the long line, I gave up and went home.

Exercise 4.10

Insert commas after the introductory verbal phrases.

1. Hoping to make a profit Carolyn invested in the stock market.

2. Trying to get to the airport on time Josephine got a ticket for speeding.

3. Snowed in for a week in the mountains we couldn't get back in time to take our final exams.

4. Having spent the day shopping unsuccessfully for shoes Tina decided to wear her old ones to the party.

5. Finding a wallet on his way to school Jerry had visions of a generous reward.

For a more detailed discussion of this use of the comma, see Chapter 8.

4.4 Misplaced Modifiers and Dangling Modifiers

When you use modifiers in your sentences, be sure that the word order of each sentence is clear and logical. Placing a modifier in an incorrect position can change or confuse the meaning of the sentence. Modifiers should be placed close to the words that they describe or qualify. Learn to identify and correct **misplaced modifiers** and **dangling modifiers**.

Misplaced Modifiers

Misplaced modifiers are exactly what the term suggests: these modifiers are called misplaced because they have been incorrectly placed next to words that they are not intended to modify.

Examples:

a. I <u>nearly</u> ate all the brownies. (misplaced modifier)

This sentence suggests that you didn't eat anything at all. You should place <u>nearly</u> in front of *all the brownies*.

I ate <u>nearly</u> all the brownies. (correctly placed modifier)

b. I heard that our nation needs additional engineers <u>on the television news</u>. (misplaced modifier)

The engineers are not needed on the television news, are they? You should place <u>on the television news</u> after the verb *heard*.

I heard <u>on the television news</u> that our nation needs additional engineers. (correctly placed modifier)

c. Coretta bought a German shepherd dog <u>alarmed by the robberies in the neighborhood</u>. (misplaced modifier)

If the dog is alarmed by the robberies, it is not going to make a good watchdog. You should place the verbal phrase modifier in front of *Coretta*.

<u>Alarmed by the robberies in the neighborhood</u>, Coretta bought a German shepherd dog. (correctly placed modifier)

Exercise 4.11

Revise the following sentences by placing the words or phrases in parentheses next to the words that they modify.

Examples: Eileen ran after the bus. (carrying a heavy briefcase)

<u>Carrying a heavy briefcase, Eileen ran after the bus</u>.

1. Nick saved $100 by making his own repairs on his car. (almost)

2. The candidate promised that he would reduce unemployment. (at the political rally)

3. Alfredo ordered a pizza to go.
   (with mushrooms and pepperoni)

   _____

4. The painters told us that they would begin painting the house. (on Wednesday)

   _____

5. Rex saw a woman in the front row jump up and run out the side exit. (suddenly)

   _____

Dangling Modifiers

A word or a phrase is called a dangling modifier when there is no word in the sentence for it to modify.

Example: <u>Showing an interest in computers</u>, personnel offices are flooded with applications.

Were the personnel offices showing an interest in computers? Of course not. The verbal phrase modifier, <u>Showing an interest in computers,</u> is left dangling. There is no word in the sentence for it to modify. To correct this problem, write the sentence as follows:

Showing an interest in computers, students are flooding personnel offices with applications.

A word such as <u>students</u> must be added to the sentence to eliminate the dangling modifier.

Another method of eliminating dangling modifiers changes the dangling word or phrase into a subordinate clause. You could correct the example given above as follows:

Because students are showing an interest in computers, personnel offices are flooded with applications.

91

Remember

You cannot get rid of a dangling modifier by moving it around in a sentence. Since there is no word in the sentence for it to modify, you must rewrite the sentence and add the word that the phrase modifies.

Exercise 4.12

Rewrite this paragraph on the lines provided. Correct the dangling modifiers in each sentence.

Expecting a robot like R2D2, the robot that was demonstrated to Willy was disappointing. Propelling itself on large wheels, Willy had hoped for useful arms and legs. Having limited mobility, stairs could not be climbed. Responding to voice command, a distance of less than seventy feet was necessary between the robot and its owner. Frustrated by the poor quality, his decision to buy a robot would have to be delayed.

_____

_____

_____

_____

_____

4.4 Misplaced Modifiers and Dangling Modifiers

_____

_____

_____

_____

_____

_____

_____

Chapter 5

Main Clauses

5.1 Identifying Main Clauses

When you studied prepositional phrases and verbal phrases, you learned that a phrase is a group of related words <u>without</u> a subject and a verb. A group of related words <u>with</u> a subject and a verb is called a **clause.** There are two kinds of clauses, **main** and **subordinate,** but this chapter will deal only with the main clause (also called an independent clause).

To identify a main clause, look first for the verb and then for the subject. The main clause can stand alone as a sentence if the first word is capitalized and the clause ends with a mark of punctuation such as a period or a question mark. The main clause may also contain words or phrases in addition to the verb and the subject.

Exercise 5.1

In the following sentences, identify the underlined group of words as a <u>phrase</u> or a <u>main clause</u>. Write your answer on the line at the right.

---

1. <u>Many people complain loudly about</u>   _____
   <u>junk mail</u>.
2. <u>It arrives in large quantities daily</u>.   _____
3. <u>Getting on these mailing lists</u> is easy.   _____
4. Companies have always exchanged   _____
   information <u>regarding consumers</u>.
5. Rented memberships and subscription   _____
   lists have been another resource <u>used</u>
   <u>by advertisers</u>.

5.2 Connecting Main Clauses

The Simple Sentence

In the preceding chapters, you have been working primarily with the **simple sentence**. The simple sentence contains *one* main clause. Which of the following two sentences is a simple sentence?

1. Mr. Hughes has dreamed of graduating.

2. For a long time since building his first race car nineteen years ago, Mr. Hughes has dreamed of graduating to the NASCAR Grand National Circuit.

Both sentences are simple sentences. Although the second sentence contains several phrases, it has only one main clause: one subject and one verb. Both sentences, as you can see, have the same subject and verb:

     S   AV   V
  (Mr. Hughes) has <u>dreamed</u>

The Compound Sentence

Which of the following two sentences contains *more than one* main clause and, therefore, is *not* a simple sentence?

1. Thousands of drivers like Mr. Hughes test themselves on America's hundreds of small dirt tracks, hoping to win $1,000, $100, or even just a trophy.

2. The race-car drivers hope to make it to the big-league tracks, and they love the thrill of driving at very high speeds.

The first sentence has only one subject and one verb:

    S   V

(Thousands) <u>test</u>

It is a simple sentence with *one* main clause.

The second sentence, containing two main clauses, is a **compound sentence.** It has two subjects and two verbs:

    S   V   S   V

(drivers) <u>hope</u> . . ., and (they) <u>love</u>

Now try two more sentences. Which one is a simple sentence? Which one is a compound sentence?

1. Trying to avoid a head-on collision with another car, the driver turned his wheel sharply to the right and crashed into a wall.

2. He wanted to pull off the road, but he could not do it quickly enough.

The first sentence is a simple sentence with one main clause. The clause contains one subject and a compound verb:

S   V   V

(driver) turned and crashed

The second sentence is a compound sentence. It has two main clauses: two subjects and two verbs.

S   V   S   AV   V

(He) wanted but (he) could do

Exercise 5.2

A. Begin by circling the subjects and underlining the verbs.

B. Identify each of the following sentences as simple or compound. If the sentence has only one main clause, write S (Simple) on the line at the right. If the sentence has two or more main clauses, write C (Compound) on the line at the right.

                 S   S

Example: (Aurelio) wanted a new bicycle, but (he) didn't have enough money for one.   __C__

1. Some people think of Iowa as flat, but some   _____

   bicyclists know better now.

2. Every year about seven thousand bicyclists   _____

   ride slowly and painfully across the state of

   Iowa.

3. The ride begins at the Missouri River along _____

   the state's western border, and it ends at its

   eastern edge along the Mississippi.

4. Many riders complain about injured knees as _____

   well as sunburns.

5. The bicyclists are surprised by the hills of _____

   Iowa, for the land had looked flat to them.

Joining Main Clauses

There are three ways to join the main clauses of compound sentences. You may use (1) a coordinating connective, (2) a semicolon, or (3) an adverbial connective. **Coordinating connectives** (sometimes called coordinating conjunctions) are words used to join words, phrases, or clauses together.

Examples: Karen and Jessica
at work or at school
Karen studies, but Jessica watches TV.

Remember These Seven Coordinating Connectives

and	for	or	yet
but	nor	so	

Put a comma before the coordinating connective when it joins two main clauses into a compound sentence.

Better Grammar

Example: Suzanne was trying to lose weight, so she avoided eating desserts.

Exercise 5.3

Change these simple sentences into compound sentences by joining the main clauses with a comma and the coordinating connectives in the parentheses. Circle the subjects and underline the verbs.

1. (but) The doctor was a well-known specialist. My father would not accept her diagnosis.

2. (and) The pole vaulter tried again to break the record. This time he succeeded.

3. (so) It is a large house. They will have room for all their furniture.

4. (for) Andrea spent four hours a day practicing the flute. She was determined to improve.

5. (or) We can drive to the beach. We can ride our bicycles.

A **semicolon** (;) may be used to connect main clauses.

Example: Suzanne read the health spa contract several times; she wanted to understand the terms before signing it.

Exercise 5.4

Circle the subjects and underline the verbs. On the lines at the right, identify each sentence as simple (S) or compound

(C). Correct the compound sentences by joining the main clauses with semicolons.

1. Lucy likes to finish her homework before _____ dinner after eating she gets sleepy.

2. Vivian brought pictures of our high-school _____ class to the reunion everyone laughed at the dated clothes and hairstyles.

3. Arturo and his brother have borrowed _____ money and opened a real estate office.

4. Our neighbor was happy about his golf _____ game today for the first time he had a lower score than his wife's.

5. The children entertained themselves for _____ half an hour by riding up and down on the escalator.

The **adverbial connectives** (sometimes called adverbial conjunctions) listed in the following box also may be used to join main clauses.

Addition: also   further   in addition   moreover

Contrast: however   instead   nevertheless   otherwise

Time: meanwhile   then

Result: as a result   consequently   thus   therefore

In Reality: in fact   indeed

Use a semicolon before the connectors and follow them by a comma.

Better Grammar

Example: Suzanne has lost ten pounds; <u>therefore</u>, she is proud of herself.

You may need to consult your dictionary to be sure you are using these words correctly.

Exercise 5.5

Circle the subjects and underline the verbs. Choose an appropriate adverbial connective from the words in the following box to connect the main clauses in the following sentences. Use each connective only once. Punctuate the sentences correctly.

---

consequently   in addition   in fact   instead   then

---

1. We had planned to bicycle through England last summer. We painted the house and built a fence.

2. I forgot my umbrella this morning. I was soaked to the skin by the time I reached the office.

3. Milt works six hours a day and overtime on weekends at a restaurant. He takes three classes at a community college.

4. First Norman reads the comics. He settles down to enjoy the sports section.

5. Cindy looked very different with her new haircut. I hardly recognized her.

Punctuation

In simple sentences, some adverbial connectives serve as adverbs and are enclosed by commas. These adverbs do not join main clauses in a sentence as the adverbial connectives do.

Examples: Eric sometimes guesses correctly the meanings of words.
He should, nevertheless, consult a dictionary.

Exercise 5.6

Punctuate the following sentences correctly.

Example: A dictionary, indeed, can tell you the meaning of a word.

1. Besides that a dictionary shows you how to spell a word.

2. A dictionary in addition shows you how to divide a word into syllables.

3. It can tell you furthermore the origin and development of a word.

4. A dictionary in fact is a good source of biographical information.

5. You must however develop the habit of consulting it frequently.

5.3 Parallel Structure

Coordinating connectives join words, phrases, or clauses that are of <u>equal</u> importance. The word to notice in this definition is <u>equal</u>. Parallel structure, the placing of similar items in similar grammatical form, gives the writer another strategy for expanding a sentence in a balanced way.

> *Example a:* Donna Chapman is a ranger.
>
> Donna Chapman, former gardener, secretary, and short-order cook, is now a ranger in a large national park.

Parallel nouns (<u>gardener</u>, <u>secretary</u>, and <u>short-order cook</u>) give the reader more information about Ms. Chapman.

> *Example b:* She loves her job.
>
> She loves her job giving information to people, keeping the park in order, and preserving the natural beauty of the wild areas.

Parallel verbal phrases (<u>giving</u> ..., <u>keeping</u> ..., <u>preserving</u> ...) add details about the nature of Ms. Chapman's job.

Faulty Parallelism

When you use parallel structure, always put the parts of the sentence that you are joining in the same grammatical form. For example, placing a noun before <u>or</u>, <u>and</u>, or <u>but</u> requires that another noun follow the connective (a swimmer, a golfer, or a jogger). Failure to do so results in **faulty parallelism** (a swimmer, a golfer, or jogging).

Incorrect: Robert liked swimming, dancing, and <u>to play basketball</u>.

Correct: Robert liked <u>swimming, dancing, and playing basketball</u>.

or

Robert liked <u>to swim, to dance, and to play basketball</u>.

Exercise 5.7

In the following paragraph, underline all the words, phrases, and clauses that are parallel to each other.

Donna Chapman, former gardener, secretary, and short-order cook, is now a ranger in a large national park. She loves her job giving information to the people, keeping the park in order, and preserving the natural beauty of the wild areas. Every morning she puts on her uniform, packs her lunch, and rides her bicycle to her station, eager to start her work. She especially likes talking to the people who come to vacation in the park. Most faces are new to her, but others are familiar. Some park "regulars" have been coming there for thirty years. Whether it is sunny or rainy, sizzling or freezing, the visitors arrive to enjoy nature and to hike in the woods with their friends and families. Dedicated and enthusiastic, Donna Chapman is at her station, answering questions and being helpful. After shifting from job to job, she has found the one occupation that suits her perfectly.

Punctuation

Use commas to separate three or more items in a series. The items may be single words, phrases, or clauses.

Example: Marty is taking courses in economics, typing, accounting, and statistics this semester.

Exercise 5.8

Insert commas where necessary.

1. Jackson Pollock dripped sand pebbles rocks and acrylic paint onto his canvases.

2. The orchestra will travel to Venezuela Argentina Peru Chile and Brazil on a tour of South America.

3. Jo Anne took a bath went back to her room closed the door turned on the radio and lay down on her bed.

4. Rita has never liked to clean to cook to iron or to shop.

5. On weekends Joseph enjoys flying hang gliders going deep-sea fishing or riding horseback.

See Chapter 8 for a more detailed explanation of this use of the comma.

5.4 Correcting Comma Splices and Fused Sentences

In 5.2, you learned that main clauses may be joined together with connecting words and appropriate punctuation marks. But sometimes students try to join main clauses without any connecting words or punctuation marks.

$$\overset{\text{S}}{} \quad \overset{\text{V}}{} \qquad\qquad \overset{\text{S}}{} \quad \overset{\text{V}}{}$$

1. The (team) won the tournament, (they) received a trophy.

$$\overset{\text{S}}{} \quad \overset{\text{V}}{} \qquad\qquad \overset{\text{S}}{} \quad \overset{\text{V}}{}$$

2. The (team) won the tournament_ (they) received a trophy.

The error in sentence 1 is called a **comma splice** (CS). Sentence 2 is called a **fused sentence** (FS).

Correct comma splices and fused sentences in any *one* of the following ways:

1. Use a comma and a coordinating connective.

   The team won the tournament, <u>and</u> they received a trophy.

2. Use a semicolon.

   The team won the tournament; they received a trophy.

3. Use an adverbial connective and a semicolon and comma.

   The team won the tournament; <u>therefore</u>, they received a trophy.

4. Use a period and a capital letter.

   The team won the tournament. They received a trophy.

Exercise 5.9

Circle the subjects and underline the verbs in each sentence. Decide if there are two main clauses. On the line at the right, write CS for comma splice, FS for fused sentence, or NE for no error. Then punctuate the sentences correctly.

1. The children ran around the park their   _____
   mothers tried to quiet them unsuccessfully.

2. The traffic was unusually heavy this   _____
   evening, it was caused by an accident at the
   intersection.

3. The smog disappeared after the heavy rains _____
   it reappeared in a few days.

4. In the early morning, many joggers are   _____
   running.

5. It was late, and all the lights in the house _____
   were out.

Exercise 5.10

Correct these comma splices and fused sentences by using coordinating connectives, semicolons, or adverbial connectives with correct punctuation.

1. More corporations are beginning to open day-care centers for their employees' children, the centers are open from nine to five.

2. Working parents take fewer days off if their children are well cared for they worry less.

3. Two-paycheck families appreciate the cost benefits, the price of a full-time babysitter would use up an entire salary.

4. Single-parent families especially appreciate the convenience of quality child-care programs child-care programs help to recruit high-quality employees.

5. Government support helps the corporations build special facilities, preschool playgrounds and indoor classrooms are often too expensive for smaller corporations to construct.

Chapter 6

Subordinate Clauses

6.1 Identifying Subordinate Clauses
••

A **main clause** is a group of words with a subject and a verb. It is called a simple sentence when the first word is capitalized and it ends with a period, a question mark, or an exclamation point.

Example: (We) <u>enjoy</u> eating ice cream. (main clause or
simple sentence)

A **subordinate clause** (or dependent clause) is a group of words with a subject and a verb that is introduced by a subordinator. It is not called a sentence because it makes an incomplete statement.

(subordinator)

Example: because (we) <u>enjoy</u> eating ice cream

The following subordinate clauses are incomplete by themselves. They should not be followed by periods.

111

Better Grammar

1. While the band took a break
2. Since you went away

They leave a question unanswered. You want to ask:

1. What happened while the band took a break?
2. What has happened since you went away?

They need another clause, the main clause, to answer these questions. You might complete the sentences as follows:

1. While the band took a break, I soaked my feet.
2. Since you went away, I found another job.

The difference between a main clause and a subordinate clause is often only the *addition* of one word at the beginning of the clause. If you add a subordinator to a main clause, you make a subordinate clause.

Example: He bought a van. (main clause)
when he bought a van (subordinate clause)

Subordinators (partial list)

Place:	where, wherever
Time:	after, before, when, whenever, as, since, until, as soon as, while, as long as
Cause or Purpose:	so that, in order that, as, because, since, that, why
Condition:	if, unless, when, whether
Contrast:	although, even though, while

112

Concession: as if, though, although

Comparison: than

Identification: that, who, what, whom, whose, which

Some of these words function as subordinators in some sentences and as prepositions in other sentences.
The <u>subordinator</u> is followed by a subject and a verb.

Example: before (I̅) <u>go</u> to work = subordinate clause

The <u>preposition</u> is followed by a noun and its modifiers.

   Prep   N
Example: before the performance = prepositional phrase

Notice that <u>like</u> is not a subordinator. Therefore, it is incorrect to say, "Like I said ..." The word <u>like</u> is <u>only</u> used as a preposition.
A sentence that has a main clause and one or more subordinate clauses is called a **complex sentence**.

Exercise 6.1

In the following complex sentences, underline the subordinate clause and put parentheses around the subordinator. Begin by circling the subjects and underlining the verbs.

Example: (Since) (butter) <u>costs</u> too much money, many (people) <u>use</u> margarine.

1. The guests left after the party was over.

113

2. The animals performed their tricks although the audience did not applaud.

3. When the instructor passed back our papers, I was delighted.

4. Mr. Hashimoto has been wearing a cast because he broke his leg.

5. While we were riding our bicycles, someone stole our car.

Sentences with More than One Subordinate Clause

1. When the instructor passed back our papers, I discovered that my grade was an "A."

In this sentence, there are two subordinate clauses. Put parentheses around the two subordinators. (You should have marked <u>when</u> and <u>that</u>.)

2. If you want to travel to Europe this summer, you must save all the money that you earned while you were working as a waitress.

In this sentence, there are three subordinate clauses. Put parentheses around the three subordinators. (You should have marked <u>if</u>, <u>that</u>, and <u>while</u>.)

Exercise 6.2

In the following complex sentences, underline the subordinate clauses and put parentheses around the subordinators. Begin by circling the subjects and underlining the verbs.

1. After dinner, while the guests sat around the table, many of them told interesting stories about their work as we all listened attentively.

2. Although she said that she loved him, he didn't believe her because he knew that she went out with many other men.

3. As long as you haven't eaten your lunch yet, you might as well wait until dinner time when we will have a big meal.

4. Before I knew what was happening, the red sports car passed my car as I drove up the hill.

5. The judge said that I should go to driving school so that I would learn about the dangers of drunk driving.

••

6.2 Using Subordinate Clauses
••

Subordination, the use of subordinate clauses, gives writers another option for adding ideas to their sentences and variety to their writing. In addition, the subordinator shows the precise relationship between the subordinate clause and the main clause of the sentence.

Example:

1. (Mario) <u>was</u> in Rome. A (thief) <u>stole</u> his wallet.
   (main clause)   (main clause)

2. (When) (Mario) <u>was</u> in Rome, a (thief) <u>stole</u> his wallet.
   (subordinate clause)   (main clause)

By using subordination in sentence 2, the writer makes the time and place of the theft exact and emphasizes one idea—the theft of the wallet. Combining these two main clauses into one complex sentence also improves the style.

Most subordinate clauses can be divided into two major groups: adverb clauses and adjective clauses. Some subordinate clauses are used as noun clauses: Mario knew <u>that he had been careless with his money</u>. The subordinate clause is the direct object of the verb "knew."

Adverb Clauses

In adverb clauses, the most frequently used subordinators specify place, time, cause, condition, and contrast when indicating the relationship between main and subordinate clauses:

Place:	where, wherever
Time:	after, before, when, whenever, as, since, until, as soon as, while, as long as
Cause:	because, since, as
Condition:	if, whether, unless, whatever, when
Contrast:	although, even though, while, whereas

Adjective Clauses

The **adjective clause** is also called a relative clause because the subordinator "relates" the rest of the subordinate clause to a word or a word group in the main clause. The subordinate clause is an adjective modifying that part of the main clause by adding information about it.

Subordinators

who   whom   whose   which   that

Examples:

1. The (people) on the bus <u>had</u> <u>offered</u> to help him, and
   (Mario) <u>thanked</u> them. (two main clauses)

2. (Mario) <u>thanked</u> the (people) on the bus ((who)) <u>had</u>
   <u>offered</u> to help him. (one main clause and one subordinate clause)

The second sentence improves an awkward sentence by subordinating the first clause in sentence 1 to the second clause.
The subordinate clause clarifies the situation by restricting
the word <u>people</u> to those who helped Mario.

Exercise 6.3

Combine the following sentences into complex sentences.

A. Form a subordinate clause by placing the subordinator
   in parentheses in the position indicated by the caret
   (^).

B. Make any necessary changes in the punctuation and
   in the capitalization.

Example: ^ Ty Cobb, nicknamed "The Georgia Peach," was
one of the greatest of all baseball players. He
was a bitter, angry man. (Use <u>although</u>.)

<u>Although</u> Ty Cobb, nicknamed "The Georgia
Peach," was one of the greatest of all baseball
players, he was a bitter, angry man.

117

Better Grammar

1. His lifetime batting record ^ was 4,191 hits in 24 seasons. It remained unbroken until the summer of 1985. (Use <u>which</u>, omit <u>It</u>.)

_____

_____

_____

2. Cobb ^ was a multimillionaire. He gave financial help to young college students, endowed a hospital in his hometown, and gave anonymous aid to indigent ballplayers. (Use <u>who</u>, omit <u>He</u>.)

_____

_____

_____

3. He remained a public idol to many. ^ Most of his fans were ignorant of his violent disposition. (Use <u>since</u>.)

_____

_____

_____

4. Cobb welcomed a fight. ^ He was sick and old. (Use <u>even when</u>.)

_____

_____

_____

5. Cobb threatened to use a loaded handgun. ^ He carried
it with him. (Use <u>that</u>, omit <u>it</u>.)

_____

_____

_____

We often combine ideas by coordinating them—that is, by
linking them with the words <u>and</u>, <u>but</u>, <u>or</u>. Coordination works
well when the parts are of equal importance, but when the
ideas are not of equal importance, it's better to subordinate one
idea to another.

Using Subordination to Correct Comma Splices and Fused Sentences

Subordination gives you another way to correct **comma
splices** and **fused sentences** by placing one idea in a subordinate clause and the other in a main clause.

Example: My brother joined the merchant marine, he
was eighteen. (comma splice)

Correction: My brother joined the merchant marine when
he was eighteen.

Exercise 6.4

Correct the following comma splices and fused sentences.
Join the ideas in the main clauses into a complex sentence by
changing one main clause to a subordinate clause. Use the
subordinator in the parentheses. Punctuate the sentence
correctly.

Example: (since) Ed joined the merchant marine he has
been in many foreign ports.

Correction: Since Ed joined the merchant marine, he has
been in many foreign ports.

Better Grammar

1. (because) The coach was fired his team never won a game.

_____

2. (when) The cat dug holes in my flower bed, I chased it away.

_____

3. (although) They lost the first game they won the second one.

_____

4. (while) We were riding our bicycles, someone stole our car.

_____

5. (who, omit she) Toni is a full-time college student, she works thirty hours a week as a musician.

_____

Punctuation

At the beginning of a sentence, use a comma after a subordinate clause.

Example: When Alex reached the parking lot, he couldn't find his car.

Do not use a comma before a subordinate clause at the end of a sentence.

Example: Alex couldn't find his car when he reached the parking lot.

___

Use commas to enclose clauses containing nonessential material. The information may add some details, but the reader could understand the main idea of the sentence if the clauses were left out.

Example: Stan, <u>who arrived late</u>, had to sit in the last row.

Omit the words enclosed by commas, and the sentence reads:

Stan had to sit in the last row.

The main idea of the sentence is unchanged.
Do not use commas to enclose clauses that are essential to the meaning of the sentence.

Example: The people <u>who arrived early</u> had the best seats.

If the subordinate clause is omitted, the main idea of the sentence is lost: The people had the best seats. The clause is needed to identify the people—those who arrived early.

Exercise 6.5

Insert commas where necessary. Some sentences do not need commas added.

1. Jeanine's dog which is a poodle digs holes in the backyard.

2. The student who will be the first speaker at graduation was in my history class last semester.

3. The *Queen Mary* which was once an ocean-going luxury liner is docked in Long Beach.

4. Their new stereo which was more expensive than ours has excellent fidelity.

5. The traffic light that is on the corner of Fifth and Grand is not working this morning.

6.3 Sentence Fragments

A **sentence fragment** is a group of words that begins with a capital letter and ends with appropriate punctuation such as a period, but the group of words does not express a complete thought or contain a complete main clause.

Some professional writers use fragments in magazines and books. We hear sentence fragments used in conversation, as in the following example:

"Did you leave school early yesterday?"
"Yes, after my music class."

Although the last bit of dialogue begins with a capital letter and ends with a period, it is not a complete sentence. It is a sentence fragment. When used in formal writing, fragments tend to confuse the reader.

Four Types of Sentence Fragments

It will be easier for you to correct fragments in your own writing if you learn to recognize four types of fragments.

Punctuating Subordinate Clauses as Sentences

Identifying the Error: When Jean came home.

This is the most common form of fragment. This subordinate clause is punctuated like a sentence.

Correcting the Error: When Jean came home, she turned on the stereo.

1. You can, of course, simply remove the subordinator, and you will have a complete sentence.

2. More than likely, however, the fragment will appear among the sentences of a paragraph you are writing. Therefore, you should connect the fragment to a sentence that is before or after the subordinate clause and change the punctuation.

   (Error) We had just finished dinner. When Jean came home. (frag.)

   (Correct) We had just finished dinner when Jean came home.

Note

When a subordinate clause is at the beginning of a sentence, place a comma after it.

Missing Subjects or Missing Verbs

Identifying the Error: 1. Swims for an hour in the pool.
2. A place to study with few interruptions.

1. Swims for an hour in the pool. <u>Swims</u> is a verb, but both nouns (<u>hour</u> and <u>pool</u>) are objects of the prepositions <u>for</u> and <u>in</u>. So this is a fragment because there is no subject.

2. A place to study with few interruptions. <u>Place</u> is a noun that could serve as a subject, and although <u>study</u> can be a verb, that is not the case here. In

this word group, <u>to study</u> is a verbal. So, again, this is a fragment.

Correcting the Error:

Add a subject and/or a verb to each phrase to make a sentence.

       S

(Correct) Carla <u>swims</u> for an hour in the pool.

      S

(Correct) Ken <u>needed</u> a place to study with few

interruptions.

Using Verbals Instead of Verbs or Participles without Auxiliaries

Identifying the Error: Riding our bicycles on the bike path.

In this case, the writer mistakes the verbal for a main verb and also leaves out the subject.

Correcting the Error:

1. Supply an auxiliary verb and, if necessary, a subject.

(We) <u>were</u> <u>riding</u> our bicycles on the bike path.

2. Attach the fragment to the sentence preceding it or to the one following it.

             (verbal phrase)

(We) <u>enjoyed</u> ourselves, riding our bicycles on the bike path.

(verbal phrase)

Riding our bicycles on the bike path, (we) met
several friends there.

3. Supply a verb and a completer. The verbal phrase
<u>riding our bicycles</u> serves as the subject of the
sentence.

(Riding our bicycles) on the bike path <u>is</u> good
exercise.

Using Lists and Examples Not Connected to a Subject and Verb

Identifying the Error: 1. The pattern, pinking shears,
straight pins, and the material.

2. For example, my Psychology 1
final last semester.

A fragment is frequently a list or an example explaining
some thought that the writer has just expressed. This kind
of fragment often begins with one of the following words:

---

also	first	including
especially	for example	such as
except		

Correcting the Error:

Although you could turn the fragment into a sentence by
supplying its own subject and verb (For example, my
Psychology 1 final last semester was too long.), generally, you
should connect the fragment to the sentence preceding it:

Better Grammar

1. First, assemble the items you will need to cut out your skirt: the pattern, pinking shears, straight pins, and the material.

2. Some examinations are not fair. for example, my Psychology 1 final last semester.

Exercise 6.6

Change the fragments to a sentence in the spaces provided.

1. Michelle has completed almost all the courses required by her major. Except for English 1, Psychology 2, and History 17.

_____

_____

2. Shelby has big plans for the sweepstakes money if he wins it. For example, traveling to many foreign countries. Including several in Africa.

_____

_____

3. This fabric offers a number of advantages for traveling in the summer. Such as being washable, quick-drying, wrinkle-free, and lightweight.

_____

_____

4. She passed the time on jury duty by knitting. And by working crossword puzzles.

_____

_____

5. The instructor reviewed the material to be covered in the chapter test. Especially calling our attention to the last three pages.

_____

_____

Exercise 6.7

Mark F for fragment and S for sentence on the lines at the right.

1. The lifeguard talking to those children _____ is Kim's sister.

2. Handle that package with care. _____

3. The kit twisting and turning before _____ falling to the ground.

4. Whenever he does the shopping. _____

5. And will come home Tuesday. _____

6. First by cutting down on unnecessary _____ purchases.

7. Turning off the light, José climbed _____ into bed.

8. The job that he wanted. _____

9. Wondering what she would do until _____ payday.

10. Because I could not find a parking _____ space.

Chapter 7
Agreement

Identifying the subject and the verb is the first step in correcting subject-verb agreement errors. The verb agrees in person and number with its subject.

The subject and the verb must agree in number.

A <u>singular</u> subject (one person or thing) takes a <u>singular</u> verb.

> The bird sings.
> The wheel turns.
> The student reads.

A <u>plural</u> subject (more than one person or thing) takes a <u>plural</u> verb.

> The birds sing.
> The wheels turn.
> The students read.

Better Grammar

From these examples, or from a review of verb endings in Chapter 2, it should be clear that the singular verb in the present tense ends in **-s**.

A subject and a verb agree if you use the correct form of the verb with the subject. Add an **-s** to the singular verb in the present tense when the subject is <u>he</u>, <u>she</u>, or <u>it</u>, or a singular noun which can be replaced by <u>he</u>, <u>she</u>, or <u>it</u>.

In order to be sure that the verb agrees with the subject, mentally change the noun subject into a pronoun and then select the correct form of the verb.

Examples:

1. Bill walks to work. (Mentally change the subject <u>Bill</u> to <u>he</u>.) <u>He</u> walks to work.

2. Sarah drives a car. (Mentally change the subject <u>Sarah</u> to <u>she</u>.) <u>She</u> drives a car.

3. This pencil needs to be sharpened. (Mentally change the subject <u>pencil</u> to <u>it</u>.) <u>It</u> needs to be sharpened.

4. The tennis players run after the balls. (Mentally change the subject <u>tennis players</u> to <u>they</u>.) <u>They</u> run after the balls.

Again, notice that for singular verb form (the one with <u>he</u>, <u>she</u>, or <u>it</u>) you add an **-s** to the end of the verb in sentences 1, 2, and 3. In sentence 4, **-s** is not added to the verb <u>run</u> because the subject <u>tennis players</u> is plural.

Exercise 7.1

Rewrite each of the following sentences, making the subjects and the verbs singular. Some sentences may require the addition of a modifier, such as <u>a</u> or <u>the</u>. Keep all verbs in the present tense.

1. Palm trees give little shade.

_____

2. The students like the Spanish class.

_____

3. Old photographs are faded.

_____

4. The bus drivers collect our fares.

_____

5. Her cars require frequent repairs.

_____

• •
7.2 Subjects and Verbs—Four Difficult Patterns
• •

Words that Come Between the Subject and the Verb

Words that come between the subject and the verb do *not* change subject-verb agreement.

Examples:

1. The <u>runners</u> on our track team <u>win</u> a trophy every year.

   The subject <u>runners</u> is plural, so the verb <u>win</u> is plural. The words <u>on our track team</u> that come between the subject and the verb do not affect the agreement.

2. The lions, waiting in front of their trainer, obey his commands.

The subject _____ is plural, so the verb _____ is plural. The words <u>waiting in front of their trainer</u>, that come between the subject and the verb do not affect the agreement. (The subject is <u>lions</u> and the verb is <u>obey</u>.)

3. The jacket that I bought with two pairs of trousers was a bargain.

The subject _____ is singular, so the verb _____ is singular. The words <u>that I bought with two pairs of trousers</u> do not affect the agreement. (The subject is <u>jacket</u> and the verb is <u>was</u>.)

Exercise 7.2

Circle the subject and enclose in parentheses any words that come between the subject and the verb. Then underline the correct form of the verb. The first sentence serves as an example to follow.

1. Today the (purpose) (of many zoos in large cities) (<u>is</u>, are) not the same as in the past.

2. Until this century human visitors to the zoo, not the animals, (was, were) the first consideration.

3. An animal in one of these new zoos no longer (spends, spend) its life in a cramped cage.

4. Open-range quarters, like those in San Diego's Wild Animal Park, (gives, give) these creatures the room to live naturally.

5. Zoo keepers, whenever possible, (works, work) to preserve and protect exotic species.

Reversed Word Order

A verb agrees with the subject even when the subject comes *after* the verb.

Examples:

1. Waiting for me at home <u>were</u> two hungry (pets.)

    Do not mistakenly identify "home" as the subject. The object of a preposition does not affect the form of the verb. The plural subject <u>pets</u> that comes after <u>were</u> requires a plural verb.

    The way to find the subject (so you will know how to make the verb agree) is to rearrange the sentence by placing the subject before the verb.

    At home <u>were</u> two hungry (pets.)

    (becomes)

    Two hungry (pets) <u>were</u> at home.

2. There <u>are</u> several (reasons) for his absence.

    The plural subject <u>reasons</u> that follows the verb <u>are</u> calls for a plural verb.

3. Here <u>is</u> your (ticket) for the plane trip.

    The singular subject <u>ticket</u> that comes after the verb <u>is</u> requires a singular verb.

    In general, when sentences begin with <u>there</u>, <u>here</u>, and <u>where</u>, the subject follows the verb. Rearrange the sentence to find the subject:

133

Here i̲s̲ your (ticket) for the plane trip.

(becomes)

Your (ticket) for the plane trip i̲s̲ here.

Exercise 7.3

Circle the subject. Underline the correct form of the verb in each sentence. The first sentence has been completed as an example.

1. There (i̲s̲, are) (disagreement) on the seriousness of indoor air pollution.

2. Some researchers say that there (is, are) much to be learned about controlling indoor air quality.

3. Experts agree that there (is, are) greater chances of problems developing in older homes.

4. The first clue that a home may have a problem (is, are) often increased humidity.

5. Increased humidity in an insulated home (signals, signal) that the rate of air change is low and other air pollutants may be building up.

Compound Subjects Joined by **and**

Compound subjects joined by and usually take a plural verb.

$$\text{S} \underline{\hspace{2cm}} \text{S} \quad \text{V}$$

Example: Ice cream and yogurt are equally delicious.

The subjects in this sentence are ice cream and yogurt. They are joined by and, so the verb "are" is plural.

Compound Subjects Joined by <u>or</u>, <u>Neither...nor</u> or <u>Either ...or</u>

When subjects are joined by these connectives, the verb agrees with the subject *closer* to the verb.

$$\text{S} \qquad\qquad \text{S} \!-\!\!-\!\!-\!\text{ V}$$

Example: Neither the instructor nor the students <u>want</u> to work hard today.

The nearer subject, <u>students</u>, is plural, so the verb <u>want</u> is plural.

Exercise 7.4

Circle the verb that best completes each sentence.

1. A radio and a cassette player (is, are) included in the price of the car.
2. The radio and the cassette player (was, were) already installed at the factory.
3. Tomatoes and onions (is, are) good in a salami sandwich.
4. Coffee or dessert (is, are) included with the dinner.
5. The lawyer or his secretary (answer, answers) the phone.

Exercise 7.5

Circle the subject closer to the verb. Underline the correct form of the verb in each sentence.

Better Grammar

1. Either cake or cookies (tastes, taste) good with ice cream.

2. Neither the union members nor the president of the company (seem, seems) willing to compromise.

3. Neither my brother nor my sisters (was, were) college graduates.

4. Either fresh flowers or a bottle of wine (make, makes) a welcome gift.

5. Neither the students nor the instructor (hears, hear) the fire alarm.

Exercise 7.6

Insert the form of the verb <u>have</u> that best completes each sentence. Choose either <u>has</u> or <u>have</u>.

1. The telephone and the front doorbell in an apartment _____ not been working

2. The tenants and the landlord _____ tried unsuccessfully to solve the problem.

3. The electrician and the telephone repairperson _____ been trying to make an appointment to fix the bells.

4. Neither the landlord nor the tenants _____ been able to hear theknock on the door.

5. Because the workers cannot get into the apartment, neither the telephone nor the front doorbell _____ been fixed.

7.3 Subjects and Verbs—Special Problems

Subjects that Are Singular

When used as subjects, the words below take singular verbs.

any	every	no	some	other words
anybody	everybody	nobody	somebody	each
anyone	everyone	no one	someone	either
anything	everything	nothing	something	neither

Examples: Neither of the children likes squash.
Each of them has set a goal.
Everyone is here.
Somebody was knocking at the door.

Neither, each, everyone, and *somebody* are the subjects of these sentences.

Exercise 7.7

Underline the correct form of the verb in the parentheses.

1. No one in my class (works, work) during the summer.

2. Each of us (needs, need) a long vacation.

3. Neither of my two best friends (plans, plan) to look for a job.

4. Everybody in the class (spends, spend) the summer relaxing.

5. Nothing (seems, seem) better than that.

Subjects that Can Be Singular or Plural

When used as subjects, these six words can be singular or plural, depending upon the noun or the pronoun to which they refer.

| all | any | more | most | none | some |

Example: (plural) Where are the letters? <u>Have</u> (any) of
them been typed yet?

(singular) The work must be completed soon.
<u>Has</u> (any) of it been started?

Exercise 7.8

Underline the correct form of the verb in parentheses.

1. Karen collects dolls; some (is, are) quite expensive.

2. How many packages did you mail? All of them (has, have) been sent.

3. We prepared the food, but none of it (was, were) eaten.

4. I want a big dish of ice cream. (Is, Are) any left in the carton?

5. We didn't eat the meat because some (was, were) undercooked.

Collective Nouns

Collective nouns represent a collection of persons, places, things, ideas, or activities.

---

audience	college	crowd	jury	school
band	committee	family	management	society
class	company	government	number	team
		group		

It is often difficult to decide whether a collective noun is singular or plural. Most of the time, use a singular verb or rewrite the sentence to make the subject clearer.

Instead of saying: "The band are tuning their instruments," you could say, "The band members are tuning their instruments."

Examples:

1. The number of courses offered this semester is small.

2. My favorite musical group is playing at the club all week.

3. Our school band is buying its own bus.

Nouns Ending in *-s* that Are Not Plural

Physics, economics, mathematics, measles, mumps, and news are considered singular even though they end in **-s,** and they take singular verbs.

Example: (Mathematics) was my favorite subject in high school.

139

Exercise 7.9

Underline the correct verb.

1. Mumps (is, are) a contagious childhood disease.
2. Physics (was, were) a major field of interest for Albert Einstein.
3. Economics (is, are) the most difficult subject in John's schedule.
4. The international news (sounds, sound) encouraging for a change.
5. Measles sometimes (cause, causes) meningitis.

Time, Money, and Weight

Words that specify *time, money,* or *weight* require a singular verb when they are considered as a unit even if they are plural in form.

Examples:

1. Two (semesters) is really a short time.
2. Five (dollars) is a modest fee for an entrance exam.

Titles

Titles of songs, plays, movies, novels, or articles require singular verbs even if the titles are plural.

Example: (The Carpetbaggers) is both a novel and a movie.

Names of Organizations and Businesses

The names of organizations and businesses that are plural in form but singular in meaning require a singular verb. Substitute a pronoun for the proper noun to determine which verb to use.

$$\overset{\text{S}}{} \qquad \overset{\text{V}}{}$$

Examples: The Taylor Brothers store <u>advertises</u> in the

newspaper every Thursday. (It advertises...)

$$\overset{\text{———— S ————}}{} \qquad \overset{\text{V}}{}$$

The House of Representatives <u>is</u> in session

today. (It is in session today.)

Special Problems of Agreement

Who, That, *and* Which *as Subjects* Who, that, and which used as subjects take singular verbs if the words they refer to are singular. They take plural verbs if the words they refer to are plural.

Examples:

1. I <u>know</u> a woman who <u>plays</u> the tuba. (The verb *plays* is singular because it agrees with the subject *who*. Who is singular because it refers to *woman,* a singular noun.)

2. Dogs that bark <u>make</u> me nervous. (The verb *bark* is plural because it agrees with its subject *that*. That is plural because it refers to *dogs,* a plural noun.)

Exercise 7.10

Write the noun that <u>who</u>, <u>which</u>, or <u>that</u> refers to on the line at the right. Then underline the correct form of the verb in parentheses.

Example: Businesses that (<u>sell</u>, sells) products <u> businesses </u>
for leisure activities compete with
television.

1. The television set has become a home-   _____
   entertainment center for Americans who
   (seeks, seek) recreation during their leisure
   time.

2. The family of four that usually (goes,   _____
   go) to a movie theater once or twice a
   week can now save money, watching cable
   television at home.

3. People with videotape cassette recorders,   _____
   which (plugs, plug) into the television set,
   schedule their favorite programs at hours
   most convenient for the family.

4. Instead of going to a videogame arcade,   _____
   many consumers play videogames that
   (hooks, hook) up to their own televisions.

5. And, of course, commercial television,   _____
   which (has, have) been keeping Americans
   at home for years, continues to consume
   one billion hours of their time each day.

7.4 Agreement of Pronoun and Antecedent

Pronouns are words that refer to nouns, other pronouns, or noun phrases. The **antecedent** (A) is the noun, pronoun, or noun phrase that a **pronoun** (P) refers to.

$$\text{A}\longleftarrow\text{P} \qquad \text{A}\longleftarrow\text{P}$$

Example: Today Jane bought her wedding dress. It is

$$\longleftarrow\text{P}$$

beautiful and fits her perfectly.

The first sentence in the example contains a pronoun (her) that refers to the noun antecedent (Jane).

The second sentence contains two pronouns that refer to two noun antecedents in the first sentence.

it (pronoun) = wedding dress (noun antecedent)
her (pronoun) = Jane (noun antecedent)

Exercise 7.11

Underline the pronouns and write the antecedents on the line at the right.

Antecedent

$$\text{A}\longleftarrow\text{P}$$

Example: Andy hung his diploma on the wall.   Andy

1. At the zoo Tanya and Rosalie fed their peanuts to the monkeys.   _____

2. The engineer completed his report.   _____

143

3. Have you renewed your driver's license yet?   _____

4. I wondered if the teacher would call on me.   _____

5. John bought two sweaters because they were on sale.   _____

Words that Separate Antecedent and Pronoun

Be sure that the pronoun agrees with the antecedent and not with another noun that may be placed closer to the pronoun than the antecedent is.

    A   P

1. <u>One</u> of the players injured in the game sprained <u>his</u> ankle.

<u>One</u> is the singular antecedent of the pronoun <u>his</u>, not the plural noun players.

    A ←   A←———P   —P

2. The <u>woman</u> who led the <u>protestors</u> in <u>their</u> march raised <u>her</u> hands in a victory sign.

<u>Her</u> agrees with the singular antecedent <u>woman</u>.

<u>Their</u> agrees with the plural antecedent <u>protestors</u>.

Exercise 7.12

Fill in the correct pronoun on the lines in these sentences. Write the word that is the antecedent on the line at the right.

Antecedent

1. The artist who sold me these paintings   _____

   signed _____ name in the corner.

2. Some of the visitors left _____   _____

   umbrellas here.

3. Mrs. Jones, who owns several apartment   _____

   buildings, has won _____ case in

   court.

4. When the birds fly south in the winter,   _____

   how do _____ know where to go?

5. Several of the students have completed   _____

   all of _____ assignments.

Compound Antecedents

Compound antecedents usually require a plural pronoun.

Example: Betty and Ellie have <u>their</u> own cars.

However, if the two antecedents are joined by <u>or</u>, <u>neither...</u> <u>nor</u>, or <u>either...or</u>, the pronoun agrees with the one closer to the pronoun.

Example: Neither my brother nor my (parents) would admit that <u>they</u> couldn't solve my sister's algebra problems.

145

Better Grammar

When one subject is plural and the other singular, place the plural subject second to avoid writing an awkward sentence.

Example (awkward) Did either the plumbers or the electrician estimate how many days he would need to complete the work?

(rewritten) Did either the electrician or the (plumbers) estimate how many days they would need to complete the work?

Exercise 7.13

Fill in the correct pronoun on the lines in these sentences. Write the word or words that are the antecedents on the line at the right.

Antecedent

1. Both Ralph and George have turned in _____ books. _____

2. Mr. & Mrs. Asano have given us _____ help. _____

3. Either Martha or Angela will bring _____ dictionary to class. _____

4. Did either the gardener or the window cleaners send a bill for _____ work? _____

5. Neither Bruce nor Richard pays _____ mother any rent. _____

146

Collective Nouns

The following nouns are usually singular if you refer to the group as a unit:

audience	committee	government	number
band	company	group	school
class	crowd	jury	society
college	family	management	team

                    A   P

Example: Our school <u>band</u> bought <u>its</u> own bus.

In this example, you are referring to the band as a unit. [f you are unsure whether to use a singular or plural pronoun, rewrite the sentence to make it less awkward.

Exercise 7.14

Write <u>its</u> or <u>their</u> on the line in each of the following sentences.

1. The committee made _____ recommendation yesterday.

2. The senior class will vote for _____ officers tomorrow.

3. Will the jury ever reach _____ decision on this case?

4. The audience sat down quietly in _____ seats.

5. Last year the company that my father works for gave _____ employees a bonus in December.

Singular Words

The words below are singular. Pronouns that refer to these words should also be singular.

any	every	no	some	other words
anybody	everybody	nobody	somebody	each
anyone	everyone	no one	someone	either
anything	everything	nothing	something	neither
				one

              A   P

Example: Has <u>everyone</u> finished <u>his or her</u> test? (not, <u>their</u> test)

The use of <u>their</u> with words like <u>everyone</u> and <u>everybody</u> is gaining acceptance. Many people would agree that it is acceptable to write:

Has everyone finished <u>their</u> test?

When writing assignments for academic purposes, try rewriting the sentence to leave out the pronoun.

Rewrite: Has everyone finished the test?

This solution also avoids the problem of sexist language and the awkward alternative of writing:

Has everyone finished <u>his</u> or <u>her</u> test?

Exercise 7.15

Complete the following sentences with appropriate pronouns or rewrite the sentences to avoid problems of awkwardness.

1. Someone left _____ books on that desk.

2. Has anyone brought _____ camera?

3. Each of the girls has paid _____ dues to the club treasurer.

4. Nobody has received _____ grades in the mail yet.

5. Everyone must show _____ employee badge to the guard at the gate.

Note: The repeated use of his/her in a paragraph or an essay can become monotonous or sound forced. You usually can avoid this problem by using a plural noun antecedent and substituting their or by using a noun marker (a, an, or the).

Agreement of Who, Whom, Which, and That with Antecedents

Who, whom, which, and that should agree not only in gender, person, and number with their antecedents, but they should also agree with them in a special way. Who and whom refer only to people.

$$A \longleftarrow P$$

Correct: 1. Marilyn, who lives next door, wants to be a model.

$$A \longleftarrow P$$

Incorrect: 2. We have a dog who can shake hands. (Write: ... dog that ....)

Which refers only to animals or to non-human things.

$$A \longleftarrow P$$

Correct: 1. Roy's car, which is twenty years old, is still running.

149

Better Grammar

$$A \longleftarrow P$$

Incorrect: 2. He is a man <u>which</u> anyone would like.
(Write: ... man whom ....)

<u>That</u> may refer to animals or things. The usual rule has been not to use <u>that</u> to refer to people. However, the use of the word <u>that</u> to refer to people is gaining wider acceptance, especially in conversation. When you are writing formal English, however, it is a good idea to use <u>who</u> and <u>whom</u> in reference to people.

Correct: 1. The <u>car that</u> I bought six months ago is falling apart.

Correct: 2. The <u>two dogs that</u> belong to my neighbor like to dig.

Informal: 3. He doesn't like <u>people that</u> don't agree with him.

Formal: 4. He has no patience with <u>people who</u> do not share his views.

Exercise 7.16

Underline the pronoun that best completes each sentence.

1. The people (who, that) live on my street belong to a neighborhood-watch group.

2. I joined the group (who, that) was formed last year.

3. The neighborhood is watched by the people (who, that) live there.

4. There are signs in the windows of the members' houses (who, that) warn criminals to stay away.

5. I like living in a neighborhood (who, that) is safe.

If you have difficulty knowing whether to use who or whom to introduce a subordinate clause, study the following explanations.

Use who to introduce a subordinate clause when it is the subject of the verb in that clause.

Example: Mark did not know who had given the money to Alan.

(Who is the subject of the verb had given.)

Use whom to introduce a subordinate clause when it is the object of a verb or a preposition in that clause.

Example: Mark did now know whom Alan had given the money to.

(Whom is the object of the preposition to.)

Exercise 7.17

Choose the correct word to complete the following sentences.

1. Anthony, surrounded by the opponent's linemen, did not know (who, whom) was running down the field.

2. Anthony depended on the signals from the coach to tell him (who, whom) to throw the ball to.

3. The coach, (who, whom) had a clear view of the whole field from the sideline, signaled the numbers of the receiver to Anthony.

4. Anthony just threw the ball with all his might, hoping that it would reach the person for (who, whom) it was intended.

5. The fans in the crowd roared when they saw the receiver, (who, whom) was waiting in the end zone, catch the ball.

- -
7.5 Unclear Pronoun Reference
- -

You will confuse your reader if there are two or more nouns the pronoun can refer to or if there is no antecedent at all for the pronoun. Learn to provide one specific antecedent for each pronoun by studying this section.

More than One Possible Antecedent

Example: Pete told Max that he was becoming bald.

There are two possible antecedents. He could refer to either Pete or Max.

Revised: Pete said to Max, "I'm getting bald."
Pete told Max that Max was getting bald.

Example: Carol dropped the glass on the plate and broke it.

The antecedent is not clear. Did the glass break? Or was it the plate?

Revised: When Carol dropped the glass on the plate, the glass broke.
The plate broke when Carol dropped a glass on it.

Example: My sister gave a speech at her graduation ceremony. <u>This</u> pleased my family.

<u>This</u> does not clearly refer to a single noun. Either <u>ceremony</u> or <u>speech</u> could be the noun antecedent.

Revised: The speech that my sister gave at her graduation ceremony pleased my family.

No Specific Antecedent

Example: I liked camp because <u>they</u> were so friendly.

The pronoun <u>they</u> cannot refer to the singular noun <u>camp</u>. Substitute a specific noun for the pronoun <u>they</u>.

Revised: I liked camp because the counselors were so friendly.

Example: Her husband is a football coach, but she thinks <u>it</u> is boring.

<u>It</u> surely cannot refer to <u>husband</u> or <u>football coach</u>. Substitute a specific noun for the pronoun <u>it</u>.

Revised: Her husband is a football coach, but she thinks <u>football</u> is boring.

Exercise 7.18

The antecedents of the underlined pronouns in these sentences are unclean Give the pronouns specific antecedents or replace the pronouns with nouns. If necessary, rewrite the sentence.

Better Grammar

1. Marla told Tess that she had lost her pen.

---

2. There are so many automobile accidents because they are so careless.

---

3. Mr. Bronowski is a great surgeon. This is a rewarding profession.

---

4. Before taking a test, Roberto studies and gets a good night's sleep, which is important.

---

5. The graduates marched solemnly down the aisle to receive their diplomas. It was so inspiring.

Chapter 8
Commas

8.1 Coordinating Connectives Between Main Clauses; Items in a Series; Introductory Phrases and Clauses

Many writers are confused about when to use commas. Study and memorize the *ten* rules discussed in this chapter, and you will not be confused about the use of commas.

1. Use a Comma Between Two Main Clauses Connected by a Coordinating Connective

Place a comma before a coordinating connective (and, but, for, or, nor, so, and yet) when it joins two main clauses.

Example: The (outfielder) dropped the fly ball, and the (runner) on third base scored.

155

Better Grammar

Unnecessary Commas The following sentence does not have a comma before the connective. In this sentence, <u>and</u> connects the two parts of a compound verb, not two main clauses.

Example: The outfielder dropped the ball <u>and</u> committed an error.

Exercise 8.1

Insert commas where necessary.

1. Andrew did not want to wear his raincoat to school yesterday nor did he want to carry an umbrella.

2. I have seen that movie star before yet I cannot remember her name.

3. Louis and Gerald tried out for the basketball team and both of them were chosen.

4. Brett and Lula were married on Friday morning but they did not leave for Hawaii until Saturday.

5. Athletes must train hard and watch their diet every day or they will not be able to compete.

Exercise 8.2

If the sentence is punctuated correctly, write *Yes* on the line at the right. If the sentence is incorrectly punctuated, write *No* on the line at the right.

1. James will have to repair his car, or take the bus to work.   _____

2. Rita has no patience, for waiting in line.   _____

156

3. The fire started in the garage, and spread   _____
   rapidly to the house.

4. Angela sometimes drinks root beer, but   _____
   prefers cola.

5. Mr. Washington frequently sends letters to   _____
   the newspaper, but the editor has never
   printed·one.

2. Use Commas to Separate Items in a Series

Use commas to separate *three or more items* in a series. The items may be single words, phrases, or clauses. A comma before the last item is optional if there are exactly three items in the series. In the following examples, you may omit the comma before *and* in sentences 2 and 3 if you wish.

Examples:

1. Marty is taking courses in economics, typing, account-ing, and statistics this semester. (words)

2. I went to the bank, did some shopping, and returned home by eleven. (phrases)

3. Leroy cut the grass, Cathy pulled the weeds in the flower beds, and Pat trimmed the hedges. (main clauses)

Unnecessary Commas No commas are necessary in the following sentence because there are only two items in the series.

Example: Tennis and swimming are her favorite sports.

157

Exercise 8.3

Insert commas where necessary.

1. Last semester Evelyn took four classes at college worked twenty hours a week and sang in the church choir on weekends.

2. My favorite breakfast cereal contains the following ingredients: malt barley oats honey and raisins.

3. He caught the pass ran along the sideline for twenty yards into the end zone but failed to score because he had stepped out of bounds on the two-yard line.

4. The students were told to bring their workbooks dictionaries lined paper and pens to every class meeting.

5. The recipe listed the following ingredients: sugar butter flour cocoa walnuts milk and peanut butter.

Exercise 8.4

If the circled comma is necessary, write *Yes* on the line at the right. If the circled comma is unnecessary, write *No* on the line at the right.

1. In high school Jason began to worry about going to college (,) choosing a career and finding a high-paying job. _____

2. The chili we ordered for lunch was hot (,) and spicy. _____

3. Namibia, Botswana, Zimbabwe (,) and Mozambique border South Africa on the east, north and west. _____

4. Dean's favorite authors used to be Ray   _____
   Bradbury (,) and Robert Heinlein.

5. We have expanded our network to include   _____
   Wisconsin (,) Indiana, and Connecticut.

3. Use a Comma After Introductory Words and Phrases

At the beginning of a sentence, use a comma after a long phrase.

Examples:

1. *By the end of the second week of school,* Ken was count-
   ing the weeks until Thanksgiving weekend.

2. *Taking out his new camera,* Ken remembered that he
   had forgotten to buy film.

The comma after a single introductory word or an introductory short phrase is *optional.* Although many writers use the
comma after these expressions, others do not.

Examples:

1. We waited for forty minutes in the rain for the bus.
   Finally, it arrived, but every seat was taken.

2. When I come home from work every evening, I eat dinner, take a shower, and do my homework. *Last of all,* I
   eat a snack and watch a television program before I go
   to bed.

3. *After work_* four of us went bowling.

4. *In that heat_* no one could sleep comfortably.

If there is any question about the meaning of the sentence, use a comma after a single word or a short phrase of introduction.

Inside, the theater was cool and dark.
While riding, the men had difficulty staying awake.

Try reading these two sentences without commas, and you will see why the comma in each case is essential to understanding the meaning.

Exercise 8.5

Insert commas where necessary. Some sentences do not need commas added.

1. Within two or three months the parking lot will be less crowded.

2. After a short pause the speaker answered the questions from the audience.

3. Best of all the food is always served hot.

4. In many tropical countries the natives take a siesta in the middle of the day.

5. John has been commuting 25 miles a day to school. Fortunately he found an apartment for rent near the college yesterday.

Exercise 8.6

If the sentence is punctuated correctly, write *Yes* on the line at the right. If the sentence is incorrectly punctuated, write *No* on the line at the right.

1. During the emergency the water was _____
turned off for six hours.

2. While working at the doughnut shop _____
Kathy lost ten pounds.

3. Despite many years of lecturing, writing, _____
composing, and performing, the noted
pianist had no intention of retiring.

4. Jan spent almost an hour shopping for _____
groceries today. Of course, she forgot to buy
the one item she needed most.

5. Before making the long drive to Seattle we _____
bought two new tires for the car.

4. Use a Comma After Introductory Subordinate Clauses

Use a comma after a subordinate clause at the beginning of
a sentence.

Example: *When you move to your new office,* send us your
address.

Unnecessary Commas Do *not* use a comma before a subordinate clause at the end of a sentence.

Examples:

1. Jay sold his old typewriter *when he bought a new one.*

2. Sue had to go to the market *because she forgot to buy
milk.*

Exercise 8.7

Insert commas where they are needed. Some sentences do not need commas added.

1. Although Jo Ellen had always known the truth about Harry she still loved him.

2. Before you can understand calculus you must understand algebra and trigonometry.

3. If the rain doesn't stop soon the rivers will overflow their banks.

4. By the time you are ready to take the test you will be able to answer all of the questions correctly.

5. The thick salmon steak was delicious even though it was a little overcooked.

Exercise 8.8

If the sentence is punctuated correctly, write *Yes* on the line at the right. If the sentence is incorrectly punctuated, write *No* on the line.

1. Wendell is moving, because the landlord raised the rent.   _____

2. After breakfast Victor and Frances drove to a nearby resort where they purchased ski-lift tickets.   _____

3. If you need a dictionary and a notebook for class, you can buy them at the student bookstore.   _____

4. Nancy is a person, who enjoys giving parties.   _____

5. Richard decided to quit smoking as soon as _____
the Christmas holidays were over.

● ●

8.2 Adjectives Before a Noun; Words that Interrupt; Direct Address

● ●

5. Use Commas to Separate Adjectives Before a Noun

Use commas to separate two or more adjectives that modify the same noun if they are not linked by a coordinating connective. You can use two tests to tell whether or not to put a comma between modifiers before a noun.

1. Use a comma if <u>and</u> can be used to connect the adjectives.
2. Use a comma if you can reverse the order of the adjectives.

Example: Bob was the most aggressive, skillful player on the court.

Use a comma because you could say:

1. Bob was the most aggressive and skillful player on the court.

or

2. Bob was the most skillful, aggressive player on the court.

Unnecessary Commas Do *not* put a comma between adjectives if <u>and</u> cannot be placed between them or if you cannot reverse their order.

———

163

Example: He was the most aggressive, skillful_basketball player on the court.

1. You would not write <u>skillful</u> <u>and</u> <u>basketball</u> <u>player</u>.

2. You cannot reverse the words—<u>basketball skillful player</u>.

Therefore, do not put a comma between <u>skillful</u> and <u>basketball</u>.

The adjectives placed before <u>basketball player</u> modify both words. Do not put a comma between the final modifier and the noun.

Exercise 8.9

Insert commas as needed in the following sentences.

1. The raindrops fell into the clear blue deep water of the pool.

2. Shana left her discarded smelly clothes scattered around her large sunlit bedroom.

3. The acrobat entertained the huge enthusiastic audience by his skillful graceful performance.

4. In the early morning the joggers run effortlessly along the deserted shell-strewn beach.

5. Marge's pink sunburnt skin looked painful to me.

Exercise 8.10

If the sentence is punctuated correctly, write *Yes* on the line at the right. If the sentence is incorrectly punctuated, write *No* on the line.

1. The young woman had a round tanned   _____
   pleasant face.

2. Calvin found it especially hard to get up   _____
   on cold, rainy, Monday mornings.

3. Mrs. Vasquez bought four ripe, Bartlett   _____
   pears for dessert.

4. We spent several hours in the noisy,   _____
   crowded amusement park.

5. Hank bought a yellow stocking cap to wear _____
   with his green, nylon, ski, parka.

6. Use Commas to Enclose Words that Interrupt

Use commas on *both* sides of a word (or a group of words) that interrupts the flow of thought in a sentence.

Examples:

1. Airline pilots, <u>by the way</u>, are often cautious automobile drivers.

2. The guests, <u>it seems</u>, are enjoying the party.

3. Several changes in the enrollment procedure, <u>however</u>, are planned for the coming semester.

Do not use just one comma; enclose the interrupting word or words between two commas.

Unnecessary Commas Do not use commas to enclose prepositional phrases that do not interrupt the flow of thought in a sentence.

Better Grammar

1. A car <u>with a flat tire</u> was parked near the exit ramp of the freeway.
2. The dwarf lemon tree grew rapidly and <u>in no time at all</u> produced fruit.
3. Lunch was served immediately <u>after the meeting</u>.

These sentences do not require any commas.

Exercise 8.11

Insert commas where necessary.

1. We hope therefore that you will send our refund soon.
2. Karen's parents as a rule drive her to school every day.
3. The jury as a result took four days to arrive at the verdict.
4. The kitchen in fact has not been cleaned since last week.
5. My opinion in the long run is based on the facts as I understand them.

Exercise 8.12

If the sentence is punctuated correctly, write *Yes* on the line at the right. If the sentence is incorrectly punctuated, write *No* on the line.

1. Many of our present tax laws, you must _____ admit, should be changed.

2. Jerome has been living in Des Moines, _____
   with his parents for nineteen years.

3. There are after all, other ways of dealing _____
   with the disposal problem.

4. Burt jumped out of the chair and, in his _____
   excitement knocked over his cup of coffee.

5. An exercise program, for example could _____
   include a thirty-minute walk after dinner.

7. Use Commas to Set Off Words in Direct Address

Use commas to set off the names and titles of people spoken to directly.

Examples:

1. "Pat, will you please call Dr. Hodge for me?" Paul said.

2. "I called you, Dr. Hodge, to ask for some information," said Pat.

3. "How often should Paul take the medicine, Doctor?" asked Pat.

These three examples show words in direct address at the beginning, in the middle, and at the end of sentences. Notice the use of commas.

Exercise 8.13

Insert commas where necessary.

1. I don't entirely agree Jim with your position.

2. Play it again Sam.

Better Grammar

3. Ladies and gentlemen of the jury you have heard the evidence.

4. Ella tell me that you love me.

5. I hope Paulette that you will practice your lesson.

Exercise 8.14

If the sentence is punctuated correctly, write *Yes* on the line at the right. If the sentence is incorrectly punctuated, write *No* on the line.

1. A vote for me my fellow Americans is a vote for good government. _____

2. Paul, do you have a job for the summer? _____

3. It is a pleasure to award first prize to you Mrs. Odim. _____

4. Your suggestion, sir is the best one we have received. _____

5. We were delighted, Marvelle, to hear about your promotion. _____

8.3 Nonessential Words, Phrases, and Clauses; Direct Quotations; Dates, Geographical Names, and Addresses

8. Use Commas to Set Off Nonessential Words, Phrases, and Clauses

Use commas to enclose words, phrases, and clauses containing nonessential material. The information in these words may add some details, but the reader could understand the main idea of the sentence if they were left out.

Examples:

1. Marcie Evan, <u>who is our pitcher</u>, will be a sportscaster next fall.

2. *Cannery Row,* <u>a novel by John Steinbeck</u>, has been made into a movie.

Omit the words enclosed by commas, and the sentences above read:

1. Marcie Evan will be a sportscaster next fall.

2. *Cannery Row* has been made into a movie.

As you can see, the main ideas of both sentences are unchanged by omitting the nonessential words. In general, if the name or title is given first, the noun appositive or adjective clause that follows is placed within commas.

Unnecessary Commas Do not use commas to enclose words, phrases, and clauses that are essential to the meaning of the sentence.

169

Better Grammar

Example: Will the person <u>who parked in the loading zone</u> move his car?

If the subordinate clause <u>who parked in the loading zone</u> is omitted, the main idea of the sentence is lost. You are left with *Will the person move his car?* In fact, the person cannot be identified; you do not know who should move his car.

Example: The novel *Cannery Row* has been made into a movie.

In this sentence the title is necessary to identify the book. Therefore, you do not use commas.

In the two examples given, you would *not* enclose the underlined words by commas because they contain material essential to the meaning of the sentences.

Exercise 8.15

Insert commas where necessary.

1. My friend Carla Caraway went to New York to get a job as a dancer.

2. A young woman alone in a strange city must learn how to take care of herself.

3. She auditioned for Judith Jamison the famous choreographer of the Alvin Ailey company.

4. Carla breathless and exhausted waited after the audition to hear the choreographer's opinion.

5. Carla joined the Ailey company one of the best dance companies in the world.

Exercise 8.16

If the sentence is punctuated correctly, write *Yes* on the line at the right. If the sentence is incorrectly punctuated, write *No* on the line.

1. Dr. Eleanor Fisher, a professor of bio-chemistry, will be a guest speaker on campus Tuesday noon.   _____

2. Mike unable to remember the answer, skipped the second question and went on to the third.   _____

3. The man jogging around the track was listening to a transistor radio.   _____

4. Farm Fresh the supermarket chain that advertises on TV stays open until 1 a.m.   _____

5. Itzhak Perlman, a renowned violinist performed with the New York Philharmonic last night.   _____

Exercise 8.17

Insert commas where required to set off nonessential words, phrases, and clauses.

1. A talented American contralto Marian Anderson who had sung at the White House was barred from singing in Constitution Hall in Washington.

2. Instead Ms. Anderson sang at the Lincoln Memorial before 75,000 people who had gathered in support of her.

3. Three Aaron Copland ballets drawing upon American themes are Billy the Kid, Rodeo, and Appalachian Spring.

4. Copland wrote Appalachian Spring for Martha Graham choreographer and dancer.

5. Ernest Hemingway an American author began his first job as a newspaper reporter at the age of eighteen.

9. Use Commas to Set Off Direct Quotations

Use commas to set off direct quotations from the rest of the sentence.

Examples:

1. "Perhaps," my brother said to me, "you should study once in a while."

2. She asked, "Won't anybody help me?"

3. "I don't want to watch television tonight," Jan said.

4. "I'll be back in an hour," Jim answered, "so don't. leave without me."

In sentence 3, although "I don't want to watch television tonight," is a main clause, do not use a period until the end of the complete statement.

Note that commas are placed inside the quotation marks.

Exercise 8.18

Insert commas where necessary.

1. "I can never do these homework assignments" Gary complained.

2. "Well" said his mother "you haven't even tried."

3. "I never learn anything in that class" he said "so what's the point?"

4. "Besides" he said to her "I have a date tonight."

5. "Gary, you should do your assignment before you go out" his mother advised.

10. Use Commas in Dates, Geographical Names, and Addresses

Use commas after every item in dates, geographical names, and addresses as shown in the following examples:

Dates: Maria drove to school on Saturday, September 5, 1989.

Geographical names: Miami, Florida, is the site of the Orange Bowl.

Addresses: James's address is 2208 N. McKnight Road, Philadelphia, Pennsylvania 19103. (The zip code is not separated by a comma from the name of the state.)

Unnecessary Commas Commas may be omitted when the day of the month is not given or when the day of the month precedes the month.

Examples: Maria drove to school in September 1989.
Maria drove to school on Saturday, 5 September 1989.

Exercise 8.19

Insert commas where necessary.

1. George will move to Las Vegas Nevada in January.

2. His address has been The Stanford Arms Hotel Apt. 10 536 W. 18th Street Rittman Indiana 46206 for the last six years.

3. We will forward his mail to his new address: The Pyramid Hotel Las Vegas Nevada 89501.

4. The Battle of Gettysburg was fought on July 4 1863.

5. The annual rodeo in Palmdale California features a bull-riding contest.

Exercise 8.20

If the sentence is punctuated correctly, write *Yes* on the line at the right. If the sentence is incorrectly punctuated, write *No* on the line.

1. Send Lynn's mail in care of Mrs. R. B. _____
Singer, 1532 Stone Canyon Drive Santa
Maria Arizona 85321 starting Friday
July 28, 1991.

2. Alfred Holmes was born on February 12, _____
1950, in Englewood, New Jersey, according
to the records.

3. Circle March 15 on your calendar as an _____
important day.

4. Sean and Kathleen left Sunday July 16 _____
for Ireland.

5. Return this form to the Department of _____
Motor Vehicles, 128 S. Cadillac Ave.,
Newbury, Montana 59711, by Monday,
July 3, 1991, to avoid paying a penalty.

Chapter 9

Punctuation and Capitalization

When you speak, you use pauses, gestures, and changes in the pitch of your voice to signal the beginnings and endings of units of thought. When you read, marks of punctuation provided by the writer guide your understanding of the writer's ideas. When you write, you also must provide guideposts for your readers to help them understand what you mean.

9.1 Period, Question Mark, and Exclamation Point

Period (.)

1. Use a period at the end of a sentence to separate it from the next one.

   Example: We made plans for a European trip. We studied maps and travel books.

2. Use a period after an abbreviation.

Examples: Mr. Jones   etc.
Prof. Anderson   p.m.
Dr. Brown   B.A.

3. Use a period after initials.

Examples: K. C. Jones   Howard C. Smith

4. It is not necessary to use a period in abbreviations that are composed of the first letter of two or more words.

Examples: UCLA   NAACP
USA   NASA
CIA   FBI

Question Mark (?)

Use a question mark at the end of a <u>direct question</u>.

Example: Do you really want to go to Europe?

Do not use a question mark after an <u>indirect question</u>, a sentence in which the question is part of the statement.

Example: We asked ourselves if we really wanted to go to Europe.

Exclamation Point (!)

Use an exclamation point after words, phrases, or clauses that express shock or excitement.

Examples: I'm falling!   Help!

Do not overuse the exclamation point. Save it for genuine expressions of emotion.

Exercise 9.1

Add periods, question marks, or exclamation points to the following sentences.

1. When did you last study punctuation

2. Mr Newman is a famous actor

3. Help Fire

4. I would be living in New York if I could afford an apartment on E 68th Street

5. He earned his B A degree from N Y U

6. Hal wondered what was wrong with him

7. What is wrong with Hal

8. Hooray We've won the game

9. When we were young, we never questioned why we were poor

10. How are you today

9.2 Semicolon and Colon

Semicolon (;)

1. The semicolon is used as a connector.

A. The semicolon joins two main clauses with closely related ideas to form a compound sentence.

Example: Please give me your history assignment; I was
absent from class yesterday.

B. The semicolon is used before adverbial connectives
like however, nevertheless, consequently, therefore,
and then to join two main clauses.

Example: The crew was cold and hungry; nevertheless,
they worked until dark.

2. The semicolon is used as a separator. The semicolon is
used between words or word groups in a series if the
items in the series contain one or more commas.

Example: Other points of interest in Europe were the
Louvre, Paris; the Colosseum, Rome; and the
British Museum, London.

Colon (:)

1. The colon is used at the end of a main clause to introduce a list.

Example: We have always wanted to visit four other countries: Poland, Hungary, Austria, and Switzerland.

2. The colon often comes after words like the following or
as follows.

Example: In Austria we would visit the following cities:
Vienna, Salzburg, and Innsbruck.

No colon is used between a verb and the objects or completers that follow it.

O

Examples: a. The tour (bus) <u>carries</u> the passengers, their

    O   O

    guide, and their luggage.

    b. The three (runners) (who) <u>represented</u> our

                                 C

    college at the track meet <u>were</u> Ron Washington,

    C   C

    Glenda Thomas, and Jorge Sandoval.

A colon after the verb <u>carries</u> would separate the verb from its objects, and a colon after the verb <u>were</u> would separate the verb from its completers. Remember that a complete sentence must come before the colon.

3. The colon is used after a salutation in a business letter.

Example: Dear Mr. Wilkins:
    Please consider me for the position of junior
    accountant in your firm.

4. The colon separates the hours and minutes when you are writing the time.

Example: Our class meets daily at 10:30 a.m.

Do not use a colon if no minutes are given.

Example: Our class meets daily at 10 a.m.

Exercise 9.2

Insert semicolons or colons where needed in the following sentences.

1. The telephone call brought David the news he had been waiting for he had been offered a job in Dallas.

2. First, Brett turned on the television then he poured himself a drink.

3. When baking a carrot cake, one should prepare the following ingredients flour, baking soda, oil, eggs, and carrots.

4. Terri has owned three cars an '80 Buick, an '84 Chevy, and an '88 Ford.

5. Three women who won prizes at the California State Fair were Alice Mills, Sacramento Betty Ford, Palm Springs and Jane Kelly, Modesto.

6. The students had planned to study in the law library however, it was closed when they arrived.

7. The charter flight was scheduled to leave at 3 45 p.m. nevertheless, at 4 p.m. the tourists were still checking in their baggage.

8. The menu lists the following entrees lasagna, fettuccini, and ravioli.

9. It has not rained much this winter therefore, we may have a shortage of water.

10. Come to our house after the movie we will have coffee in the comfort of our home.

9.3 Quotation Marks

Direct Quotations

Quotation marks are used primarily in direct quotations. Put quotation marks around the exact words of the speaker.

Examples:

1. Jimmy called, "Anyone for tennis?"

2. "I would rather play golf," replied Lee.

Note the punctuation for direct quotations:

Use a comma before the direct quotation.
Use quotation marks around the speaker's exact words.
Use a capital letter for the first word of the direct quotation.

Split Quotations

Examples:

1. "But, Linda," he said, "you and Cheryl have never ridden on the Colossus."

2. "You go ahead and ride on it," she answered. "We'll stay here and watch you.

Note the punctuation for split quotations:

In 1, the word <u>you</u> begins with a small letter because the words on either side of <u>he said</u> are the two parts of a single sentence.

In 2, there are two sentences. The first one begins with <u>You</u> and ends with <u>she answered</u>. Therefore, the <u>W</u> of <u>We'll</u> is capitalized as the first word of the second sentence.

End Punctuation in Quotations

Periods and commas are always placed <u>inside</u> quotation marks.

Examples:

1. "I would rather play golf," replied Lee.

2. "We'll stay here and watch you."

Question marks and exclamation points are placed <u>outside</u> quotation marks except when the quotation itself is a question or an exclamation.

Example: Did Jimmy say, "I want to play tennis"?

Exceptions:

1. Jimmy called, "Anyone for tennis?" (The quotation is a question.)

2. The crowd shouted, "Touchdown! Touchdown!" (The quotation is an exclamation.)

Quotations within Quotations

Single quotation marks are used to enclose quoted material within a direct quotation.

Example: He never tires of saying, "Remember Patrick Henry's words: 'Give me liberty or give me death.'"

Unnecessary Quotation Marks Do not enclose an indirect quotation in quotation marks. It is a report in different words of what a speaker or writer said. The word "that" usually indicates the following words are an indirect quotation.

Examples:

1. Joan said, "This assignment is Greek to me" (direct quotation)
   Joan said that the assignment was Greek to her. (Indirect quotation, do *not* use quotation marks.)

2. Marcus swore, "I'll never eat at Joe's pizza Palace again." (direct quotation)
   Marcus swore that he would never eat at Joe's Pizza Palace again. (Indirect quotation, do *not* use quotation marks.)

The Use of Quotation Marks and Underlining in Titles

A. Use quotation marks for short works.

1. title of article
2. title of chapter
3. title of short story

4. title of song

5. title of poem

B. In handwritten or typed work, underline the words that would be italicized in printed material.

1. title of book

2. title of magazine

3. title of newspaper

4. title of play, movie, work of art

5. title of record album, compact disc, or video

6. foreign words

7. words used as words

C. Never use quotation marks around the title of your own composition.

Examples:

1. Have you read the article "Getting the Airmail off the Ground" in the May issue of <u>Smithsonian</u>?

2. We decided to rent <u>Gone with the Wind</u> and <u>Fantasia</u> to watch at home.

3. The English instructor assigned two stories for us to read: "A Perfect Day for Bananafish" and "Uncle Wiggily in Connecticut" in the paperback <u>Nine Stories</u> by J.D. Salinger.

4. I bought two CDs at the record store: <u>Maiden Voyage</u> by Herbie Hancock and <u>Miles Ahead</u> by Miles Davis.

5. "Guiding Children's Book Selection," a chapter in <u>Children & Books</u>, contains standards for evaluating books.

6. The word <u>freedom</u> is difficult to define.

Exercise 9.3

Use quotation marks or underline as needed in the following sentences.

1. Few people who have read Shirley Jackson's The Lottery or William Faulkner's A Rose for Emily can forget those short stories.

2. Have you seen The Tempest at the Old Globe Theater yet? he asked.

3. Ben said that he had just returned the book Beloved, by Toni Morrison, to the library.

4. The manager ran out of the store and shouted, Stop that shoplifter!

5. Can you believe that Mr. Marquez said, Read the next four chapters by tomorrow?

6. The article A Private Solution to a Public Problem in this morning's Times offers one more proposal to ease the state's financial crisis.

7. When Rose was three years old, her favorite poem was The Owl and the Pussycat.

8. Cheers, Roseanne, and L.A. Law are three television shows that Ron always watches.

9. Poetry and advertising have much in common, according to a chapter entitled Poetry and Advertising in the book, Language in Thought and Action.

10. Lauren obtained material for her speech from the article, College Tuition, in The Atlantic magazine.

9.4 Hyphen and Dash

Hyphen (-)

1. Use a hyphen to join two or more words that serve as a single adjective describing a noun.

Example: My son and I had a heart-to-heart talk.

2. Use a hyphen to divide a word at the end of a line of writing or typing. If you are unsure about the correct syllable division, consult a dictionary.

Example: Hazel and Hugh discussed their son's problems together.

Never divide a word of one syllable at the end of a line. Whenever possible, avoid dividing a word.

3. Use a hyphen with fractions, compound nouns, and compound numbers.

Example: thirty-five   forty-ninth   father-in-law
self-improvement   one-half

Exercise 9.4

Insert hyphens where they are needed in the following sentences.

1. A fifty year old man has won the marathon race.

2. Unfamiliar with the city, Steven made a left hand turn into a one way street.

3. I have all my wool sweaters dry cleaned.

4. The sharp eyed detective noticed the run down heels of the sus pect.

5. My sister in law Renata bought a second hand typewriter for seventy two dollars.

6. Margot works as a free lance writer; she edits self help books.

7. Two thirds of the Senate voted for the proposed insurance bill cov ering high risk drivers.

8. The snipers were hiding in the bullet scarred high rise building.

9. As the mayor elect, Mr. Barr was called on to lecture the upper class students of the high school on self reliance.

10. Dennis half heartedly tried self hypnosis to stop smoking.

Dash (—)

A dash signals an interruption in the sentence. Use dashes before and after interrupters.

Examples:

1. Some—but not all—of the problems were difficult.

2. I had volunteered to work this summer—but why bother about that now?

Note: On a typewriter, strike the hyphen key twice to form the dash. Do not overuse the dash. It should not be used as a substitute for commas, semicolons, or colons just because you are unsure about which to use.

• •

9.5 Capital Letters
• •

Always capitalize:

1. The first word of a sentence and the first word of a line of poetry.

He ran down the street.

2. The first word of a direct quotation.

He said, "The restaurant is on fire!"

3. The name of a person.

Albert Einstein

4. The personal pronoun *I*.

I, I'm

5. The names of continents, countries, nationalities, states, cities, bodies of water, places, and streets.

Asia, Greece, American, California, Dallas, Pacific Ocean, Griffith Park, Main Street

6. The names of the days of the week, months, holidays (but not the seasons).

Sunday, May, Mother's Day, Labor Day

7. The names of commercial products (but not the type of product).

Dentyne gum, Pillsbury flour, Ivory soap

8. The names of companies, organizations, government agencies and offices.

General Motors Co., Democratic Party, Department of Motor Vehicles, Federal Bureau of Investigation

9. The titles of persons,   **Mr., Dr.,** Reverend,
books, magazines,   President Lincoln, "Dream
newspapers, articles,   Deferred," *The Jeffersons*
stories, poems, films,
television shows, songs,
papers that you write.
Note: Do not capitalize
small words like *the, in,*
or *a* within titles.

10. The names of schools,   **W**est Los Angeles College,
colleges, and universities, Department of English,
academic departments,   Associate of Arts, History
degrees, and specific   101
courses.

Exercise 9.5

Capitalize where necessary.

1. anh nguyen has become an american citizen.

2. i'm passing english 1, but i'm failing history 21.

3. when mary went to new york, she visited the metropolitan museum of art.

4. i have already seen the play, *phantom of the opera.*

5. sue's favorite lunch consists of ritz crackers, kraft cheese, and coca-cola.

6. when darlene went to sears, she bought wamsutta sheets for her new water bed.

7. are you going to watch the sugar bowl game on new year's day?

8. in the spring i usually spend saturdays working in my garden.

9. yellowstone national park is the largest national park in the united states.

10. my instructor told me to read a novel by hemingway this weekend, but i watched television.

Chapter 10

Usage

Words that sound alike or look alike can cause many problems in spelling. Study the following words and refer to these pages when you are writing your paragraphs.

10.1 A / An / And

1. Use <u>a</u> before words beginning with consonants or consonant sounds.

Examples: <u>a</u> chair, <u>a</u> boy, <u>a</u> tree, <u>a</u> picture, <u>a</u> youth

2. Use <u>an</u> before words beginning with vowels *(a, e, i, o u)* or a silent *h*.

Examples: <u>an</u> apple, <u>an</u> egg, <u>an</u> idea, <u>an</u> honor, <u>an</u> opal

3. <u>And</u> connects words, phrases, and clauses. It is a coordinating connective.

Examples: Don <u>and</u> I are going to the concert.

10.2 Accept / Except

1. <u>Accept</u> is a verb. It means to receive gladly, to agree to.

Example: I <u>accept</u> your invitation with pleasure.

2. <u>Except</u> is a preposition. It means excluding, but.

Example: Everyone was here <u>except</u> Jerry.

Exercise 10.1

Fill in the blanks with the correct words:

1. Please _____ my apology.

2. Marilyn cleaned every room in the house _____ the bathroom.

10.3 Advice / Advise

1. <u>Advice</u> is a noun. It means an opinion, from one not immediately concerned, about what could or should be done about a problem.

Example: Sally loves to give <u>advice</u> to everyone.

2. <u>Advise</u> is a verb. It means to offer advice; to counsel. Note: Pronounce the *s* like a *z*.

Example: My counselor <u>advised</u> me to petition for graduation soon.

Exercise 10.2

Fill in the blanks with the correct words:

1. Can the professor _____ me what courses to take next semester?

2. Will you follow his _____ ?

10.4 Affect / Effect

1. <u>Affect</u> is usually used as a verb. It means to have an influence on; to touch or move the emotions of someone.

Example: We have learned that using drugs <u>affects</u> our health.

2. <u>Effect</u> is usually used as a noun. It means the final result; the outcome.

Example: The <u>effect</u> of a drug on the nervous system is quickly observed.

Exercise 10.3

Fill in the blanks with the correct words:

1. The recent cold weather _____ the fruit crop.

2. The _____ of the budget cut was felt by all the employees.

•••

10.5 Already / All Ready
•••

1. <u>Already</u> is an adverb. It means by this time; before; previously.

Example: I have <u>already</u> eaten lunch, thank you.

2. <u>All ready</u> is an adjective. It is used to express complete readiness.

Example: The tourists were <u>all ready</u> to board the plane.

Exercise 10.4

Fill in the blanks with the correct words:

1. Everyone is _____ to go to the beach.

2. The students had _____ studied for the test.

10.6 Dessert / Desert

1. <u>Dessert</u> is a noun. It means the last course of a lunch or a dinner.

Example: My favorite <u>dessert</u> is apple pie.

2. <u>Desert</u> is used as a noun to mean barren land, an area of little rainfall.

Example: There is a large <u>desert</u> in Africa.

3. <u>Desert</u> is used as a verb to mean to leave or abandon.

Example: The soldier <u>deserted</u> his post during the battle.

Exercise 10.5

Fill in the blanks with the correct words:

1. Maria prepared fried bananas for _____ .

2. Many flowers bloom in the _____ in the spring.

3. James's father _____ his family.

10.7 Its / It's

1. <u>Its</u> is the possessive form of the pronoun it.

Example: The cat licked <u>its</u> fur.

2. <u>It's</u> is the contraction of <u>it is</u> or <u>it has</u>.

Example: <u>It's</u> time to eat.

Many writers are tempted to add <u>'s</u> to the pronoun <u>it</u> to form the possessive. To avoid this error, read <u>it's</u> as <u>it is</u> whenever you see it to ensure that you are using the contraction of <u>it is</u> rather than the possessive of <u>it</u>, which should always be <u>its</u>.

Exercise 10.6

Fill in the blanks with the correct words:

1. _____ been raining all day.

2. The bear stuck _____ paw into the beehive.

10.8 Know / No

1. <u>Know</u> is a verb. It means to understand; to be familiar with; to be certain of.

Example: Ed <u>knows</u> where Angie lives.

2. <u>No</u> is a negative. It means not any; not one.

Example: You have <u>no</u> reason to stay in bed today.

Exercise 10.7

Fill in the blanks with the correct words:

1. Some professors _____ their students well.

2. Lisa has _____ more money in her wallet.

10.9 Lead / Led

1. Lead is a noun. It is pronounced like *led*. It means a soft, bluish white element used in pencils. If it is used as a verb, it is pronounced "leed." It means to show the way by going in advance; to conduct.

Examples: Lead is a dense metal.
The conductor will lead the orchestra.

2. Led is the past tense and past participle of the verb lead.

Example: The guide led us out of the forest.

Exercise 10.8

Fill in the blanks with the correct words:

1. Early alchemists tried to make gold out of _____ .

2. The sergeant _____ his men into battle.

197

······································
10.10 Loose / Lose
··

1. <u>Loose</u> is an adjective. It means not tight fitting; too large; not fastened.

Example: The string on that package is too <u>loose</u>.

2. <u>Lose</u> is a verb. Pronounce the *s* like a *z*. It means to misplace; to fail to win.

Example: I hope my horse won't <u>lose</u> the race.

Exercise 10.9

Fill in the blanks with the correct words:

1. I will _____ the key if I don't buy a new key ring.

2. Linda likes to wear _____ slippers on her feet.

···
10.11 Past / Passed
···

1. <u>Past</u> is a noun. It means the time before the present. It can be used as an adjective to describe that which has already occurred.

Example: Try not to think about the <u>past</u>.

198

2. <u>Passed</u> is the past tense and past participle form of the verb <u>pass</u>. It means succeeded in, handed in, or went by.

Example: Andrea waved and smiled as she <u>passed</u> by us. Larry <u>passed</u> in his term paper on time.

Exercise 10.12

Fill in the blanks with the correct words:

1. Henry liked to tell us about his _____ experiences.

2. Tom _____ by our house last night about this time.

10.12 Personal / Personnel

1. <u>Personal</u> is an adjective. It means something private or one's own. Pronounce this word with the accent on the first syllable.

Example: My diary is my <u>personal</u> property.

2. <u>Personnel</u> is a noun. It means the group of people employed by a business or service. Pronounce this word with the accent on the last syllable. It may take either a singular or a plural verb.

Example: The president of the company sent a memo to all of the <u>personnel</u>.

Exercise 10.11

Fill in the blanks with the correct words:

1. Please don't ask so many _____ questions.
2. She was vice-president in charge of _____ in our company.

• •
10.13 Principal / Principle
• •

1. Principal is usually used as a noun. It means a person who is a leader, someone who is in charge. When it is used as an adjective, it means leading or chief.

Example: The principal of the high school spoke at the assembly.

2. Principle is a noun. It refers to basic truths, rules of human conduct, and fundamental laws.

Example: Our constitution is based on the principles of democracy.

Exercise 10.12

Fill in the blanks with the correct words:

1. I know him to be a man of high _____ .
2. The _____ partner in the law firm signed the contract.

10.14 Quiet / Quite

1. Quiet means silent, free of noise,

Example:: I need a quiet place to study.

2. Quite means entirely, really, rather.

Example: You have been quite busy all day.

Exercise 10.13

Fill in the blanks with the correct words:

1. The Smith family live on a very _____ street.

2. The street is not _____ as _____ as it used to be.

10.15 Suppose / Supposed

Suppose is a verb. It means to assume to be true; to guess; to think.

Example: Do you suppose it will rain today?

Note: The verb suppose is often used in tbe passive and is followed by to. Do not forget to add the **d** to the verb: supposed.

Supposed to, in this sense, means to expect or require.

Example: He is <u>supposed to</u> go to the store.

The example means that he is expected to go to the store.

Exercise 10.14

Fill in the blanks with the correct words:

1. This is _____ to be one of the best restaurants in town.

2. I _____ we will arrive home by noon.

10.16 Then / Than

1. <u>Then</u> is an adverb. It means at that time; next in time, space, or order.

Example: Rhonda <u>then</u> decided to leave.

2. <u>Than</u> is used in comparative statements to introduce the second item.

Example: This suitcase is heavier <u>than</u> that one.

Exercise 10.16

Fill in the blanks with the correct words:

1. First we ate dinner, and _____ we went to the concert.

2. Mike gets up earlier _____ Jay does.

••
10.17 There / Their / They're
••

1. There shows direction. It means at that place. It is often used to introduce a thought, as in there is or there are.

Example: Put the tape recorder over there.

2. Their is the possessive form of the pronoun they. It means belonging to them.

Example: The fans received their tickets in the mail.

3. They're is a contraction of the two words they are.

Example: They're very thoughtful people.

Exercise 10.16

Fill in the blanks with the correct words:

1. I hear that _____ giving a party in _____ new home.

2. _____ is going to be a parade on St. Patrick's Day.

10.18 Through / Though / Thought

1. <u>Through</u> means finished. It also means to go in one side and out the other.

Examples: He is <u>through</u> with his work.
We walked <u>through</u> the park after dark.

2. <u>Though</u> means the same as although; despite the fact that.

Example: <u>Though</u> Jim had left home early, he arrived at work late.

3. <u>Thought</u> is the past tense and the past participle of <u>think</u>. It can also he used as a noun, and it means an idea.

Example: I <u>thought</u> you had gone home.

Exercise 10.17

Fill in the blanks with the correct words:

1. I _____ you drove to New England last year.

2. _____ I closed the door quickly, the cat ran

_____ it.

10.19 To / Two / Too

1. <u>To</u> means in the direction of, when it is used as a preposition.

Example: Pierre is going <u>to</u> Canada this summer.

Sometimes the word <u>to</u> is the first word in a verbal phrase.

Example: We are going <u>to move</u> to a new apartment next month.

2. <u>Two</u> is the same as the number 2.

Example: "You have <u>two</u> phone messages," Selena told her boyfriend.

3. <u>Too</u> means also; in addition to; very; overly so.

Example: The soup was <u>too</u> hot to eat.

Exercise 10.18

Fill in the blanks with the correct words:

1. _____ of the masked men approached the bank teller.
2. This dress is _____ old _____ wear _____ the party.

10.20 Use / Used

l. <u>Use</u> is a verb. It means to employ; to make use of. Pronounce the *s* like *z*.

Example: We <u>use</u> a broom to sweep the floor.

2. <u>Used</u> is often followed by the word *to*. It means accustomed to; familiar with; was in the habit of.

Example: Selma was <u>used to</u> working eight hours a day.

Exercise 10.19

Fill in the blanks with the correct words:

1. John is not _____ to staying up late.

2. Accountants _____ adding machines often.

10.21 Weather / Whether

1. <u>Weather</u> is a noun. It refers to the state of the atmosphere at a given time or place.

Example: The <u>weather</u> in Kansas City is usually cold in December.

2. <u>Whether</u> is a subordinator. It means if it is so that; if it is the case that; in case; either.

Examples: We should find out <u>whether</u> the museum is open on Sundays.
He passed the test, <u>whether</u> by skill or luck.

Exercise 10.20

Fill in the blanks with the correct words:

1. Airline pilots frequently check the _____ conditions along the route.

2. Rosetta did not know _____ to laugh or to cry.

10.22 Whose / Who's

1. <u>Whose</u> is the possessive form of the pronoun <u>who</u>. It means belonging to whom.

Example: <u>Whose</u> tennis shoes are these?

2. <u>Who's</u> is a contraction of the two words <u>who is</u>.

Example: <u>Who's</u> that man over there?

Exercise 10.21

Fill in the blanks with the correct words:

1. Tanya is someone _____ never at a loss for words.

2. I don't know _____ book is on the table.

10.23 Your / You're

1. Your is the possessive form of the pronoun *you*. It means belonging to you.

Example: Your car is in the parking lot.

2. You're is the contraction of the two words you are.

Example: You're going to enioy this book, Lorraine.

Exericse 10.22

Fill in the blanks with the correct words:

1. _____ going to the concert with us tomorrow.

2. You bought _____ ticket a few weeks ago.

Answer Key

Chapter 1

Exercise 1.1

  X   N   N   X   N   X
1. on, highway   2. Rain, last   3. drivers, cautious

  N   N   N   N
4. surface, road   5. Buick, brakes

Exercise 1.2

        N   N   N
1. Mr. Cuadros gave us two free tickets to the basketball game.

            N   N   N
2. Would you like a bowl of chicken soup and a fresh fruit salad?

            N   N   N
3. I bought a digital watch for thirty dollars at the Kmart.

  N   N   N
4. Lori wore a new green wool dress to her job interview.

Better Grammar

$$\text{N} \qquad\qquad \text{N} \qquad\qquad\qquad \text{N}$$

5. The young doctor had a pleasant smile and a reassuring manner.

Exercise 1.3

1. dogs 2. dates 3. tricks 4. tests 5. sales 6. words
7. sentences 8. paragraphs 9. operators 10. students

Exercise 1.4

1. skies 2. days 3. ladies 4. penalties 5. keys 6. turkeys
7. counties 8. candies 9. armies 10. batteries

Exercise 1.5

1. brushes 2. watches 3. buses 4. waltzes 5. taxes
6. glasses 7. boxes 8. messes 9. rashes 10. stitches

Exercise 1.6

1. selves 2. halves 3. hooves or hoofs 4. shelves 5. proofs
6. lives 7. thieves 8. wolves 9. cliffs 10. wives

Exercise 1.7

1. sopranos 2. vetoes 3. tomatoes 4. potatoes 5. pianos
6. radios 7. zeros or zeroes 8. ratios 9. heroes
10. dominos or dominoes

Exercise 1.8

1. mice 2. teeth 3. women 4. children 5. men

Exercise 1.9

1. the cats' names 2. their owners' commands 3. the baby's
crib 4. the baby's mother 5. Ginny's food

Exercise 1.10

1. Saturday's 2. weeks' 3. Year's 4. day's 5. penny's

Exercise 1.11

1. no apostrophe   2. friends'   3. refugees'   4. no apostrophe
5. no apostrophe   6. students'   7. no apostrophe
8. customer's or customers'   9. parents'   10. no apostrophe

Exercise 1.12

1. I enjoy eating out instead of cooking at home. Living in Seattle, I have a choice of many different kinds of restaurants. My favorite restaurant is a Japanese one near my home. It is very small and very popular, so I usually have to wait for a table.
2. If a person wants to learn to play a musical instrument well, he or she will have to develop self-discipline. The serious music student, for example, must be willing to give up watching two or three hours of television a day and, instead, spend his or her time practicing.
3. During the past year or two, the price of food has risen sharply. Every time I go to the market, you can see increases in several items. Not so long ago, your twenty dollars bought quite a few bags of groceries, but now I can carry twenty dollars' worth of food home in one bag.
4. I received a camera for a graduation present last year. It worked fine at first, but after a few months, I could tell that something was wrong with it. The pictures were so blurry that I couldn't recognize the people in them. The repairperson at the camera shop wanted too much money to repair it, so I stopped using it. I would be wasting my money to buy film for that lemon.
5. My brother likes his job as a lifeguard at the beach. He doesn't have to wear a coat and tie to work, and he is out in the fresh air all day. He has an important job. He doesn't just watch pretty girls; he is responsible for the lives of all the people who come to enjoy the ocean.

Exercise 1.13

1. theirs   2. hers   3. theirs   4. his   5. mine

Better Grammar

Exercise 1.14

1. You're   2. They're   3. Who's   4. It's   5. They're   6. hers
7. theirs   8. its, your   9. Whose   10. You're

Exercise 1.15

1. C   2. I   3. C   4. me   5. C

Chapter 2

Exercise 2.1

1. stops, stopped   2. hurries, hurried   3. trips, tripped
4. glare, glared   5. watches, watched

Exercise 2.2

1. plans   2. works   3. saves   4. opens   5. watches   6. waits
7. listens   8. changes   9. snows   10. removes

Exercise 2.3

1. met   2. came   3. gave   4. made   5. threw   6. rode   7. ate
8. had   9. held   10. kept

Exercise 2.4

1. letting   2. jumping   3. hitting   4. returning
5. swimming   6. occurring   7. dripping   8. wrapping
9. screaming   10. getting

Exercise 2.5

1. stops, stopped, stopped, stopping   2. carries, carried,
carried, carrying   3 watches, watched, watched, watching
4. tries, tried, tried, trying   5. hopes, hoped, hoped, hoping

Exercise 2.6

1. is, was/were, been, being   2. freezes, froze, frozen, freezing
3. runs, ran, run, running   4. chooses, chose, chosen,
choosing   5. shakes, shook, shaken, shaking

Exercise 2.7

1. <u>Do</u> <u>shop</u>   2. <u>might</u> have <u>received</u>   3. <u>have</u> <u>found</u>   4. <u>could</u>
<u>send</u>   5. <u>can</u> <u>order</u>

Exercise 2.8

1. <u>have</u> <u>been</u> <u>helped</u>   2. <u>can</u> <u>see</u>   3. <u>can</u> <u>examine</u>   4. <u>may</u> <u>be</u>
<u>done</u>   5. <u>must</u> <u>cut</u>

Exercise 2.9

1. run   2. sung   3. seen   4. heard   5. broken   6. known
7. flown   8. brought   9. eaten   10. said

Exercise 2.10

1. <u>is</u>(n't)   2. <u>should</u> (always) <u>practice</u>   3. <u>must</u> (certainly) <u>give</u>
4. <u>may</u> <u>travel</u>   5. <u>could</u> <u>close</u>

Exercise 2.11

1. will want   2. will earn   3. will begin   4. will stay
5. will ask

Exercise 2.12

1. will   2. would   3. will   4. would   5. will   6. would

Better Grammar

Exercise 2.13

1. has, predicted 2. have, kept 3. have, planned 4. have, brought 5. have, bought

Exercise 2.14

1. had shown 2. had promised 3. had had 4. had run 5. had chosen

Exercise 2.15

1. will have learned 2. will have paid 3. will have lived 4. will have gone 5. will have spoken

Exercise 2.16

1. Last Tuesday night I went to the library because I had a test in history on Wednesday morning. It <u>was</u> too noisy at home to study. My brother <u>was</u> playing the stereo, my mother was vacuuming, and my little sister and her friend <u>were</u> chasing each other around the house. How <u>was</u> I supposed to concentrate with all that commotion?
2. My friend Greg loves peanut butter. Every morning he <u>spreads</u> peanut butter on his toast or waffles. He <u>snacks</u> on peanut butter cups at school, and, of course, he <u>eats</u> peanut butter sandwiches for lunch every day. Nowadays, he bakes his own peanut butter cookies because his mother <u>has</u> refused to make them anymore. Greg <u>is</u> a hopeless case; he even covers a slice of chocolate cake with peanut butter.
3. My wife and I bought a golden retriever puppy last year. We made the mistake on the first few nights of allowing the puppy to sleep on a rug by our bed because he <u>missed</u> his brothers and sisters. Later when we made a bed for him in the laundry room, he <u>howled</u> and <u>scratched</u> on the door for several hours every night. After a while the neighbors <u>called</u> on the telephone to complain about the noise. We thought that he <u>would</u> never give up. The puppy finally learned to sleep by himself, and the neighbors <u>started</u> speaking to us again.

Chapter 3

Exercise 3.1

Subject	Auxiliary Verb	Main Verb
1. Scotsman	Does	wear
2. Americans	can	satisfy
3. festivals	are	held
4. events	———	include
5. contestants	are	throwing

Exercise 3.2

The following are possible responses:

1. Come 2. Put 3. Shut 4. Meet 5. Get

Exercise 3.3

1. [Since 1789], [between the ages], for fourteen and eighteen], [as congressional pages], [in our nation's capital]

2. [during vacation], [in Washington, D.C.], [for a year], [at Page School], [in the Library of Congress]

3. [for members], [of Congress], [from 9 a.m.], [to 5 p.m.]

4. [of the present system], [at home], [with their parents]

5. [despite the pressures], [of a busy schedule], for national political life]

Exercise 3.4

1. [on top of the car], [of luggage] 2. [instead of a salad], [with his dinner] 3. [in front of me], [about the long wait], [in line] 4. [After two innings], [at Yankee Stadium], [because of rain] 5. [together with several council members], [in a panel discussion], [on the city's transit problems]

Better Grammar

Exercise 3.5

Subject	Verb	Direct Object
1. uncle	plays	————
2. children	asked	questions
3. you	did order	food
4. Marilyn	sang	————
5. Steve	can play	guitar

Exercise 3.6

        S   LV   C

1. My ⟨daughter⟩ is a first-year student at Jackson Community College.

        S   LV   C

2. ⟨Everyone⟩ seemed happy about the election results.

           S Aux   LV   C

3. The traffic ⟨light⟩ is finally turning green.

        S   S   Aux   LV   C

4. ⟨Mario and Kevin⟩ have just become partners.

     Aux   S LV   C

5. Can ⟨you⟩ be the moderator of our next discussion?

Exercise 3.7

1. He, it 2. you, she 3. you, we 4. They 5. I

Exercise 3.8

1. it 2. us 3. her 4. you, them 5. me

Exercise 3.9

1. him 2. He, I 3. us 4. I 5. he, I

Exercise 3.10

1. she'll 2. they've 3. he'd 4. he's 5. I'll 6. I'm 7. we've
8. here's 9. it's 10. we're

Exercise 3.11

Your sentences will vary.

1. S-LV-NC 2. S-V-O 3. S-V 4. S-V-O 5. S-V 6. S-LV-AC
7. S-V 8. S-LV-NC 9. S-V-O 10. S-LV-AC

Chapter 4

Exercise 4.1

1. New York City's, its 2. His, city's 3. Today's, America's
4. salt's, our 5. engineer's, people's

Exercise 4.2

1. box, fought 2. turning, home 3. winning, rookie, head
4. excited, place, goal 5. winning, laughing, shouting,
football

Exercise 4.3

It is [a] [beautiful] [sunny] day in [a] [popular] [theme] park
in [the] United States. Mr. and Mrs. Tomita on [their] [first]
trip to [this] country, listen attentively to [a] [tour] [guide's]
claim that [thirty-five thousand] adults and children visit [the]
park [every] day. [Most] visitors to [this] [magical] place are
[attracted] by [an] [amazing] variety of shows, rides, exhibits,
and restaurants. [Both] Mr. and Mrs. Tomita, however, are
impressed by [the] [clean] surroundings. They are staying at
[the] [vacation-land's] hotel where [all] [the] rooms have
immaculately [clean] [blue] [plastic] furniture, [green] and
[beige] walls, and beds [covered] with [purple-green] spreads.
[The] [hotel's] [parking] lot, with [its] carefully [planted] vege-

tation, is also sparkling [clean.] [The] [smallest] scrap of litter is sucked underground and rushed via pipes to [a] [fabulous] [trash] compactor. Even [the] [friendly] birds do [their] part by picking [some] [bread] crumbs off [the] [restaurant's] patio at [the] hotel. Mr. and Mrs. Tomira know that they will enjoy themselves in [this] [spotless] [American] [tourist] attraction.

Exercise 4.4

1. cluttered, noisy   2. frigid, ice-covered   3. battered, rusty; luxurious, shiny   4. graceful, elegant   5. old-fashioned, clumsy, worn-out

Exercise 4.5

1. less interesting   2. least dangerous   3. less expensive
4. least creative   5. less sleepy

Exercise 4.6

1. most important   2. easier   3. better   4. bigger, more powerful   5. most recent   6. greater   7. more efficient
8. simpler or more simple   9. largest   10. best, lowest

Exercise 4.7

The following are possible sentences.

1. Kimiko arrived <u>at 8:00 o'clock</u> after a long flight <u>from Tokyo</u>.
2. The pilot landed the plane <u>smoothly</u> and <u>silently</u>.
3. All the passengers <u>on the plane</u> applauded <u>loudly</u>.
4. Kimiko walked <u>quickly</u> toward the exit door to <u>deplane</u>.
5. She was thrilled to be <u>in Chicago</u> after so many years.

Exercise 4.8

1. most reluctantly   2. less efficiently   3. more systematically
4. most definitely   5. more easily

Exercise 4.9

1. Today 1,500 Seminole (Indians) live [on the reservation built on 120,000 acres of swamp in the Florida Everglades.]

2. A (group) [of these Indians, living near Tampa,] has defied the law.

3. [In addition to a shrine and a museum,] the (Seminoles) have built a drive-thru smoke shop there.

4. The (Indians) have been selling cigarettes [without charging sales tax.]

5. [From the first,] state and local law (enforcers) did not like these Indians [to sell cigarettes.]

Exercise 4.10

1. profit, Carolyn   2. time, Josephine   3. mountains, we
4. shoes, Tina   5. school, Jerry

Exercise 4.11

1. Nick saved almost $100 by making his own repairs on his car.
2. The candidate promised at the political rally that he would reduce unemployment.
3. Alfredo ordered a pizza with mushrooms and pepperoni to go.
4. The painters told us on Wednesday that they would begin painting the house.
or The painters told us that they would begin painting the house on Wednesday.
5. Rex suddenly saw a woman in the front row jump up and run out... exit.
or Rex... jump up suddenly... exit.

Exercise 4.12

The following is a possible revision. Yours may vary.

Expecting a robot like R2D2, Willy was disappointed by the robot that was demonstrated to him. Willy had hoped the robot would have useful arms and legs, but it propelled itself on large wheels. Having limited mobility, the robot could not climb stairs. A distance of less than seventy feet was necessary between the robot and its owner for the robot to be able to respond to voice commands. Frustrated by the poor quality, Willy decided to delay his decision to buy a robot.

Chapter 5

Exercise 5.1

1. main clause   2. main clause   3. phrase   4. phrase   5. phrase

Exercise 5.2

Subject	Auxiliary Verb	Verb	Type of Sentence
1. people	—	think	
bicyclists	—	know	compound
2. bicyclists	—	ride	simple
3. ride	—	begins	
it	—	ends	compound
4. riders	—	complain	simple
5. bicyclists	are	surprised	
land	had	looked	compound

Exercise 5.3

1. The (doctor) was a well-known specialist, but my (father) would not accept her diagnosis.

2. The pole (vaulter) tried again to break the record, and this time (he) succeeded.

3. (It) is a large house, so (they) will <u>have</u> room for all their furniture.

4. (Andrea) <u>spent</u> four hours a day practicing the flute, for (she) was <u>determined</u> to improve.

5. (We) can <u>drive</u> to the beach, or (we) can <u>ride</u> our bicycles.

Exercise 5.4

1. (Lucy) <u>likes</u> to finish her homework before   C dinner; after eating (she) <u>gets</u> sleepy.

2. (Vivian) <u>brought</u> pictures of our high-school   C class to the reunion; ((everyone)) <u>laughed</u> at the dated clothes and hairstyles.

3. (Arturo) and his (brother) <u>have</u> <u>borrowed</u> money   S and <u>opened</u> a real estate office.

4. Our (neighbor) <u>was</u> happy about his golf game   C today; for the first time (he) <u>had</u> a lower score than his wife's. (or: game; today)

5. The (children) <u>entertained</u> themselves for half   S an hour by riding up and down on the escalator.

Exercise 5.5

1. (We) <u>had</u> <u>planned</u> to bicycle through England last summer; instead, (we) <u>painted</u> the house and <u>built</u> a fence.

2. (I) <u>forgot</u> my umbrella this morning; consequently, (I) <u>was</u> <u>soaked</u> to the skin by the time (I) <u>reached</u> the office.

3. (Milt) <u>works</u> six hours a day and overtime on weekends at a

restaurant; in addition, (he) takes three classes at a community college.

4. First (Norman) reads the comics; then, (he) settles down to enjoy the sports section.

5. (Cindy) looked very different with her new haircut; in fact, (I) hardly recognized her.

Exercise 5.6

1. Besides that, a furthermore, the however, develop
2. dictionary, in addition, shows
3. you,
4. dictionary, in fact, is
5. You must,

Exercise 5.7

1. gardener, secretary, short-order cook
2. giving information, keeping the park, and preserving the natural beauty
3. puts on her uniform, packs her lunch, and rides her bicycle
4. Most faces are new, but others are familiar.
5. sunny or rainy, sizzling or freezing
6. to enjoy nature and to hike in the woods
7. Dedicated and enthusiastic
8. answering questions and being helpful

Exercise 5.8

1. sand, pebbles, rocks, and acrylic paint
2. Venezuela, Argentina, Peru, Chile, and Brazil
3. bath, went... room, closed... door, turned... radio, and lay... bed
4. to clean, to cook, to iron, or to shop
5. flying hand gliders, going deep-sea fishing, or riding horseback

Exercise 5.9

1. The ⟨children⟩ <u>ran</u> around the park; their   <u> FS </u>
   ⟨mothers⟩ <u>tried</u> to quiet them unsuccessfully.

2. The ⟨traffic⟩ <u>was</u> unusually heavy this evening;   <u> CS </u>
   ⟨it⟩ <u>was</u> <u>caused</u> by an accident at the intersection.

3. The ⟨smog⟩ <u>disappeared</u> after the heavy rains;   <u> FS </u>
   ⟨it⟩ <u>reappeared</u> in a few days.

4. In the early morning, many (⟨joggers⟩) <u>are</u>   <u> NE </u>
   <u>running</u>.

5. ⟨It⟩ <u>was</u> late, and all the ⟨lights⟩ in the house   <u> NE </u>
   <u>were</u> out.

Exercise 5.10

The following are possible revisions. Your sentences may vary.

1. More corporations are beginning to open day-care centers for their employees' children; the centers are open from nine to five.
2. Working parents take fewer days off if their children are well cared for because they worry less.
3. Two-paycheck families appreciate the cost benefits, for the price of a full-time babysitter would use up an entire salary.
4. Single-parent families especially appreciate the convenience of quality child-care programs; in fact, child-care programs help to recruit high-quality employees.
5. Government support helps the corporations build special facilities; preschool playgrounds and indoor classrooms are often too expensive for smaller corporations to construct.

Chapter 6

Exercise 6.1

1. The (guests) <u>left</u> (after) the (party) <u>was</u> over.
2. The (animals) <u>performed</u> their tricks (although) the (audience) <u>did</u> not <u>applaud</u>.
3. (When) the (instructor) <u>passed</u> back our papers, (I) <u>was</u> <u>delighted</u>.
4. Mr. (Hashimoto) <u>has been wearing</u> a cast (because)(he)<u>broke</u> his leg.
5. (While) (we) <u>were riding</u> our bicycles, (someone) <u>stole</u> our car.

Exercise 6.2

1. After dinner, (while) the (guests)<u>sat</u> around the table, (many) of them <u>told</u> interesting stories about their work (as) (we) all <u>listened</u> attentively.
2. (Although) (she) <u>said</u> (that) (she) <u>loved</u> him, (he)didn't <u>believe</u> her (because) (he) <u>knew</u> (that) (she) <u>went</u> out with many other <u>men</u>.
3. (As long as) (you) <u>haven't eaten</u> your lunch yet, (you) <u>might</u> as well <u>wait</u> until dinner time (when) (we) <u>will have</u> a big meal.
4. (Before) (I) <u>knew</u> ((what)) <u>was happening</u>, the red sports (car) <u>passed</u> my car (as) (I)<u>drove</u> up the hill.
5. The(judge)<u>said</u> (that)(I)<u>should go</u> to driving school (so that) (I) <u>would learn</u> about the dangers of drunk driving.

Exercise 6.3

1. His lifetime batting record, which remained unbroken until the summer of 1985, was 4,191 hits in 24 seasons.
2. Cobb, who was a millionaire, gave...
3. Since most of his fans were ignorant of his violent disposition, he remained...
4. He welcomed a fight even when he was sick and old.
5. Cobb threatened to use a loaded handgun that he carried with him.

Exercise 6.4

1. The coach was fired because his team never won a game.
2. When the cat dug holes in my flower beds, I chased it away.
3. Although they lost the first game, they won the second one.
4. While we were riding our bicycles, someone stole our car.
5. Toni, who is a full-time college student, works thirty hours a week as a musician.

Exercise 6.5

1. dog, which is a poodle, digs
2. no comma
3. Mary, which... liner, is
4. stereo, which... ours, has
5. no comma

Exercise 6.6

The following are possible sentences. Your sentences may vary.

1. Michelle has completed almost all the courses required by her major, except for English 1, Psychology 2, and History 17.
2. Shelby has big plans for the sweepstakes money if he wins it. For example, he hopes to travel to many foreign countries, including several in Africa.
3. This fabric offers a number of advantages for traveling in the summer, such as being washable, quick-drying, wrinkle-free, and lightweight.

4. She passed the time on jury duty by knitting and by working crossword puzzles.
5. The instructor reviewed the material to be covered in the chapter test and especially called our attention to the last three pages.

Exercise 6.7

1. S   2. S   3. F   4. F   5. F   6. F   7. S   8. F   9. F   10. F

Chapter 7

Exercise 7.1

1. tree	gives
2. student	likes
3. photograph	is
4. driver	collects
5. car	requires

Exercise 7.2

Subjects	Aux. Verbs and Main Verbs	Words Between Subject and Verb
1. purpose	is	(of many zoos in large cities)
2. visitors	were	(to the zoo, not the animals)
3. animal	spends	(in one of these new zoos no longer)
4. quarters	give	(like those in San Diego's Wild Animal Park)
5. keepers	work	(whenever possible)

Exercise 7.3

Subject	Verb
1. disagreement	is

2. much	is
3. chances	are
4. clue	is
5. humidity	signals

Exercise 7.4

1. are 2. were 3. are 4. is 5. answers

Exercise 7.5

1. taste 2. seems 3. were 4. makes 5. hears
   (cookies) (president) (sisters) (bottle) (instructor)

Exercise 7.6

1. have 2. have 3. have 4. have 5. has

Exercise 7.7

1. works 2. needs 3. plans 4. spends 5. seems

Exercise 7.8

1. are 2. have 3. was 4. Is 5. was

Exercise 7.9

1. is 2. was 3. is 4. sounds 5. causes

Exercise 7.10

Antecedents	**Verbs**
1. Americans	seek
2. family	goes
3. recorders	plug
4. videogames	hook
5. television	has

Better Grammar

Exercise 7.11

Pronouns	Antecedents
1. their	Tanya and Rosalie
2. his	engineer
3. your	you
4. me	I
5. they	sweaters

Exercise 7.12

Pronouns	Antecedents
1. her or his	artist
2. their	visitors
3. her	Mrs. Jones
4. they	birds
5. their	students

Exercise 7.13

Pronouns	Antecedent
1. their	Ralph or George
2. their	Mr. and Mrs. Asano
3. her	Either Martha or Angela
4. their	either gardener or window cleaners
5. his	Neither Bruce nor Richard

Exercise 7.14

1. its   2. their   3. its   4. their   5. its

Exercise 7.15

Pronouns	Antecedents
1. his or her	Someone
2. his or her	anyone
3. her	each

| 4. his or her | Nobody |
| 5. his or her | Everyone |

Exercise 7.16

1. who   2. that   3. who   4. that   5. that

Exercise 7.17

1. who   2. whom   3. who   4. whom   5. who

Exercise 7.18

1. Maria said to Tess, "I have lost my pen."
2. There are so many automobile accidents because drivers are careless.
3. Dr. Bronowski is a great surgeon. Surgery is a rewarding profession.
4. Before taking a test, Roberto studies and gets a good night's sleep. Rest is important.
5. The graduates marched solemnly down the aisle to receive their diplomas. The ceremony was so inspiring.

Chapter 8

Exercise 8.1

1. Andrew did not want to wear his raincoat to school yesterday, nor did he want to carry an umbrella.
2. I have seen that movie star before, yet I cannot remember her name.
3. Louis and Gerald tried out for the basketball team, and both of them were chosen.
4. Brett and Lula were married on Friday morning, but they did not leave for Hawaii until Saturday.
5. Athletes must train hard and watch their diets every day, or they will not be able to compete.

Better Grammar

Exercise 8.2

1. No   2. No   3. No   4. No   5. Yes

Exercise 8.3

1. Last semester Evelyn took four classes at college, worked twenty hours a week and sang in the church choir on weekends. (*or* week, and)
2. My favorite breakfast cereal contains the following ingredients: malt, barley, oats, honey, and raisins.
3. He caught the pass, ran along the sideline for twenty yards into the end zone but failed to score because he had stepped out of bounds on the two-yard line. (*or* zone, but)
4. The students were told to bring their workbooks, dictionaries, lined paper, and pens to every class meeting.
5. The recipe listed the following ingredients: sugar, butter, Hour, cocoa, walnuts, milk, and peanut butter.

Exercise 8.4

1. Yes   2. No   3. Yes   4. No   5. Yes

Exercise 8.5

1. Within two or three months, the parking lot will be less crowded.
2. After a short pause, the speaker answered the questions from the audience.
3. Best of all, the food is always served hot.
4. In many tropical countries, the natives take a siesta in the middle of the day.
5. John has been commuting 25 miles a day to school. Fortunately, he found an apartment for rent near the college yesterday.

Exercise 8.6

1. No   2. No   3. Yes   4. Yes   5. No

Exercise 8.7

1. Although Jo Ellen had always known the truth about Harry, she still loved him.
2. Before you can understand calculus, you must understand algebra and trigonometry.
3. If the rain doesn't stop soon, the rivers will overflow their banks.
4. By the time you are ready to take the test, you will be able to answer all of the questions correctly.
5. The thick salmon steak was delicious even though it was a little overcooked.

Exercise 8.8

1. No   2. Yes   3. Yes   4. No   5. Yes

Exercise 8.9

1. The raindrops fell into the clear, blue, deep water of the pool.
2. Shana left her discarded, smelly clothes scattered around her large, sunlit bedroom.
3. The acrobat entertained the huge, enthusiastic audience by his skillful, graceful performance.
4. In the early morning, the joggers run effortlessly along the deserted, shell-strewn beach.
5. Marge's pink sunburnt skin looked painful to me.

Exercise 8.10

1. No   2. No   3. No   4. Yes   5. No

Exercise 8.11

1. We hope, therefore, that you will send our refund soon.
2. Karen's parents, as a rule, drive her to school every day.
3. The jury, as a result, took four days to arrive at the verdict.
4. The kitchen, in fact, has not been cleaned since last week.
5. My opinion, in the long run, is based on the facts as I understand them.

Better Grammar

Exercise 8.12

1. Yes   2. No   3. No   4. No   5. No

Exercise 8.13

1. I don't entirely agree, Jim, with your position.
2. Play it again, Sam.
3. Ladies and gentlemen of the jury, you have heard the evidence.
4. Ella, tell me that you love me.
5. I hope, Paulette, that you will practice your lesson.

Exercise 8.14

1. No   2. Yes   3. No   4. No   5. Yes

Exercise 8.15

1. My friend Carla Caraway went to New York to get a job as a dancer.
2. A young woman, alone in a strange city, must learn how to take care of herself.
3. She auditioned for Judith Jamison, the famous choreographer of the Alvin Ailey company.
4. Carla, breathless and exhausted, waited after the audition to hear the choreographer's opinion.
5. Carla joined the Ailey company, one of the best dance companies in the world.

Exercise 8.16

1. Yes   2. No   3. Yes   4. No   5. No

Exercise 8.17

1. A talented American contralto, Marian Anderson, who had sung at the White House, was barred from singing in Constitution Hall in Washington.

2. Instead, Ms. Anderson sang at the Lincoln Memorial before 75,000 people who had gathered in support of her.
3. Three Aaron Copland ballets, drawing upon American themes, are *Billy the Kid, Rodeo,* and *Appalachian Spring.*
4. Copland wrote *Appalachian Spring* for Martha Graham, choreographer and dancer.
5. Ernest Hemingway, an American author, began his first job as a newspaper reporter at the age of eighteen.

Exercise 8.18

1. "I can never do these homework assignments," Gary complained.
2. "Well," said his mother, "you haven't even tried."
3. "I never learn anything in that class," he said, "so what's the point?"
4. "Besides," he said to her, "I have a date tonight."
5. "Gary, you should do your assignment before you go out," his mother advised.

Exercise 8.19

1. George will move to Las Vegas, Nevada, in January.
2. His address has been The Stanford Arms Hotel, Apt. 10, 536 W. 18th Street, Rittman, Indiana 46206, for the last six years.
3. We will forward his mail to his new address: The Pyramid Hotel, Las Vegas, Nevada 89501.
4. The Battle of Gettysburg was fought on July 4, 1863.
5. The annual rodeo in Palmdale, California, features a bull-riding contest.

Exercise 8.20

1. No 2. Yes 3. Yes 4. No 5. Yes

Chapter 9

Exercise 9.1

1. When did you last study punctuation?
2. Mr. Newman is a famous actor.
3. Help! Fire!
4. I would be living in New York if I could afford an apartment on E. 68th Street.
5. He earned his B.A. degree from NYU.
6. Hal wondered what was wrong with him.
7. What is wrong with Hal?
8. Hooray! We've won the game!
9. When we were young, we never questioned why we were poor.
10. How are you today?

Exercise 9.2

1. for; he
2. television; then
3. ingredients: flour
4. cars: an
5. Sacramento; Betty Ford, Palm Springs; and
6. library; however,
7. 3:45 p.m.; nevertheless,
8. entrees: lasagna
9. winter; therefore,
10. movie; we

Exercise 9.3

1. "The Lottery," "A Rose for Emily"
2. "Have you seen <u>The Tempest</u> at the Old Globe Theater yet?"
3. <u>Beloved</u>
4. "Stop that shoplifter!"
5. "Read... tomorrow"?
6. "A ... Problem," <u>Times</u>

7. "The Owl and the Pussycat"
8. Cheers, Roseanne, L.A. Law
9. "Poetry and Advertising," Language in Thought and Action
10. "College Tuition," The Atlantic

Exercise 9.4

1. fifty-year-old
2. left-hand, one-way
3. dry-cleaned
4. sharp-eyed, run-down sus-
5. sister-in-law, second-hand, seventy-two
6. free-lance, self-help
7. Two-thirds, cov-, high-risk
8. bullet-scarred, high-rise
9. major-elect, upper-class, self-reliance
10. half-heartedly, self-hypnosis

Exercise 9.5

1. Anh Nguyen, American
2. I'm, English 1, I'm, History 21
3. When Mary, New York, Metropolitan Museum of Art
4. I, *Phantom of the Opera*
5. Sue's, Ritz, Kraft, Coca-Cola
6. When Darlene, Sears, Wamsutta
7. Are, Sugar Bowl, New Year's Day
8. In, I, Saturdays
9. Yellowstone National Park, United States
10. My, Hemingway, I

Chapter 10

Exercise 10.1

1. accept   2. except

Exercise 10.2

1. advise   2. advice

Better Grammar

Exercise 10.3
1. affected 2. effect

Exercise 10.4
1. all ready 2. already

Exercise 10.5
1. dessert 2. desert
3. deserted

Exercise 10.6
1. It's 2. its

Exercise 10.7
1. know 2. no

Exercise 10.8
1. lead 2. led

Exercise 10.9
1. lose 2. loose

Exercise 10.10
1. past 2. passed

Exercise 10.11
1. personal 2. personnel

Exercise 10.12
1. principles 2. principal

Exercise 10.13
1. quiet 2. quite, quiet

Exercise 10.14
1. supposed 2. suppose

Exercise 10.15
1. then 2. than

Exercise 10.16
1. they're, their 2. There

Exercise 10.17
1. thought 2. Though, through

Exercise 10.18
1. Two 2. too, to, to

Exercise 10.19
1. used 2. use

Exercise 10.20
1. weather 2. whether

Exercise 10.21
1. who's 2. whose

Exercise 10.22
1. You're 2. your

Glossary

Action verbs tell what the subject does, did, or will do.

Adjective clauses are **subordinate clauses** that are also called **relative clauses** because the **subordinator** "relates" the rest of the subordinate clause to a **noun** or **pronoun** in the **main clause.** The subordinate clause acts like an **adjective** modifying that part of the main clause by adding information about it.

Adjectives make **nouns** or **pronouns** more specific or concrete by limiting and describing them.

Adverb clauses are **subordinate clauses** that are introduced by a **subordinator,** which specifies time, place, cause, condition, or contrast when indicating the relationship between the **main** and the **subordinate clause.**

Adverbial connectives *(however, nevertheless, then)* are words that are used with a semicolon and a comma to join **main clauses** together. They are also called **adverbial conjunctions** or **conjunctive adverbs.**

Adverbs modify **verbs, adjectives,** or other **adverbs** and answer one of the following questions: When? Why? How? Where?

Agreement is the matching in **number, gender,** and **person** between words. **Subjects** and **verbs** must agree, and **pronouns** must agree with their **antecedents.**

Antecedents are **nouns, pronouns,** or **noun phrases** to which a noun refers.

Auxiliary verbs are helping verbs used with main verbs to form **verb phrases.**

237

Better Grammar

Base forms of verbs are the present forms of the verbs with no *-s* at the end.

Collective nouns (such as *family)* refer to a collection of persons, places, things, ideas, or activities.

Comma splices are grammatical errors that occur when **main clauses** are joined with only a comma and no **connectives.**

Common nouns name people, places, things, ideas, or activities in general.

Comparatives are the forms of **adjectives** or **adverbs** used to compare two people, places, ideas, things, or actions.

Completers follow **linking verbs** to describe or rename the subject.

Complex sentences are composed of a **main clause** and one or more **subordinate clauses.**

Compound antecedents are two or more **antecedents** joined by a **coordinating connective.** When joined by *and,* they require a plural pronoun. When joined by *or, neither... nor,* or *either ... or,* they require a pronoun that agrees with the antecedent closer to the pronoun.

Compound objects are two or more **direct objects** joined by a **coordinating connective.**

Compound sentences contain two or more **main clauses** joined by a **connective** and by appropriate punctuation.

Compound subjects are two or more **subjects** joined by a **coordinating connective.**

Compound verbs are two or more **verbs** joined by a **coordinating connective.**

Connectives are the words used to connect words, phrases, and clauses.

Contractions are words that are formed by combining two words with an apostrophe for the omission of letters.

Coordinating connectives *(and, but, or, for, nor, so, yet)* are words used with a comma to join words, phrases, and **main clauses** together. They are also called **coordinating conjunctions.**

Dangling modifiers are **adjectives** or **adverbs** that do not modify any word in the sentence. Sentences with dangling modifiers can be rewritten by inserting a word for the modifier to limit or describe.

Direct objects are the **nouns** or **pronouns** that answer the question "What?" or "Whom?" after an **action verb. Objects** also follow **prepositions.**

Glossary

Faulty parallelism is the failure to place similar items in similar grammatical form.

Fused sentences are grammatical errors that occur when **main clauses** are joined with no punctuation or **connectives.**

Gender indicates whether a third-person **pronoun** is masculine, feminine, or neuter.

Indefinite pronouns (such as *anyone* or *someone)* usually take a singular verb and require a singular pronoun.

Irregular verbs do not follow any spelling rules to form the past tense.

Linking verbs connect the subject to its description. Common linking verbs include *become, feel, seem, appear*, and the forms of the verb *be.*

Main clauses (also called **independent clauses**) are groups of related words with a subject and a verb that can stand alone as a sentence if the first word is capitalized and the clause ends with a mark of punctuation such as a period or a question mark.

Misplaced modifiers are **adjectives** or **adverbs** that have been placed next to words they do not modify. They confuse the reader and should be moved closer to the words they modify.

Modifiers describe, limit, or make specific another word in the sentence.

Noun markers are **adjectives** that point to the **noun** that follows them,

Noun phrases are groups of words that include a **noun** and its **modifiers.**

Nouns name people, places, things, ideas, or activities.

Number indicates whether a **pronoun** is singular or plural.

Parallel structure is the placing of similar items in similar grammatical form.

Participles are verb forms that may function as part of a **verb phrase** (was *laughing)* or as an **adjective** (The *winning* team, *laughing* and *shouting,* ran off the field). The **present participle** is formed by adding *-ing* to the base form of the verb. The **past participle** of a regular verb is formed by adding *-d* or *-ed* to the base form.

Perfect tenses are formed by using a form of the **auxiliary verb** *have* and the **past participle** of the main verb.

Person indicates the person speaking, the person spoken to, or the person or thing spoken about.

Phrases are groups of words without a **subject** and a **verb.** Examples are **noun phrases, verb phrases,** and **prepositional phrases.**

239

Better Grammar

Plural nouns refer to more than one person, place, thing, idea, or activity.

Possessive nouns are nouns that change spelling to indicate a belonging-to relationship.

Prepositions are the words used to show position, direction, or relationship.

Present participles are formed by adding *-ing* to the base form of a verb.

Pronouns are used to take the place of a noun or to refer to a noun. A **personal pronoun** shows **person, number,** and **gender.**

Proper nouns name specific people, places, things, ideas, or activities.

Regular verbs add *-d* or *-ed* to form the past tense.

Relative pronouns are **subordinators** (such as who or which) that introduce a **subordinate clause.** The relative pronoun must agree with the **noun** or **noun phrase** in the **main clause** as its **antecedent.**

Sentence fragments are groups of words that begin with a capital letter and end with a period, but do not express a complete thought or contain a **main clause.**

Sentences must contain at least one **subject** and one **verb** and express a complete thought.

Simple sentences are **sentences** that contain one **main clause.**

Subjects are the people or things the **verb** is asking or telling about.

Subordinate clauses (also called **dependent clauses**) are groups of related words with **subjects** and **verbs** that are introduced by a **subordinator,** They make incomplete statements, so they must be attached to a **main clause** to be a complete sentence.

Subordinators are words that are used to introduce a **subordinate clause.** Examples: *because, that, although.*

Superlatives are the forms of **adjectives** or **adverbs** used to compare three or more people, places, ideas, things, or actions.

Tense is the change of verb form to indicate when the action occurred.

Verbal phrases include a **verbal** plus a **noun** and/or a prepositional phrase. Examples: to choose a pet, choosing a pet; chosen for its intelligence.

Verbals are formed from **verbs** and are used to introduce **verbal phrases.** They include one of the three following forms: to plus the base form of the verb, a present participle, or a past participle.

Verbs are the words in sentences that indicate the action of the sentence.

Index

Better Vocabulary in 30 Minutes a Day

By
Edie Schwager

Acknowledgments

My heartfelt thanks go to Michael J. Schwager, who happens to be my son and is also a fellow writer and editor. Besides his pursuits as an author and writing consultant, he's a computer guru. He offered insightful suggestions about the text and helped make sure that the book got to Career Press on time, and in the electronic form the publisher needed.

Special thanks go to Doris S. Michaels, my literary agent, for her diligence, competence, patience and generosity of spirit. I received the assignment to write this book because of her, and her enthusiasm motivated me from our first conversation about the project to the last word.

My father, Michael Cohen, always told me that if you're going to do a job, do it right, no matter what it is. Above everything except family, he revered education and learning. He taught me by example that one of the highest human endeavors is gathering knowledge and using it to exercise wisdom. This book is dedicated to his memory.

So hats off to all the Michaels!

Thanks to everyone at Career Press—especially Ron Fry, president; Betsy Sheldon, editor in chief; Ellen Scher, associate editor; Jane A. Brody, editor; and Fred Nachbaur, marketing manager—for their encouragement and all their efforts.

Contents

Preface

Eating potato chips

Have you ever noticed that you can't look up just one word? It's like eating potato chips. You can never eat just one. Before you catch yourself, your eye spies another word whose meaning you want to know, and that entices you to look up that one, too. This never-ending process is called enriching your mind.

This book will help you by adding to your vocabulary. It will encourage you to use words correctly and confidently, as dynamic tools that explain or persuade.

Whether English is your native language or your second language, your constant use of this book will accomplish several things: It will stimulate you to become interested in the meanings and origins of words, introduce you to new ideas and concepts, acquaint you with the fun and mystery of mythology and history, and add to the sum of your knowledge.

The Athenian playwright Aristophanes (c. 450-385 BC) wrote that "by words, the mind is excited and the spirit elated."

Much more recently, H. G. Wells, author of *The Time Machine* and other futuristic novels, wrote that "human history becomes more and more a race between education and catastrophe" (*The Outline of History*, 1920).

The ultimate tools

Words can work magic. Despite generals, wars are not won on the battlefield. Eventually, all sides have to sit down at the negotiating table. Wars are finally won with words.

Most human transactions are won or lost through words.

Only humans have a written language

Only human beings have the ability to use a system of words to convey ideas—that is, to communicate with language. Other animals can communicate to one another (for instance, with certain sounds or body movements), but not with words. Only we humans have that power.

Expressing yourself well

The way you express yourself is your showcase to the world. To use another figure of speech, it's the window through which your family, your friends, your teacher, your colleagues and the rest of the world perceive you.

It's within your power to create the image you want to present. Your words are as important as your actions, and are often more memorable.

People who are good conversationalists, who can express themselves grammatically and understandably, are in a more favorable life situation.

People who can write clearly, without ambiguity, are pearls of great price.

Opening your mind to new challenges, new ideas and new words can be one of the most exciting and pleasurable intellectual experiences you'll ever have. One effective way to do that is by using this book diligently.

What is English?

Our language didn't come out of thin air. It's an amalgam, a glorious intermingling of words that originated with diverse cultures, tastes, styles and manners.

Most of our simpler and more practical words come from the Germanic and Scandinavian side of our language heritage. It will not escape your notice that the majority of the etymologies in this book's entries contain the abbreviations *L* (Latin) and *Gk* (Greek). That's because most words having to do with culture and learning come from Latin and Greek roots. In addition, almost the entire English medical and scientific vocabulary comes from Latin and Greek.

English has thousands of borrowings from other languages as well. Those are among the most exotic words— for example, *harem, mikado, bazaar, kiosk*. French has contributed more than 15,000 words to English. Spanish and Italian were also generous. The Netherlands gave us words having to do with the shipbuilding and shipping industries. Scandinavian warriors invading and then settling in the Danelaw area of England brought words that became part of the language.

After the conquest of England by the Normans in 1066, French became the country's official language, but the common people continued to speak English. Between 1066 and the 14th century, a dialect of French intermixed with English known as Anglo-French became the official language, and the language of the court and the law. Over the centuries, these words were intermixed with the Germanic and other words that already existed in English.

How did English evolve into the language as we know it? That's a subject that would fill an entire library, but it helps to know that English owes a great deal to Romance languages such as Portuguese, Italian, French, Spanish and Romanian. The Netherlands, the Scandinavian and Slavic countries, and other European cultures also contributed substantially to our vocabulary.

Robert Burchfield, in *The English Language*, wrote that "every major historical, political, and social event, every discovery and every new belief, since *c*. 450 has brought change to the English language, and not least to the meanings of words."

Evolution and revolution

Language changes, the meanings of words change, politics, styles and cultures change. We all benefit by and contribute to these developments.

More scientific, medical and technologic advances have taken place in the past 100 years than in all the preceding centuries put together. Fortunately, our language is flexible and capacious enough to absorb these changes and to build new terms on them.

In every country the common people—workers, artisans, business people—make the everyday practical language, the vulgate. Others, such as the engineers, artists, physicians, and scientists, contribute the more technical and specific terms. Thus the language grows and changes.

Idiosyncratic idioms

English is an extremely idiomatic language, full of colorful and vivid imagery. We use phrases without a second thought as to their literal meaning. Language evolves through interactions between and among humans. Although we think in words, our actions take place without conscious thought as to how they are to be expressed in spoken language.

When we say something is "as easy as pie," we're not thinking about pie at all. "Holding your own" *what*? People in my area go on vacation not "down to" the shore but "down the shore," even though the Atlantic Ocean is more east of here than south.

So the idioms go. They don't have to be logical. That's just the way it is. However, language in general has to be logical if it is to be communicated effectively.

Some idioms, like humans, have a life. They are born, they flourish, and then they die. Others remain with us for centuries, usually because there is a contemporaneous use for them.

Although we use idiom constantly in both written and spoken language, writing gives us the golden opportunity to use logic too. Good writing presupposes clear thinking. Knowing the right words gives us, as the idiom goes, a leg up.

I never make misteaks

Words have shades and hues of meaning, subtleties and nuances. Many errors are caused by the irrational, irritating, unphonetic and difficult spelling of English words. These characteristics make learning English tough, especially for nonnative speakers. The difficulty is compounded by the innumerable *homonyms* and *homophones* in English, words that sound or look alike but mean different things. The section called "Word Roots" contains several examples.

Other difficulties arise when people who were reared where British English reigns supreme immigrate to this country and have to contend with American English spelling. Still other mistakes stem from poor reading (or *no* reading) or studying habits, substandard education, lack of access to a library, lack of a personal library and, above all, a lack of interest or motivation, otherwise known as *apathy*.

English is the world's lingua franca

There is no world language, and there may never be, but English approaches it. It is the language used to record more than 80 percent of the world's computer information.

English is the lingua franca, the commercial language, of the world. If you want to do business abroad, you must know English. If you want to venture into the international computer networks, you must know English.

Here's your user's manual!

In the main section of this book, "Words Are Tools," the lexicon is arranged alphabetically, so that you'll be able to find the exact word you want quickly and easily, without being distracted or interrupted by other sections.

The illustrative sentences give you a good idea of how each word can be used in context. For instance, when the entry is a verb, the corresponding noun or adjective is also given.

The section titled "Word Roots," also arranged alphabetically, will help you build your vocabulary using an architectural style. You'll soon be able to figure out the meanings of unfamiliar words by recognizing the roots and their affixes. You already know many of them, so you can concentrate on the words you don't see every day. Prefixes and suffixes are collectively known in the trade as *affixes*.

Some definitions in "Words Are Tools" are informal, to get a point or two across. Ditto for "Word Roots" and my commentaries.

You will note that some words in one section are repeated in another. That's for memory reinforcement and refreshment.

12

Diacritical or accent marks are not used in words that have already been integrated into the English language.

Note the "Key to Abbreviations" used in the book: F, Gk, Ger, F, L, ME, ISV, etc. You'll find it just before the main section of this book.

And, finally, at the end of the book, a chance to practice your new vocabulary skills! You can undoubtedly figure out what "Word Aerobics" are. I coined this phrase because that kind of exercise is challenging and a lot of fun for me.

Look it up!

Mark Twain, who was noted for his zingers, wrote, "The man who does not read good books has no advantage over the man who cannot read them." That goes for women too.

Guessing at what a word means works sometimes, but beware of fake (fake folk) etymology. In the words profession, this alert is called a caveat, as in caveat emptor, which means "Buyer, beware!" For instance, words that contain ped can refer to feet (pedal, biped, pedicure), children (pediatrics), teaching (pedagogy, pedantry), or lousiness (pediculosis). Not to mention soils (pedogeography) or botany (peduncle, which has nothing to do with relatives but is a flower-bearing stalk).

English is an extremely versatile language. One word can have many meanings: Consider the word *down*. You think it's a simple word, but if you look it up in the *big* dictionary, *Webster's Third New International Dictionary of the English Language*, you'll see that the entries for this little word consume an inordinate amount of space. It can be several parts of speech: a noun (*down* off a duck, ups and *downs*, the *downs* of England's countryside); an adjective (the computers are *down* again, *down* payment); an adverb (tore the Sears building *down*, keeping your expenses *down*, kept *down* by lack of education); a preposition (perspiration dripping *down* his T-shirt, went *down* the mountain); or a verb (*downed* by a superior wrestler, *down* the soda pop too quickly, *down* the tools in a sitdown strike).

Innumerable other words in our language can be several different parts of speech.

The watchphrase is **look it up!**

The best and the brightest

In my work I depend on the monumentally scholarly Merriam-Webster books, notably the following:

- *Webster's Third New International Dictionary of the English Language, Unabridged,* known briefly and affectionately in this book as *Webster's Third.*

- *Webster's New Biographical Dictionary.*

- *Webster's Word Histories.*

In addition, I find *Bartlett's Familar Quotations,* 16th ed., edited by Justin Kaplan, and several other excellent books of quotations indispensable resources.

The other books in my voluminous (no pun intended) library that I used in writing this book are too numerous to mention. Some day I hope to catalog them. (I should live so long.)

I am eternally grateful to these wonderful scholars and all the other lexicographers, philologists, etymologists, linguists and verbophiles who have contributed immeasurably to our vibrant, vigorous and *living* language.

The next move

The ball's in your court. As you use this book, you'll find that you can comprehend and will be familiar with terms used in, for example, *The New York Times*, which is one of the best newspapers in the world and certainly one of the best edited. Many words in this book are straight out of *The Times*, since it has always been the Gold Standard for me. Naturally, any single work such as this book can only scratch the surface. It's up to you to prospect deeper for more gold.

As you increase and improve your vocabulary, you'll also find that you're more confident and comfortable in your speech. Your reading and writing will come much easier. Success in your life may very well hinge on your ability to communicate lucidly and powerfully. I don't necessarily mean monetary success; social and artistic success is every bit as important for fulfillment.

Alexander Pope wrote:

> A little learning is a dangerous thing;
> Drink deep, or taste not the Pierian spring:
> There shallow draughts intoxicate the brain,
> And drinking largely sobers us again.

Pope also wrote:

> True ease in writing comes from art, not chance,
> As those move easiest who have learn'd to dance.
> 'Tis not enough no harshness gives offence,
> The sound must seem an echo to the sense.

You, too, can learn to dance.
Never stop learning.

Key To Abbreviations

AF	Anglo-French
Ar	Arabic
E	English
F	French
Ger	German
Gk	Greek
Heb	Hebrew
ISV	International Scientific Vocabulary
It	Italian
L	Latin
LHeb	Late Hebrew
LL	Late Latin
ME	Middle English
MF	Middle French
ML	Medieval Latin
NL	New Latin
OE	Old English
OF	Old French
OHG	Old High German
OL	Old Latin
ONF	Old North French
OSp	Old Spanish
Russ	Russian
Skt	Sanskrit
Sp	Spanish
Sw	Swedish
Y	Yiddish

Words Are Tools

A

abridge—to shorten, abbreviate (from L *ad*, toward, *breviare*, to abbreviate)

*It's easy to write a long memo. To **abridge** it usually takes much longer.*
*The collegiate dictionaries are **abridgments** of larger works.*

In American English, *fledgling, acknowledgment* and *judgment*, like **abridgment**, are spelled without an *e* after the *g*, although *abridgement* is also correct. The British style generally is to retain the *e* in these and similar words.

Synonyms for **abridgment** include *abstract, brief* and *epitome*.

Blaise Pascal summed it up when he wrote (in 1657), "I have made this letter longer than usual because I lack the time to make it shorter."

abrogate—to give up, repeal, set aside (L *ab*, from, *rogare*, to ask)

*Constantine refused when asked to **abrogate** his throne.*
*Free citizens should not **abrogate** their rights under the Constitution.*

19

*Treaties are sometimes **abrogated** by irresponsible nations.*

Synonyms for **abrogate** include *annul*, *void* and *nullify*.

abstinence—self-denial, abstaining (OF, from L *abstinentia*)

*Some religions prescribe **abstinence** from alcohol and certain foods during holy days.*
***Abstinence** does not always make the heart grow fonder.*

The verb is **to abstain.**

abstruse—hard to understand, concealed, mysterious (from L *abstrusus*, hidden)

*The workings of statisticians are too **abstruse** for those of us who are unfamiliar with mathematics.*
*Many worthwhile subjects are **abstruse** until you start to study them.*

accretion—increase, increment, accumulation (from L *accretio*, increase)

*The United States was formed by **accretion** of land bought or otherwise acquired from other countries.*
*The **accretion** of sand dunes takes eons, but can be undone by one hurricane.*

Carl Sandburg wrote that "the United States *is*, not *are*. The Civil War was fought over a verb."

acerbic—(a-SIR-bik) acid, biting, sarcastic (from L *acerbus, acer,* sharp)

*Groucho Marx was celebrated for his **acerbic** wit as well as his rolling eyes, fake mustache and meaningful leer. In one of his motion pictures, he said, "I never forget a face, but in your case I'll make an exception."*

*The district attorney was notorious for his **acerbic** dueling with defense lawyers.*

The film Laura *featured Clifton Webb as the **acerbic** Waldo Lydecker, a critic in the full sense of the word.*

acme—peak, the top, the best (Gk *akme,* highest point)

*Known as the "Waltz King" and the composer of the immortal "The Beautiful Blue Danube," Johann Strauss was considered the **acme** of waltz composers.*

*Levi Strauss invented the **acme** of jeans.*

*Vintage grapes reach their **acme** when climatic conditions are also at their **acme**.*

Wiley Coyote, the Roadrunner's nemesis in Loony Tunes cartoons, favored products made by the **Acme** company, but they never performed to his satisfaction.

acrimony—bitterness, rancor, sharpness (MF *acrimonie,* from L *acer,* sharp, *acrimonia*)

*Debates in the Congress are often full of **acrimony** rather than reason.*

*Alimony payments are sometimes accompanied by **acrimony**.*

acrophobia—fear of heights (Gk *akros*, topmost, extreme, L and Gk *phobia*, abnormal fear)

> *She has never visited the Grand Canyon or Sandia Mountain because she has **acrophobia**.*

> Some people refuse to fly in airplanes. They're not afraid to fly—they're just afraid of heights.

acropolis—city on a height (Gk *acr*, topmost, *polis*, city)

> *The magnificent Parthenon in Athens is the main attraction on the **Acropolis**.*
> *There are many other temples on the **Acropolis**, but the Parthenon is the most world-renowned. It has undergone considerable renovation to restore the damage caused by acid rain, earthquakes and millions of visitors.*

adamant—unyielding, inflexible, stubborn (L *adamas*, steel, hardest gem, diamond)

> *We are persistent in our beliefs; others are **adamant**.*
> *To be **adamant** in the face of logic is fruitless.*

> **Adamantine** is a synonym for **adamant**.

adherent—follower, advocate, proponent (MF *adhérent*, from L *adhaerens*)

> *He was a firm **adherent** of the Teddy Roosevelt philosophy of government: "Speak softly and carry a big stick; you will go far."*

> This word is also an adjective:

*An ingenious invention, Velcro, is an **adherent** hook-and-loop tape.*

Returning from a walk in the Swiss countryside in the early 1950s, George deMescal found cockleburs on his jacket. He wondered what made them so tenacious. When he examined the prickly plants under the microscope, he saw that cockleburs are covered with hooks, and that they became embedded in his jacket.

Velcro is used in aerospace and other applications.

The name Velcro comes from *vel*vet and *cro*chet.

adverse—unfavorable, unfortunate, critical (MF, from L *adversus*)

*Under **adverse** weather conditions, Jason sailed off in the Argos with his brave companions for the adventure of his life.*

*The playwright was visibly downcast when he read the **adverse** reviews of his latest work.*

Don't confuse this with *averse*, which means having a feeling of distaste, repugnance, dislike or antipathy.

aegis—(EE-jis) protection, auspices, leadership (L, from Gk *aigis*, shield of Zeus)

*The task force operated under the **aegis** of the United Nations.*

*Under the **aegis** of the Czarina, Rasputin became the power behind the throne.*

Zeus, the top brass in Greek mythology, wore an **aegis**, a shield or breastplate. His daughter, also wore a symbol of their preeminence. The shields were made of *aigis*, which originally meant goatskin. The symbolic meaning has been extended to auspices or sponsorship.

aggregation—a grouping together (L *ad*, to, *grex*, herd, flock)

> *New Jersey probably has the largest **aggregation** of pharmaceutical firms in the United States.*
>
> *Arthur Goldberg became general counsel for the **aggregation** of local unions known as the Congress of Industrial Organizations.*

agoraphobia—fear of crowds or open spaces (Gk *agora*, assembly, marketplace, *phobia*, abnormal fear)

> *The recluse was afflicted with **agoraphobia**, which prevented him from leaving his home for years at a time.*

People with **agoraphobia** are afraid of being embarrassed or caught helpless in crowds or in the midst of an open space.

This word came into general use in 1873 with publication of an article by Dr. C. Westphal, and became part of the psychological and psychiatric lexicons.

alar—wing, winglike (L *ala*, wing)

> *Angels are usually portrayed with spectacular **alar** appendages.*

This is a handy four-letter word for crossword puzzle and Scrabble fans. The plural of *ala* (wing) is *alae*. A synonym for winged or **alar** is *alate*.

aleatoric—improvisatory, random, chancy (L alea, die, dice)

> *Life is full of **aleatoric** events.*

Composer John Cage is preeminent in the field of
aleatoric *music.*

A favorite pastime of the ancient Romans was gambling with dice. Julius Caesar, on crossing the Rubicon, said, *"Iacta alea est!"* "The die is cast!" His gamble eventually paid off with a tremendous military victory.

alternative—a choice or option (L *alternus*, interchangeable)

Lord Cardigan's order apparently gave the Light Brigade no **alternative** *to charging the Russian lines at Balaclava.*

Desmond had three **alternatives***: He could go to college, enter the NBA draft system or choose a business career.*

This word should be distinguished from *alternate*, which means by turns, or one after the other. Traffic reports give "alternate" routes when they should be giving **alternative** routes.

The plural **alternatives** reminds me of the story about the devoted son who came to his mother's home to thank her for the two neckties she had given him for his birthday. When he entered the house, he saw her face fall. "Hi, mom. Something wrong?" he asked. She answered with another question: "What's the matter? You didn't like the *other* tie?"

ambidextrous—skillful with either hand (L *ambi*, both, *dexter*, on the right, skillful)

Plumbers and other artisans are **ambidextrous** *because they have to be able to work in any uncomfortable position with either hand.*

25

*Foreign correspondents must be not only inquisitive— they must be politically **ambidextrous** as well.*

Although left-handed people were as skillful or talented as the right-handed in ancient Rome (as they still are), the bias in Latin is plain to see. This word is often used metaphorically to mean versatile or flexible.

ambience—surrounding atmosphere, environment, etc. (F *ambiant*, surrounding)

*Professional military people are more comfortable in their own **ambience** than in the company of armchair soldiers.*

*Sundecks on ships have a pleasant **ambience** about them.*

Some diners go to expensive restaurants for the **ambience** as much as the food.

ambiguous—unclear, having more than one meaning (L *ambiguus*, from *ambigere*, to wander about, waver, from *ambi*, about, *agere*, to do)

*Cary Grant received an **ambiguous** telegram reading "How old Cary Grant?" Grant, known for his sense of humor, replied, "Old Cary Grant fine. How you?"*

The best antonym for **ambiguity** is clarity, a quality much to be desired in English composition.

ameliorate—to improve, make better (F *améliorer*, alter, L *melior*, better)

*The agency wished to **ameliorate** the condition of the refugees, but it was hampered by a lack of funds.*

ampersand—and, the symbol &, also called short *and*

> *The **ampersand** should be used only in company names.*

Every other use is tacky, but it's all right to use it once in a while in informal cursive writing. This symbol is taken from *and* plus *per se* (meaning by itself) plus *and*. Now you know why the shorthand symbol is used.

anachronistic—out of chronologic sequence (Gk *ana*, not, *chronos*, time)

> *Romance and historical novelists should be careful to avoid **anachronistic** events.*

In an episode of *Murder, She Wrote*, the obnoxious shock jock showed his ignorance by suggesting to Jessica Fletcher that she arrange an **anachronistic** conference with Dostoevsky about making a television series of *Crime and Punishment*.

ancillary—related, subordinate, complementary, auxiliary (L *ancilla*, maidservant)

> *Acoustics and design are **ancillary** to the study of architecture.*
> *Radiation is an **ancillary** treatment for certain kinds of cancer.*

android—automaton with human form, humanlike (Gk *andr*, man, *oeides*, oid, like)

> *Robots are the most **android** of all the automatons.*
> Star Trek *fans will remember Data, an endearing **android**, who was capable of human emotion.*

anesthesia—unconsciousness or state of no pain (Gk *an*, not, *asthesis*, feeling)

> *A new, experimental drug was used to induce* ***anesthesia*** *during the five-hour operation on the quarterback's knee.*

Anesthetics, the agents or drugs used, should be distinguished from **anesthesia**.

antecedent—predecessor, ancestor (L *ante*, before, *cedere*, to go)

> *Americans point with pride to their* ***antecedents***, *who immigrated to this country at great cost and sacrifice for political or economic freedom.*

This word can also be used as an adjective:
> *Typewriters were* ***antecedent*** *to word processors.*
> *The verb should agree in number with its* ***antecedent*** *subject.*

arcane—mysterious, secret, concealed (L *arcanus*)

> *The film* Raiders of the Lost Ark *depicted the search for the* ***arcane*** *Holy Grail.*
> *Medieval alchemists were engaged in an* ***arcane*** *quest: to find the way to make gold from base metals.*

Alchemists were also engaged in even more **arcane** pursuits: to find a panacea for all diseases and to discover a way to prolong life indefinitely.

argent—silver, silvery (L *argentum*)

> *The sea shone with an* ***argent*** *glow in the moonlight.*

28

*That day, the Aurora Borealis was **argent**, although in other climes Anouk had seen it in Technicolor.*

The explorer Sebastian Cabot may have given **Argentina** its name because of the beautiful silver jewelry and ornaments the inhabitants wore.

artifact—object made by humans, not a natural object (L *ars*, art, skill, *facere*, to make)

*The National Museum of Anthropology in Mexico City has fascinating collections of **artifacts** from Central American civilizations, including the Aztec and the Mayan.*

This word is also correctly spelled **artefact**.

asterisk—the symbol *, sometimes called star (Gk *asteriskos*, little star, *aster*, star)

Some day a jokester may come up with a song titled "Twinkle, Twinkle, Little Asterisk." But that would be redundant.

astronavigation—celestial navigation, "steering by the stars" (Gk *aster*, star, L *navis*, ship, *agere*, to lead, drive)

*Airplane pilots use **astronavigation** as well as instruments to steer by.*
*On Jan. 30, 1996, an amateur **astronomer** in Japan, Yuji Hayakutake, discovered a new comet, which was immediately named after him.*

The authority at the Fels Planetarium in Philadelphia tells me that Hayakutake is not the brightest comet in 440 years and not the closest in 440 years (there have been others), but taking both characteristics together, it is the brightest and the closest.

aural—relating to the ear or sound (L *auris*, ear)

*Although some species of fish have no **aural** apparatus, they can sense motion or vibrations in the water, perhaps through some form of sonar.*

This word sounds exactly like *oral*, which has to do with the mouth and not the ear, so the one word is often mistaken for the other.

auriferous—bearing or carrying gold (L *aurum*, gold, *iferous*, bearing)

*The 1849 Gold Rush came soon after prospectors at Sutter's Mill found **auriferous** rocks.*
*On Oscars night, a famous movie critic wisecracked that the starlet was downright **auriferous** but that the gold of her hair was spurious.*

austral—southern (L *australis*)

*Exploring the **austral** seas was only for the bravest, because that part of the world was still uncharted.*
*The smallest continent, **Australia**, which is an island as well, was so named because it is in the southern Pacific Ocean.*

avuncular—like an uncle (L *avunculus*, maternal uncle, the diminutive of *avus*, grandfather)

*Milton Berle was called "Uncle Miltie" because of his sometimes **avuncular** air on his television show.*

B

bagatelle—a trifle, something of little consequence (F, from It *bagattella*)

> *For the Chief Executive Officer, one Mercedes was a mere bagatelle.*

A short piece of music or verse is often called a **bagatelle**. There is also a game called **bagatelle** that is similar to billiards.

barbaric—savage, uncivilized (Gk *barbaros*, foreigner)

> *Because of terrible means of destruction, modern wars are much more **barbaric** than those in bygone days.*
> *Stravinsky's ballet* Rite of Spring *caused a near-riot in Paris because of its unfamiliar **barbaric** rhythms and discords.*

A year later, audiences cheered Stravinsky's ballet and carried him out to the street on their shoulders "like a prizefighter," as a gendarme later said.

behemoth—monster (Heb *behemah*, beast)

> *The Trojan Horse, the **behemoth** brought to the gates of Troy by the Greeks, became a disastrous "gift" for the city's unfortunate inhabitants.*
> *With its far-flung empire, AT&T is one of the **behemoths** of the communications industry.*

*Baldwin locomotives, one of which is housed inside the Franklin Institute in Philadelphia, were called **behemoths** because of their immensity.*

belligerent—warlike, carrying on war, quarrelsome, argumentative (L *bellum*, war, *gerere*, to carry on, wage)

*Many have feared that the **belligerent** nations might take the world to the brink of war.*

*Jan's **belligerent** words provoked a confrontation.*

Other words from the same root are *antebellum* (before the war) and *bellicose* (combative).

bellwether—a sheep carrying a bell (ME, from *belle*, bell, *wether*, ram)

***Bellwethers** are used to lead or guide the flock into the meadow or the fold.*

*Bradburn, Inc. is the **bellwether** of the widget cartel.*

This word is sometimes misspelled "bellweather," but it has nothing to do with the weather.

bemused—dazed, sometimes bewitched or bothered as well, but always bewildered

*Effects of the confusing evidence could be seen in the **bemused** expressions of the jurors.*

Children at the circus are amused, not **bemused**, except perhaps by the magic antics of the clowns.

beneficence—goodness, kindness, favor, support, promotion (L *bene*, well, *facere*, to make, do)

>*Tragedies and misfortunes may cause some people to lose their faith in the inherent **beneficence** of the human race.*
>
>*Mother Theresa's **beneficence** is visible in her face.*

biennial—every two years, once in two years (L *bi*, two, *annum*, year)

>*The commission prepares for the state's **biennial** sports competitions far in advance.*
>
>*Some crops are not profitable because they can be reaped only **biennially**.*

>**Biennial** should be carefully distinguished from *biannual*, which means twice a year; *semiannual* means every half-year or twice a year.

bigamous—relating to bigamy, the act of marrying one person while still being married to another (L *bi*, two, Gk *gamos*, marriage)

>*In* Madama Butterfly, *Lieutenant Pinkerton enters into a **bigamous** marriage with his American fiancee.*
>
>*Polygamy (multiple marriages) has never been legal in the United States, and mere **bigamy** is out too.*

biodegradable—capable of being destroyed by natural means (L *bio*, life, *gradus*, step, pace)

>*For the sake of the planet and for economic and public relations reasons, many manufacturers are using **biodegradable** packing material rather than Styrofoam.*

---

blatant—obtrusive, noisy, offensive (unknown, but perhaps from L *blatire*, to gossip or chatter)

> ***Blatant*** *disregard of civility can result in senseless tragedies such as freeway shootings.*
> *The **blatancy** of Western culture is often lampooned in the foreign media.*

bovine—cowlike, patient, sluggish (LL *bovinus*, from L *bos*, ox, cow)

> *Ladd's **bovine** eyes were brown and unblinking.*
> *Jocelyn's **bovine** temperament was a great help in her research.*

broach—to introduce, announce, present (ME *brochen*, from OF *broche*)

> *Nature enthusiasts took the opportunity to **broach** the subject of a hike along the Appalachian trail.*

> Don't misspell this word "brooch," which means an ornamental pin.

buff—enthusiast, fan (probably from the buff coats worn around 1820 by volunteer firemen in New York City, who presumably were enthusiastic about putting out fires)

> *Theater **buffs** are delighted when their opinions coincide with those of the sometimes hypercritical critics.*
> *Carr's mystery plots are elaborate, and so they appeal only to true **buffs** like you and me.*

> The slang term "fan" is short for *fanatic*.

C

cacophony—unpleasant or discordant sound (Gk *cakos*, bad, *phonia*, sound)

> *He loved the city with all its **cacophony**—street sounds, noisy air-conditioners spewing cool air, the sudden screech of brakes.*
>
> *The unfamiliar **cacophony** of the katydids, owls, and other nocturnal creatures disturbed the city boy's sleep.*

Cacophony is the antonym, the opposite, of *euphony*, which means good or pleasant sound.

caduceus—(ka-DOOS-ee-us) herald's wand, staff (L)

> ***Caducei** are favorite logos to denote swiftness, for example the winged staff with two serpents curled around it, used by the Medical Corps of the United States Air Force.*
>
> *Aesculapius, the Greco-Roman god of medicine, carried a different **caduceus**, a simple wooden staff with a forked top, with one serpent coiled around it.*

The **caduceus** of Aesculapius became the official insignia (insigne is also correct) of the American Medical Association and the familiar symbol of the medical profession in general.

carcinogenic—causing or tending to cause cancer (NL, from *carcin*, cancer, *genic*, producing)

*Many air pollutants, including industrial burnoff and tobacco smoke, are known to be **carcinogenic**.*

The constellation Cancer, portrayed in the Zodiac as a crab, lies between Leo and Gemini.

cardiology—the study and science of the heart and its diseases (Gk *kardia*, heart, *logos*, study, word, account)

*An important subspecialty of internal medicine is **cardiology**.*

carnivore—flesh-eater (L *carn*, flesh, *vorare*, to devour)

*Animals are not the only **carnivores**; insect-eating plants are also **carnivorous**.*

cartographer—one who makes maps (F *carte*, map)

*The Flemish geographer Gerhardus Mercator, who died in 1594, is perhaps the most famous **cartographer**.*

The Mercator "flat" projection is still seen in illustrations of old maps.

catharsis—purifying, cleansing, purging (Gk *katharsis*)

*Confession of sins is often thought of as **catharsis** of the soul.*
*Castor oil is an old household **cathartic** remedy.*

caustic—biting, acidic, corrosive (Gk *kaustikos*, burning)

> *Sulfuric acid is a **caustic** agent used in the laboratory to dissolve certain materials.*
> *Satirists use **caustic** humor to good advantage.*

Many Goldwynisms, solecisms attributed to Samuel Goldwyn, were never said by him, but they make for good anecdotes. His gag writers often teasingly attributed their own jokes to him. When a director told Goldwyn that a particular screen writer was too **caustic**, he is said to have replied, "Too **caustic**? The hell with it, we'll make the picture anyway."

Oscar Levant, a great performer of Gershwin music, was also noted for his **caustic** wit. He said about Doris Day's acting career that he "knew her before she was a virgin."

cerulean—deep blue, azure (L *caeruleus*)

> *The skies that autumn morning were a dazzling **cerulean**.*

charisma—an unusual quality of leadership (Gk)

> *President John F. Kennedy possessed **charisma**, and for the most part he used it well politically.*
> *Extraordinary teachers have the kind of **charisma** that inspires their students.*

This word is often mistakenly used to mean ordinary charm or persuasiveness. **Charisma** has a much stronger meaning, often having to do with leadership, and is much less common.

charlatan—quack, faker, fraud, pretender (It *ciarlatano*)

*In medical circles, **charlatans** who claim to be able to cure all diseases are called quacks.*

The German physician Franz Anton Mesmer, who practiced therapeutic hypnotism in Vienna, was thought to be a **charlatan** in his time, and he died in obscurity. Some researchers now believe that he was practicing psychosomatic medicine, an idea whose time had not yet come.

chauvinism—warmongering, unquestioning patriotism (F *chauvinisme*)

***Chauvinism** can blind its adherents to better, more rational ways to solve problems among nations than wars.*

Chauvin was a soldier whose life was fanatically dedicated to Napoleon. He even became a character in a play.

The usage of **chauvinism** has been extended to mean excessive partiality for any group, or just the opposite—extreme hostility toward members of the other sex in general.

chutzpah—nerve, gall, extreme self-confidence (Y, from Heb)

*The proverbial example of **chutzpah** is the man who kills his parents and then throws himself on the mercy of the court because he is an orphan.*

The Greek equivalent of **chutzpah** is *hubris*.

circadian—occurring daily or in about 24-hour cycles (L *circa*, about, *dies*, day)

> *"Morning persons" differ from night owls by virtue of different **circadian** rhythms.*

circuitous—roundabout, indirect (L *circuitus*, from *circum*, around, about, *ire*, to go)

> *The yellow brick road to Oz was so **circuitous** that Dorothy and her companions grew tired and frustrated.*
>
> *Politicians are particularly adept at speaking **circuitously** about crucial (and other) issues.*

claustrophobia—abnormal fear of being closed in (L *claustrum*, bar, bolt, lock, L and Gk, *phobia*, fear)

> *Patients may be so **claustrophobic** that they refuse to enter the narrow chamber used for computerized tomography.*
>
> *His **claustrophobia** in adult life was traced to painful episodes in his childhood, when he was locked in a closet all day for misbehaving.*

climax—highest point (L from Gk *klimax*, ladder)

> *For some Shakespeare enthusiasts, the play within a play is the **climax** of Hamlet.*
>
> *The American Revolution reached its **climax** when General Washington and his troops crossed the Delaware River and won the battle of Trenton.*

cogitation—reflection, thinking, meditation (L *cogitare*, from *co* + *agere*, to turn over in the mind)

> *An occasional pause for* ***cogitation*** *refreshes the mind.*
> *After much anxious* ***cogitation****, the pilot decided to land the single-engine plane on the freeway.*

comatose—in an unconscious or lethargic state (Gk *koma*, deep sleep)

> *After the accident, Dr. Bancroft's patient was left in a* ***comatose*** *state, but seven years later she woke up, to the astonishment of her family and the entire medical group.*
> *Speeches that go on too long can cause a* ***comatose*** *state and snores in the audience.*

compendium—short or abridged work, condensation of a larger work (L, shortcut)

> *Reader's Digest is a* ***compendium*** *of book excerpts and articles of general interest.*

This word is mistakenly used to mean a large, capacious work. It means quite the opposite.

complacency—undue self-satisfaction, smugness (L *com*, *placere*, to please)

> ***Complacent*** *players lose baseball games—and football games—and tennis tournaments.*
> *Displeased with the* ***complacency*** *of the school district, the parents held a town meeting to change its priorities.*

complaisant—eager to please (MF *complaire*, to acquiesce, L *complacere*, to please greatly)

> *Middle-level executives were too* **complaisant** *for the feisty new president, who openly labeled them "yes-men."*

contretemps—embarrassing or dangerous situation (F, *contre*, counter, *temps*, time)

> *Khrushchev, one of the main players in this* **contretemps** *at the United Nations, banged his shoe on the desk in a rage.*
> *Mistranslation of a Russian phrase caused a* **contretemps** *that led to some unfortunate decisions. Gorbachev had warned the United States to "take heed," but it was mistranslated as "take care," a clear threat.*

> *KON-tra-tawn* is the best English pronunciation I can offer, as the word is pronounced through the nose.

convoluted—curved, tortuous, coiled (L *com*, with, *volvere*, to enfold)

> *The human brain is so* **convoluted** *that it presents difficult choices for neurosurgeons; they sometimes operate on patients who have life-threatening disorders.*
> **Convoluted** *events call for unconvoluted solutions, but these are seldom achieved.*

> By extension this word means *complicated*.

corporeal—relating to a physical body, material (L *corpus*, body)

> *Religious institutions tend to be concerned more with spiritual concerns than* **corporeal** *ones.*

---

corrigendum—error to be corrected (L *corrigere*, to correct)

*Acknowledging her mistake, the researcher agreed to have a **corrigendum** appear in the next issue of the journal.*

*Most newspapers print **corrigenda** in the same section where the original errors appeared.*

cosmopolitan—having a world view, worldly (Gk *kosmos, polites*, citizen)

*People who travel a great deal tend to be more **cosmopolitan** than stay-at-homes.*

*The isolationist always finds himself at odds with the **cosmopolitan**.*

coup de grace—(koo-di-grahs) blow of mercy (F)

*In medieval times, a dagger called a misericord was used to administer the **coup de grace** to a criminal.*

Warriors sometimes used a misericord to end a comrade's suffering. Another *coup de grace* is the final, single shot of a firing squad.

*Terminally ill because of poor management, the Bireme Company received the **coup de grace** from the bankruptcy court.*

covert—concealed, hidden (F *couvrir*, to cover, L *coopertus*, covered)

*It is no secret that almost every country in the world has spies conducting **covert** operations.*

The opposite of **covert** is *overt*.

---

craven—cowardly, fainthearted (from ME *cravant*, cowardly)

> *Bert Lahr's most famous role was as the **craven**
> lion in* The Wizard of Oz.
> *Running away from an unfair fight is not **craven**.*

credible—believable (L *credere*, to believe)

> *Jurors thought the witnesses were **credible**, and
> acquitted the defendant.*

The opposite of **credible** is *incredible*, unbelievable.
Don't confuse **credible** with *creditable*, which means
worthy or respectable.

criterion—standard, standard of reference (Gk)

> *Integrity is one important **criterion** by which people
> are judged.*
> *Speed and maneuverability are **criteria** used to
> classify Air Force jets.*

cryogenics—science of freezing (Gk *krymos*, icy cold, ISV
genic, producing, forming)

> *The aerospace industry uses **cryogenics** extensively,
> and so do frozen-food companies.*
> *Researchers use **cryogenics** in their study of human
> tissues.*

cryptic—puzzling, hidden, secret (Gk *kryptos*)

> *Computer manuals are often **cryptic** to the average
> user.*

---

*The Oracle at Delphi gave such **cryptic** answers that the hearers could interpret them any way they wished.*

In the Oedipus legend of Greek mythology, the Sphinx at Thebes was the destroyer sent by the gods to kill all passersby who could not solve the **cryptic** riddle: "What walks on four feet in the morning, on two at noon, and on three in the evening?" The only one to solve the riddle was Orestes, who answered: "Man crawls on all fours as a baby, walks upright in the prime of life, and uses a staff in old age." The Sphinx then killed herself.

culpable—guilty, blameworthy (L *culpare*, to blame)

*The public's verdict was that those who witnessed the hold-up and stood by silently were as **culpable** as the perpetrators.*

cyberspace—the universe of computers and the networks that link them (from Gk *kybernetes*, steersman, governor)

*Meeting in **cyberspace** can be exciting and productive, but beware the frauds and malefactors who also have access to it.*

D

dearth—lack, scarcity (ME *derthe*, from *dere*, costly, dear)

*The **dearth** of rainfall in 1992 left the reservoir too low in water and full of sediment.*

debacle—collapse, downfall (F *débâcler*, to unbolt, unbar)

*The fateful year 1929 saw a **debacle** on Wall Street that ruined millions of investors and caused banks all over the United States to fail.*

decimate—to destroy, injure or damage to an extreme (L *decimus*, tenth, from *decem*, ten)

*In former times, to **decimate** was to kill every tenth man, especially in a military sense.*

Nowadays, **decimate** is used too loosely to indicate an injury of a somewhat serious kind.

deleterious—hurtful, harmful (Gk *deleterios*)

*Dietitians tell us that too much fat in the diet may cause **deleterious** plaques in the blood vessels.*
*Acid rain is **deleterious** to our cities' statues and other monuments.*

demography—statistical and sociologic science and study of human populations and subpopulations (F *démographie*, from Gk *demos*, population, people, *graphos*, written)

***Demography** is a fascinating field for workers talented in mathematics and interested in populations.*

Demographers can tell us how many people live in the United States, where they work, how they study and are educated, what percentage of drivers use a certain kind of gasoline, the number of buyers of cereals or other grocery products, and thousands of other valuable facts.

Demographers are employed by business, industry, organizations, and governing bodies, to name just a few. They are indispensable to the federal government and the Congress, which base many expenditures on **demographers'** statistics.

deprecate—to disapprove, frown on (L *deprecari*, to avert by prayer)

*Don't be too quick to **deprecate** other people's beliefs.*

derogatory—disparaging, detracting (L *derogatus*)

*Their parents wisely made no **derogatory** remarks about the children's behavior in public, and saved their criticism until they all got home.*

deterrent—discouragement, restraint (L *deterrere*, to deter)

*Capital punishment has been abolished in some countries, because they do not believe it is a **deterrent** to crime.*

digitize—to put into digital form (L *digitus*, finger, toe, digit)

*A scanner **digitizes** drawings or photographs so that you can edit them on your computer.*
__Digitizing__ is a necessity for people who want to apply for certain computer positions at this plant.

dilettante—connoisseur, amateur enthusiast, dabbler (It *dilettante*, from *dilettare*, from L *delectare*, to delight)

*As a connoisseur of the arts, she was superb. As a painter, she was a **dilettante**.*

This word can mean either amateurish or expert. Art critics are careful to use the right words in describing artists or would-be artists.

dismal—unpleasant, evil, unlucky, disagreeable (ME, from ML *dies*, day, *mali*, evil, bad)

*Medieval calendar makers considered two days in each month, 24 in a year, to be **dismal**, that is, unlucky.*

*The greatest expectations sometimes have **dismal** results.*

The ancient Romans had a similar designation, the ides, a period between the 13th and 15th of the month. Julius Caesar was warned to beware the ides of March—with good reason, for it was during one of those **dismal** days that he was assassinated.

disparate—different, unequal, unlike (L *disparare*, to separate, from *disparatus*, from *parare*, to prepare)

*Singapore is an island with three **disparate** cultures, Chinese, Malay and Indian.*

English is one of the official languages, along with Chinese, Malay and Tamil.

*Joanne Woodward won an Academy Award for her portrayal in 1957 of a woman with **disparate** personalities (*The Three Faces of Eve*).*

You will recognize the root *parare* in the motto of the United States Coast Guard: "Semper Paratus," "Always Prepared."

disseminate—spread about, make widespread (L *disseminatus*, from *dis*, apart, *semen*, seed)

> *The town crier, ringing his bell in the center of the common, would shout "Hear ye! Hear ye!" and* **disseminate** *the latest news three times each day except Sunday.*

diurnal—daily, occurring every day (L *diurnalis*)

> *The earth's rotation is a* **diurnal** *motion.*
> *Everyone needs a respite from* **diurnal** *duties.*

dolorous—sad, painful, regrettable (L *dolor*, pain)

> *Her extravagance was born of deprivation in the* **dolorous** *days of the Great Depression.*

downtime—unproductive period

> *Factory workers can ill afford a* **downtime**.
> *The Chief Financial Officer complained that there were too many* **downtimes** *in the factory's computer division.*

draconian—extremely severe or harsh

> *The original boycott was brought on by the* **draconian** *measures of tax collectors.*

Sometimes this word is correctly capitalized, since it originates with Draco, an Athenian legislator, who lived about 621 BC, and was noted for his severe code of laws.

The term *boycott* stems from Charles Boycott, an English land agent in Ireland, who refused to reduce rents and was forever after ostracized.

dyslexia—a disturbance of the ability to read (NL, from *dys*, difficult, abnormal, from Gk *lexis*, word)

> **Dyslexia** *did not prevent these diligent students from completing their education.*
>
> *Some of the world's foremost achievers, such as Leonardo da Vinci and Thomas A. Edison, have been* **dyslexic**.

E

ebullient—bubbly, exuberant, enthusiastic (L *bullire*, to bubble)

> *Barbara Walters'* **ebullient** *personality serves her well as a television interviewer.*
>
> *Old Faithful has an* **ebullient** *energy that can be seen several times a day.*

eclectic—selective, having many different sources (Gk *eklegein*, to pick out, select)

> *One* **eclectic** *branch of psychiatry blends the principles of Freud, Jung and Adler, as well as more current theorists.*
>
> *Taste in music can be* **eclectic** *without being either stuffy or vulgar.*

McGuffy's readers were called **eclectic** because they stressed the "three R's," readin', writin' and 'rithmetic.

effervescent—bubbly, exuberant (L *effervescere*, to begin to boil)

> *Even as a child, Beverly Sills was so **effervescent** that she was nicknamed "Bubbles."*
> *Speedy Alka-Seltzer was an animated character advertising the **effervescent** antacid tablets.*

effete—used up, exhausted, outdated (L *ex*, out, *fetus*, fruitful)

> *Snobbishness is a hallmark of **effete** social climbers.*
> *In her novels, Jane Austen skillfully and elegantly portrays the **effeteness** of late-18th-century gentility.*

egalitarian—believing in equality (F *égalité*, equality, L *aequalitas*, equality)

> *The avowed objective of the French revolutionists was **egalitarianism**, and on July 14, 1789, they led thousands of Parisians in storming the Bastille to free political prisoners.*

egregious—flagrant, outrageous, notorious, in conspicuous bad taste (L *e*, out of, *grex*, herd, flock)

> *The House of Lords was outraged by the member's **egregious** tirade against the Prime Minister.*

Even experts make **egregious** errors in every field of human endeavor.

As Fiorello La Guardia once said, "When I make a mistake it's a beaut!"

elusive—fleeting, evasive, baffling (L *eludere*, to elude)

Agatha Christie's **elusive** perpetrators were pursued relentlessly by the immortal Belgian sleuth, Hercule Poirot.
James Joyce's meanings are **elusive** to all but a few scholars who have devoted years of study to his idiosyncratic novels.

empathy—the capacity for associating with someone else's feelings (translation from G *einfühlung*)

A person who has **empathy** can put himself or herself in another person's shoes, even without having gone through the same experience.

encomium—praise (L, from Gk *enkomion*, a laudatory poem)

The highest **encomium** came from a fellow Nobel Laureate.

endemic—native, indigenous, confined to a particular region (Gk *endemos*, from *en*, in, *demos*, populace)

Medicinal herbs are **endemic** in the rain forests.
Because of the ease of worldwide transportation, especially by jet plane, few diseases are **endemic**.

enervate—to take energy or vigor away (L *e*, out of, *nervus*, nerve)

*Corruption has **enervated** many a metropolitan police force.*

*Discouragement can **enervate** the most courageous.*

This word is sometimes mistakenly taken to mean energize. It means the opposite.

ennui—(ahn-wee) boredom, weariness, dissatisfaction (OF *enui*, annoyance)

*Yawning, a conspicuous sign of **ennui**, is a sign that the lecturer should cut it short.*

entomology—scientific study of insects (F, from Gk, from *e*, out, *temnein*, to cut)

*The word **entomology**, a zoologic term meaning the study of insects, is often facetiously used instead of* etymology, *the study of words.*

ephemeral—temporary, fleeting, transient (Gk *ephemeros*, lasting a day, from *epi*, upon, on, *hemera*, a day)

*The popularity of many works of art is as **ephemeral** as the morning dew.*

*News on the electronic media is **ephemeral**, but the printed word lasts indefinitely.*

*Napoleon's rule of France was **ephemeral**, lasting only 100 days.*

Alfred Kahn, a professor of economics but undoubtedly also a philosopher, wrote that life is just a concatenation of **ephemeralities**.

epicenter—center, focus of an earthquake (L, from Gk *epi*, on, L *centrum*, center)

> *Anchorage, Alaska, was the **epicenter** of a 1964 earthquake that registered 8.4 on the Richter scale.*
> *Boston, which playfully claims for its nickname the Hub of the Universe, is the **epicenter** of culture and medicine in New England.*

epigram—terse, witty, pithy or wise saying (Gk *epi*, on, *graphein*, to write)

> *Benjamin Franklin's* Poor Richard's Almanack *was full of **epigrams** that are still quoted extensively.*

Why "Poor Richard"? Franklin sometimes used the pseudonym or *nom de plume* Richard Saunders.

epitome—summary, abridgment, apex, acme, embodiment (Gk *epi*, upon, *temnein*, to cut)

> *A short or condensed work is an **epitome** of a larger one.*
> *Beau Brummell was the **epitome** of London sartorial splendor.*

epizootic—epidemic among animals (Gk *epi*, on, *zoion*, animal)

> *"Mad cow" disease was **epizootic** in Great Britain in early 1996.*

ergo—therefore, hence (OL *e* + *rogo*, from the direction of)

> *California is the most populous state in the union; **ergo** it has the greatest number of representatives in the Congress.*
> *"Humana sum; **ergo** erro." "I am human; therefore I err."*
> *"Cogito **ergo** sum." "I think, therefore I am" (René Descartes).*

erratum—error (L)

> *Even the best dictionary can contain an **erratum**, which may be corrected in a subsequent edition.*

The plural is **errata**. A word related in meaning is *corrigendum*, which means something to be corrected.

esoteric—difficult to understand, mysterious (Gk *esoterikos*)

> *The tax laws are so **esoteric** that most of us need accountants to prepare our returns.*

Rhyming slang used by Cockneys in London is too **esoteric** for outsiders. Here are some examples: "mince pies" for *eyes*, "trouble and strife" for *wife*, "apples and pears" for *stairs* and "half-inch" for *pinch*.

esthetics—philosophy or science of beauty, art, and taste (Gk *aesthetikos*, of sense perception)

> ***Esthetics** embraces painting, sculpture, decoration, music and all the other arts.*

Dr. Albert Barnes, who assembled a splendid collection of Impressionist paintings in the early 1900s, was a keen student of **esthetics**.

This word is also correctly spelled **aesthetics**.

estivate—to pass the summer in one place (L *aestivare*, to spend the summer)

Summer visitors to Maryland's Eastern Shore tend to **estivate** *in a state of relaxation bordering on torpor.*

To *hibernate* is to spend the winter in one place in a state of inactivity or lethargy.

etymology—science and study of the origins of words (L *etymologia*, from Gk *etymon*, the literal meaning of a word according to its origin, from *etymos*, true)

Knowing the **etymology** *of a word can help in understanding its meaning.*
Etymologists *study the evolution, origins and interrelation of languages.*

eugenics—science dealing with improvement of human qualities (Gk *eu*, good, well, *genes*, born)

Geneticists have made great strides not only in mapping genes but in **eugenics**, *that is, in improving inheritable characteristics.*

More has been discovered about chromosomes and genes in the last 50 years than in the entire previous history of science.

eulogy—praise, speech in praise (Gk *eu*, good, well, *logia*, logy)

> *It is customary in some countries to have a relative deliver the **eulogy** at the funeral of a family member.*
> *The speech introducing the day's moderator was a **eulogy** in itself.*

euphonious—sounding good (Gk *eu*, good, sweet, *phonos*, sound)

> *The whistles, cheers and laughter of the crowd were always **euphonious** to the Harlem Globetrotters.*

> The antonym, the opposite, of **euphony** is *cacophony* (bad sound).

euphoria—feeling good (Gk *eu*, good, well, *phoros*, carrying, bearing, tendency)

> *Writing a good composition brings about a well-deserved and gratifying **euphoria**.*
> *Being on cloud nine is being **euphoric**.*

exculpate—vindicate, to clear of blame (L *ex*, out, *culpare*, to blame)

> *A P.I. (private investigator) was hired to find evidence that would **exculpate** the defendant.*
> ***Exculpatory** information must be brought to the attention of both prosecution and defense.*

extrapolate—extend, expand (L *extra*, out, E *polate*)

> *Pharmacologists cannot necessarily **extrapolate** the effects of drugs in animals to their effects in humans.*

---

*The world population in particular years beyond the year 2000 can be **extrapolated** from current statistics.*

extraterrestrial—outside the earth (L *extra*, outside, *terra*, earth, world)

*Satellites in outer space are constantly searching for intelligible **extraterrestrial** sounds.*
The film E.T. *tells the touching story of an **extraterrestrial** being and its friendship with a compassionate human boy.*

extrovert—outgoing person (L *extra*, out, *vertere*, to turn)

*An **extrovert** can be the life of the party or just a nuisance who cavorts around the room with a lampshade on his head.*

This word is also correctly spelled **extravert**.

F

fauna—animals, animal life (L *faunus*, faun)

*Zoologists all over the world go to the Serengeti National Park in Tanzania to study its magnificent **fauna**.*

The phrase "flora and fauna" often refers to the plant life (flora) and the animal life (fauna) of a particular region.

faux pas—misstep, social blunder, error (F, false step)

*Leaving a party without saying goodbye to the hosts is a **faux pas**.*
*"Oops" is a sometimes acceptable apology for a mild **faux pas**.*

This French phrase, which has passed painlessly into our language, is pronounced *foh-pah*, not *fox-pass*.

ferrous—iron-bearing, containing iron (L *ferrum*, iron, *ous*, having, being full of)

*Construction contractors use **ferrous** products extensively, especially those made of steel.*

fiat—edict, command (L, let it be done, from *fieri*, to become)

*Tolerance and equality can never be achieved solely by **fiat**.*
*The conscience has its own **fiats**.*

filial—relating to a son or daughter (L *filius*, son)

*In the field of Chinese ethics, **filial** piety, children's reverence for parents, is considered the paramount virtue and the basis for all moral human relations.*
*Although she was only a niece, Ashley had a **filial** love for her Aunt Bess.*

flagrant—notorious, glaring, conspicuous (L *flagrare*, to burn)

***Flagrant** disregard of civility and reasoned thinking led to a rash of frivolous lawsuits.*

*The nuclear-power plant engineer was adjudged guilty of a **flagrant** dereliction of duty after he was discovered asleep at his monitoring post.*

flora—plants, flowers, foliage, usually of a region (L)

*Spectacular displays of **flora** can be enjoyed at Longwood Gardens in Kennett Square, Pennsylvania.*

Strangely enough, the bacteria residing in the intestine are called **flora**.

foible—weak point, flaw, shortcoming, failing (F *faible*, weak)

*P. G. Wodehouse wrote humorous novels about the **foibles** of the idle, but lovable, rich.*

In French, the *faible* is the part of a sword blade from the middle to the point, and therefore the weaker part.

You can see where our word *feeble* originates.

formication—feeling of insects creeping on oneself (L *formica*, ant)

*All during the journey through the thick undergrowth, she had a dreadful feeling of **formication**, although the pests could not be seen.*

forte—(fort) strong point (MF, strong)

*Judy won the national bee, because spelling is her **forte**.*

59

The *forte* of a sword is the strong part, from the middle to the hilt.

The Italian *forte* means loud, and is pronounced in two syllables, unlike the French word.

fragile—delicate, frail, tenuous, weak (MF, from L *fragilis*)

*Their confidence is based on a **fragile** foundation.*

*Most perennial plants are too **fragile** to withstand the harsh Eastern winters, but they bloom again in the spring.*

frenetic—frenzied, frantic, hectic (Gk *phrenitikos*, inflammation of the brain, from *phren*, mind)

***Frenetic** activity was seen throughout the museum before the opening of the opulent Faberge exhibition.*

*The **frenetic** screams of the Grateful Dead fans could be heard even outside the stadium.*

G

gaffe—mistake, faux pas (F)

*The most conspicuous **gaffes** made in newspapers are factual errors.*

*Knowing the tight deadlines, careful readers usually forgive the typographic **gaffes**.*

gambit–opening move, a chess opening in which a piece is sacrificed for later advantage (It *gambetto*, gambit, tripping up, from *gamba*, leg)

> *The aerospace company's **gambit** eventually paid off for the major stockholders, who had wisely held on to their shares.*
>
> *Operation Overlord, which began on D-Day with the storming of the Normandy coast, was the supreme **gambit** of the Allies.*

garrulous–talkative (L *garrulus*, from *garrire*, to chatter)

> *Norman Rockwell loved to paint the **garrulous** characters he saw sitting around the cracker barrel swapping lies.*
>
> Synonyms for **garrulous** are *verbose, prolix, wordy, chatty* and *loquacious.*

genealogy–history of ancestry (Gk *genea*, race, family, *logia*, logy, study)

> *It is said that many American presidents could trace their **genealogies** to the kings and nobles of England.*
>
> *The Mayflower would have sunk outside Southampton harbor if all the people who now claim **genealogy** back to it had actually been on it.*

generic–general, not specific, not individual, not proprietary, characteristic of a group (F *génerique*, from L *genus*, class, group, kind)

> ***Generic** drugs are over-the-counter (OTC) products.*
>
> *By design, the Rockettes have a **generic** look.*

Trademarked or proprietary drugs, the opposite of **generic** drugs, are patented by their manufacturers for a finite term.

genuflect—to bend the knee, to be servile or humble (L *genu*, knee, *flectere*, to bend)

> *The mavericks who refused to* **genuflect** *before their political masters were drummed out of the party.*
> *Wedding pictures show the royal couple* **genuflecting** *before the Archbishop of Canterbury.*

geriatric—relating to old age (Gk *geras*, old age, E *atric*)

> *In the United States the* **geriatric** *population is growing at a faster rate than any other group, a process called the "graying of America."*

germane—relevant, pertinent (ME, MF *germain*, having the same parents)

> *Angry words are seldom* **germane** *to the subject in contention.*
> *Economic issues are always* **germane** *to social or political issues.*

glitch—slip, misstep, mistake, malfunction (probably from G *glitschen*, to slip, slide)

> *A faulty cotter pin caused a* **glitch** *in the satellite's liftoff.*
> *There's many a* **glitch** *'twixt the cup and the lip.*

Gordian—pertaining to something seemingly insoluble, an extreme difficulty (from Gk *Gordios*)

> *To cut the **Gordian** knot is to solve a seemingly insoluble problem with a brilliant stroke.*

Gordius, the mythologic founder of Phrygia, tied a knot in a chariot thong that could be unraveled only by someone proclaimed by the oracle to become the ruler of Asia. All who had come to that place failed in the attempt, but Alexander the Great simply cut the Gordian knot with one blow of his sword.

This word is also spelled with a lowercase *g*.

gratuitous—given freely, unnecessary, groundless, not called for by the circumstances (L *gratus*, pleasing, grateful)

> *Harsh criticism is usually **gratuitous**.*
> *Don Rickles is famous for his **gratuitous** insults of celebrities.*

A generous tip or **gratuity** is gladly given for services above and beyond the call of duty.

gravamen—burden, material part or basis (L *gravis*, heavy)

> *The **gravamen** of the Bill of Complaint was negligence on the houseowner's part to keep the sidewalk clear of snow.*

gravitate—go in the direction of (L *gravitas*, weight)

> *The younger children **gravitated** to others of the same age.*

*Their conversations at the dinner table inevitably and disastrously **gravitated** toward religion and politics.*

gregarious—social, sociable (L *gregarius*, from *grex*, herd, flock)

*Human beings create cities because we are **gregarious** by nature.*

Spinoffs of this word include *aggregate* and *congregate* (to come together), and *segregate* (*separate*).

gremlin—mischievous imp, bad influence (origin unknown)

***Gremlins** were loose in the hangar that day, with mechanics dropping tools on coworkers' toes and oil being spattered on walls and floors.*

grist—grain for grinding (OE *grist*)

*Every experience, every conversation was **grist** for Studs Terkel's mill, and he used them skillfully in his books.*

H

hagiography—study or biography of saints (Gk *hagios*, holy, saints, *graphein*, to write)

*St. Augustine is a prominent name found in every **hagiography**.*

Hagia Sophia (Gk, holy wisdom), Santa Sophia, was originally a Christian church in Constantinople (now Istanbul). It became a mosque in 1453. The present edifice, itself a masterpiece of Byzantine architecture and an art museum, was built in 532-537 by Emperor Justinian.

hedonist—someone who lives for pleasure (Gk *hedone*, pleasure)

Life on the Riviera was ideal for the **hedonist**.
The reckless pursuit of **hedonism** *led to the billionaire's downfall.*

herbivorous—grass- or plant-eating (L *herba*, grass, *vorare*, to devour)

Giraffes and giant pandas are **herbivorous**.

So are vegetarians.

Herculean—strong, of giant proportions, of great difficulty (from Hercules)

Designing the space shuttle Endeavor was a **Herculean** *task for the aerospace engineers.*

Hercules (L, from Gk Herakles), a hero in Greco-Roman mythology, possessed great strength and accomplished tasks that were impossible for anyone else.

In 1984 Arnold Schwarzenegger played the villainous, homicidal Terminator, but later films cast him in a better light as Hollywood's Action Hero of Choice, the **Hercules** of Hollywood.

hibernate—to be dormant or lethargic during the winter (L *hibernus*, of winter, wintry)

> *Bears are not the only creatures that **hibernate**; icy streets and storms cause humans in harsh climates to **hibernate** also.*

> To *estivate* is to be dormant or lethargic during the summer months.

hirsute—hairy, shaggy (L *hirsutus*)

> *In the movie* Planet of the Apes, *written by Rod Serling, the **hirsute** apes are the sympathetic masters and humans their savage subjects.*

holistic—emphasizing the relationship between parts and wholes (Gk *holos*, complete, entire)

> ***Holistic** medicine treats the patient in his or her entirety rather than as a bearer of disease.*

homily—lecture, discourse (Gk *homilos*, crowd, assembly)

> *The pope delivered a **homily** called "Urbis et Orbis," "to the city and the world," in which he pleaded for peace in troubled or warring countries.*

homogeneous—of the same or similar kind, equivalent (Gk *homogenes*, from *homo*, the same, *genos*, race, kind)

> *Japan has one of the most **homogeneous** populations in the world.*

*Mormons, members of the Church of Latter-Day Saints, tend toward **homogeneity** in their ethics, principles and beliefs.*

homograph—the same word, or spelled the same but meaning different things (Gk *homo*, same, *graphos*, written)

Invalid *and* invalid *are **homographs**. One means an ill person; the other, something null and void.*

Invalid, an ill person, is accented on the first syllable. **Invalid**, describing a nullity, is accented on the second syllable.

The French comic dramatist Moliere cast himself in his own play, *The Imaginary **Invalid** (Le Malade Imaginaire)*, but collapsed from a severe hemorrhage during a performance and died the same day.

Homographs can also mean words that are spelled the same but mean completely *opposite* things.

Cleave means to separate or to cling together.

Apparent can mean seemingly evident or clearly evident, readily perceptible.

To *sanction* means to approve or to punish.

Also see *homonym* and *homophone*.

homonym—words spelled the same and sometimes with the same pronunciation, but meaning different things (Gk *homonymos*, having the same name)

Lean *means slim or thin; to lean means to depend. They are **homonyms**.*

Homonym and **homophone** are ordinarily used synonymously and interchangeably, since there is only a slight difference between them.

Also see *homograph* and *homophone.*

homophone—words with the same pronunciation but spelled differently and meaning different things (Gk *homo,* same, *phonos,* sound)

Write, right *and* rite *are **homophones**, that is, they all sound the same but mean completely different things.*

Also see *homograph* and *homonym.*

honorific—expressing honor or respect (L *honorare*)

*Sports writers conferred the **honorific** "Sultan of Swat" on Babe Ruth. He was major-league baseball's home run king, with 714, until Hank Aaron eclipsed his record in 1974 and finished with 755.*
*Oliver Wendell Holmes, Jr., a justice of the United States Supreme Court, was given the **honorific** "The Great Dissenter" because of his well-considered and elegantly written dissenting opinions.*

horology—the science of measuring time, the art of constructing timepieces (Gk *hora,* period of time, time of day, *logy,* study)

*The sundial, an early product of **horology**, can still be seen in some gardens.*
***Horologists** construct grandfather clocks that show not only the hour but the phases of the moon.*

hortatory—urging, attempting to persuade, advisory (L *hortatus*)

*The candidate's speech was more **hortatory** than enlightening.*

The word *exhortation* comes from the same root.

hubris—gall, nerve, arrogance, excessive self-confidence (Gk *hybris*)

*Celebrities who refuse to give autogra, hs under any circumstances are guilty of **hubris**.*
*Mussolini manifested all the **hubris** of power.*

You may never see or use the word *sophrosyne*, which is the opposite of **hubris**. It means temperance, prudence or self-control.

hyperbole—gross exaggeration (Gk *hyperbole*, excess, extravagant)

***Hyperbole** is saying, "If I've told you once I've told you a thousand times."*
***Hyperbole** is the last refuge of the linguistically insecure.*

The shortened form **hype** is used extensively in describing movies and television series.

hypercritical—overly critical, faultfinding in trivial matters (Gk *hyper*, over, above, *kritike*, criticism)

*Those who care for children should never be **hypercritical**, for harsh words may ring forever in a child's mind.*

69

hypothermia—abnormally low body temperature (Gk *hypo*, under, beneath, *therme*, heat)

Dramatic pictures of the boy's rescue from the icy pond were seen on the evening television news. He had been under water for 20 minutes and was suffering from severe **hypothermia.**

I

icon—image, idol (Gk *eikon*, resembling)

The Hermitage, a museum in St. Petersburg, Russia, contains innumerable **icons** *of saints.*
Although they were British, the Beatles became an American **icon.**
A Wall of Fame in the restaurant bears the caricatures of local sports **icons.**

Icon is also used in computer language to denote a small picture or graphic representation—on the screen of a program, file or function—that the user can choose. The **icon**, which is usually in a box, can be called up by clicking a mouse.

idiosyncrasy—a characteristic peculiar to one entity or person, eccentricity (Gk *idio*, personal, distinct, personal, individual, *synkrasis*, mixing, blending)

Her refusal to make left turns into streets was only one of her driving **idiosyncrasies.**

A small group of subjects reported **idiosyncratic** *reactions to the investigational drug.*

One eccentric businessman in Boston never paid any attention to the one-hour difference during Daylight Saving Time. His clients were forced to bow to this **idiosyncrasy**, and his friends forgave it.

illicit—unlawful (L *in*, not, *licitus*, lawful)

Some characters in the opera Carmen *were engaged in an* **illicit** *activity, smuggling.*
Evidence obtained by **illicit** *means is tainted, and therefore inadmissible in court.*

illuminate—to light up, enlighten (L *in*, into, *lumen*, light)

Backlighting was used to **illuminate** *the stained-glass rose windows of the cathedral.*
St. Gregory the **Illuminator** *(240-332 AD) was the founder and patron saint of the Armenian church.*
Floodlights **illuminated** *the Field of Dreams, and the fans came.*

impecunious—poor, penniless (L *im*, not, *pecunia*, money)

Dickens wrote about people who were **impecunious** *but nonetheless rich in character and compassion.*

impervious—impenetrable, not open (L *im*, not, *pervius*, from *per*, through, *via*, road, way)

Police officers often wear vests that are **impervious** *to most kinds of bullets.*

*Lord Worcester's haughty manner gave the impression that he was **impervious** to insults.*

incredible—unbelievable, unlikely, improbable (L *in*, not, *credere*, to believe)

*Marco Polo's tales of riches and spices in far-off lands were **incredible** at first to his fellow Venetians.*

Bystanders in a Texas town looked on *incredulously* as cowboys rounded up cattle that had escaped from an overturned trailer truck. These words should be differentiated: Things are **incredible**; people are *incredulous*.

indigenous—native, originating in that region (L *indigena*, native)

*Corn is **indigenous** to the United States.*

*Digitalis, an herb **indigenous** to Eurasian countries, is used as a cardiac stimulant.*

infinitesimal—tiny, almost zero (NL *infinitesimus*, infinite in rank, from L *infinitus*, infinite)

*Differences between identical twins are **infinitesimal**.*

*In building bridges, or other massive engineering work, even an **infinitesimal** error can have disastrous results.*

Constructors of the 180-foot-high campanile nicknamed the Leaning Tower of Pisa made a seemingly **infinitesimal** error by building on a foundation only about 10 feet deep. Today the tower is almost 17 feet out of perpendicular.

iniquity—wrongful conduct, sin, wickedness (L *in*, not, *aequus*, unjust, unequal)

> *Communities work with the legal system in trying to remedy the **iniquity** of child abuse.*
>
> *What is **iniquity** to fundamentalists may simply be a difference of opinion.*

You should be careful to distinguish this word from **inequity** by pronouncing each carefully. An **iniquity** is more serious than an inequity, for example an inequity in wages, although that may be a sin, too.

innuendo—insinuation, hint (L *innuere*, to hint)

> *Gossip columnists and certain television personalities use **innuendo** to titillate their audiences.*
>
> *To paraphrase an adage attributed to the 19th-century Baptist preacher C. H. Spurgeon, **innuendo** (a lie, in the original) travels round the world while truth is putting her boots on.*

insouciant—(in-soos-ee-ant) indifferent, nonchalant, without a care (F *insoucier*, from *in*, not, *soucier*, to disturb, trouble, from L *sollicitare*, to disturb, agitate)

> *Eustace Tilley, the splendidly dressed man on the annual cover of* The New Yorker *magazine, has an **insouciant** air about him, because he is ignoring a butterfly flitting around his head.*

73

interregnum—lapse, period between two regimes (L *inter*, between, *regnum*, dominion)

> *Anne of Austria was chosen regent for the* ***interregnum*** *between the king's death and the dauphin's accession to the throne, but Cardinal Mazarin held the real power.*
>
> *Lame-duck congresspeople are always the victims of the* ***interregnum*** *between election and inauguration.*

intransigent—uncompromising, unshakable, immovable (Sp *intransigente*, from L *in*, not, *transiger*, to compromise)

> *The Stamp Act of 1765 aroused the fury of the American colonists. The British parliament reversed its* ***intransigent*** *stand and repealed the act only a year later.*
>
> Businessmen, lawyers, journalists and merchants vehemently opposed the Act, which levied a tax on all papers, newspapers, journals, legal documents, and advertisements issued in the American colonies. Because the colonists were not represented in Parliament, they condemned the Act as taxation without representation.

introvert—one turned inward toward oneself (L *intro*, within, toward, *vertere*, to turn)

> *Poets and other writers are often more* ***introverted*** *than nonwriters, perhaps because of the solitary nature of the writing process.*
>
> **Introverts** are often called wallflowers. Their opposites are *extroverts*.

iota—an infinitesimal amount, the smallest part, jot (Gk, ninth letter of the Greek alphabet)

*The champion showed not an **iota** of courtesy to the challenger during the weigh-in period, even though they had been friends and sparring partners.*

Iota is the smallest letter in the Greek alphabet.

J

jaundiced—yellowish (MF *jaune*, yellow, L *galbinus*, yellowish-green, from *galbus*, yellow)

***Jaundiced** people, who are affected by an abnormal flow of bile, usually have a yellowish cast to their skin.*

By extension, **jaundiced** can also mean having a hostile, envious or unfavorable view. Alexander Pope wrote that everything looks yellow to the **jaundiced** eye.

jocular—given to jesting, humorous, playful (L *jocularis*, from *joculus*, little jest, from *jocus*, joke)

*The comic's serious demeanor in his private life was belied by his **jocular** manner on stage.*

The word **jocund**, meaning merry, lively, pleasant, cheerful, has the same root.

joust—tournament, mock combat (OF *jouster*, to joust)

> *The roommates often engaged in good-natured verbal jousts.*

Original **jousters** were knights on horseback who tried to knock their armored opponents to the ground.

judicious—wise, prudent (L *iudicium*, judgment)

> *A judicious choice of investments brought prosperity to Green in her later years.*
> *Judicious words and pacific actions finally brought an end to the community's conflict over a proposed housing development.*

juxtaposed—placed side by side (L *juxta*, near, next to, *positus*, placed)

> *When space is a consideration, office modules can be juxtaposed, but at the expense of privacy.*
> *In constructing neighborhoods, juxtaposing houses is more economical than building detached ones.*

K

kaleidoscope—infinite variety, a viewing instrument containing colored pieces of glass (Gk *kalos*, beautiful, *eidos*, form, *scopein*, view)

> *Betsy could amuse herself for a half-hour at a time with her favorite gift, a kaleidoscope.*

Sunset over the Grand Canyon was an unforgettable **kaleidoscope**.

keystone—wedge-shaped stone at the top of an arch

*In baseball the **keystone** sack is second base. Pennsylvania is nicknamed the **Keystone** State because of its central geographic position among the original 13 colonies.*

kibbutz—a collective farm in Israel (Heb *gibbus*, gathering)

*My friend Menachem lives on a **kibbutz** near the Jordan River.*

The plural is **kibbutzim**.

*On many **kibbutzim** the adults' living quarters fan off a central dining hall and children's quarters.*

kinetic—relating to motion, active, lively (Gk *kinetos*, moving)

*Elvis Presley had a **kinetic** energy that communicated itself to the audience.*
*Leonard Bernstein's **kinetic** force was a predominant influence on 20th-century American music.*

kleptomania—irresistible urge to steal (Gk *kleptein*, steal)

*Shoplifting may be **kleptomania**, which is considered a sickness, but it is a crime nonetheless.*

kremlin—fortress or walled citadel of a Russian city (Russ *kreml*)

*Many cities had kremlins, but the **Kremlin** in Moscow is the most famous.*

The **Kremlin**, triangular and occupying 90 acres, was the residence of the czars until Peter the Great moved the capital of Russia to St. Petersburg (later Leningrad, but now St. Petersburg again). In 1918 the capital was transferred back to Moscow, and the **Kremlin** became the administrative and political focus of the Soviet Union.

kudos—renown, praise, fame (Gk *kydos*)

*Volunteer firefighters are quiet heroes who deserve much **kudos**.*

Merriam-Webster dictionaries say that **kudos** is both singular and plural. Although the plural verb is seldom used, this is a correct usage: "Throughout the year, Rachel received various other **kudos**, including her high school's prestigious scholar-athlete award for basketball." This 16-year-old dynamo also excels in softball and field hockey. She is also a proud member of the National Honor Society.

L

lacerate—to tear, rend, mangle (L *lacerere*, to tear)

*This latter-day Romeo claims that his heart bears many **lacerations**.*

*The skeletons of crabs and purple shells **lacerated** the honeymooning couple's bare feet as they walked on the Monterey beach.*

laconic—concise, undemonstrative, terse (Gk *Lakonikos*)

*As usual, the **laconic** George understated the seriousness of the situation.*

This word derives from Laconia, an ancient Greek district, of which Sparta was the capital. The Spartans were famous for their succinct way of speaking and writing. Philip, the King of Macedon, threatened them when he said "If I enter Laconia, I will raze it to the ground." The Spartan magistrates **laconically** replied, "If."

largo—slow, broad (It, from *largus*, generous, abundant)

*In music the **largo** movement is a particularly slow one.*

The cast of the 1948 movie thriller *Key **Largo*** included Humphrey Bogart, Lauren Bacall, Edward G. Robinson, Claire Trevor and Lionel Barrymore.

lassitude—weariness, lethargy, debility (L *lassus*, weary)

*Sleeping sickness is characterized by **lassitude**.*

*Between cases, Sherlock Holmes suffered from a **lassitude** that made Dr. Watson, his companion, concerned that the detective might reawaken his addiction to cocaine.*

leonine—like a lion (L *leo*, lion)

*The back of Leopold Stokowski's **leonine** head was immortalized in the film Fantasia.*
*Some sphinxes had **leonine** heads. Others had the faces of women.*

lethargy—drowsiness, apathy (Gk *lethe*, forgetfulness)

*Politicians complain that the American people seem to suffer from extreme **lethargy** on Election Day.*

This word comes from Greek mythology. Lethe was a place of oblivion in the lower world.

lexicographer—a maker of dictionaries, student of words (Gk *lexis*, word, *graphos*, writing)

*Samuel Johnson and Noah Webster were two of the most prominent early **lexicographers**.*
*Johnson called a **lexicographer** "a harmless drudge."*

A related word is **lexicon**, which you're looking at now.

liaison—close bond, interrelationship (F *lier*, to tie, bind, *aison*, ation)

*Henry's group was the **liaison** between the airlines and the U.S. Department of Transportation.*

*Dangerous **Liaisons** is a magnificently crafted movie about depravity, cruelty and deceit among the aristocracy in pre-Revolutionary France.*

This film was adapted from a novel by Choderlos de Laclos titled *Les Liaisons Dangereuses*, which the author said was fully intended to shock. It succeeded then, and it still succeeds.

ligature—bond, connection (L *ligare*, to tie, bind)

> *Sutures are used as **ligatures** in surgery.*
> *In printing, **ligatures** are one or more letters of the alphabet joined or combined into one, for example, æ.*

Oliver Wendell Holmes, Sr., a physician who disliked pretentiousness, wrote that he would never use a long word where a short one would do. There were professors, he said, who **ligate** arteries. Other surgeons only tie them, and it stops the bleeding just as well.

lilliputian—tiny, small, undersized (from Lilliput, an imaginary country)

> *In his brilliant* Gulliver's Travels, *Jonathan Swift describes Gulliver's first journey, to **Lilliput**, where the **Lilliputians**, fearful of this giant, captured him and kept him in chains.*

Sometimes the adjective of **lilliputian** is spelled with a capital *L*.

logorrhea—excessive talkativeness, running off at the mouth (Gk *logos*, word, *rhea*, flowing)

> *Speakers should never succumb to the temptation of **logorrhea**.*

---

logotype—symbol used for identification (Gk *logos*, word, *typos*, impression, image, model, type)

> *A red flying horse is used as the **logotype** for Mobil gasoline.*

This word is almost always abbreviated in speech to **logo**, meaning an individualized symbol for instant recognition. The *fleur-de-lis* is the **logo** of the Boy Scouts of America.

loquacious—talkative, garrulous (L *loquax*)

> *There is a time to keep silent and a time to speak, and even a time to be **loquacious**.*

lupine—wolfish, wolflike (L *lupus*, wolf)

> *Robin's friends thought that his sideburns gave him a **lupine** appearance.*
> *The stalker who haunted Chicago streets even had a **lupine** walk.*

M

magnanimous—generous in spirit (L *magnus*, great, *animus*, spirit)

> *Even enemies can be **magnanimous** in victory.*
> ***Magnanimity** is rarely foolish.*

malevolent—mean-spirited, injurious, filled with spite or
  hatred (L *male*, badly, *velle*, to will)

> *The clouds hovered over the ball park like*
> ***malevolent*** *spirits.*
>
> *Dorothy was frightened by the **malevolent** shrieks*
> *of the Wicked Witch, but she courageously refused to*
> *give up the ruby slippers.*

malign—to act maliciously, slander, vilify (L *male*)

> *Caldwell took the opportunity to **malign** his*
> *competitors, asserting that their goods were inferior.*
>
> *The vice president sued the newspaper, alleging that*
> *it had **maligned** him unfairly because of his stock*
> *trades.*

malleable—open-minded, impressionable, capable of being
  molded or transformed (L *malleare*, to hammer)

> *Youth should be **malleable**, middle age should be*
> *confident and old age should be **malleable** once again.*

manumission—freeing, as of a slave (L *manu*, from the
  hand, *mittere*, to let go, send)

> *In the antebellum South, **manumission** for a price*
> *was practiced by the more greedy slaveowners.*
>
> *Tess celebrated her **manumission** from an oppressive*
> *relationship with Jack.*

masochism—extreme self-denial, self-punishment (from Leopold von Sacher-**Masoch**, a German novelist)

*Some critics consider ice hockey, with its attendant broken front teeth and frequent bloody melees, an exercise in **masochism**, while fans see it as a fast, exciting sport.*

masterful—domineering, arrogant, imperious (ME *maister*, master)

*General Scott's **masterful** command earned him the enmity of his subordinate officers.*
In the film The King and I, *Yul Brynner portrays the **masterful** King of Siam.*

This word is often mistakenly used to mean *masterly*. The two should be distinguished, since for most people—and society—it is more desirable to be *masterly* than **masterful**.

masterly—with the skill of a master, artistic, skillful, talented (ME *maister*, master)

*The museum exhibited the **masterly** works of Ansel Adams, whose black-and-white photographs made him preeminent in his field.*
*Michelangelo's **masterly** ceiling in the Sistine Chapel has never been equalled.*

mauseoleum—tomb, gloomy, ornate structure (Gk *mausoleion*)

*Napoleon's **mausoleum** is under the huge dome of the Hôtel des Invalides in Paris.*

---

*Probably the most famous of all **mausoleums** is the Taj Mahal at Agra, India.*

These structures are named after **Mausolos**, a Greek ruler in 353, whose tomb is in Halicarnassus.

The Invalides, a historic landmark in Paris, was originally a hospital for disabled veterans. It is now a military museum complex.

The Taj Mahal, ordered built by the Mogul emperor of India Shah Jahan, was completed in 1648 as a memorial to his beloved wife, Mumtaz Mahal. Deservedly considered one of the most beautiful buildings in the world, it is in a perfect state of preservation.

maven—connoisseur, expert, knowledgeable person (Y, from LHeb)

*An oenophile is a lover of wine or a wine **maven**.*
*Her best friend was a **maven** when it came to Italian cuisine.*
*Besides being a world-renowned playwright, George Bernard Shaw was a drama **maven**, and wrote many memorable reviews of other people's plays.*

maximal—highest, greatest, most effective (L *maximus*)

*To get the **maximal** effect from this medication, take it on an empty stomach.*
*The Marxists' motto was "The **maximal** good for the greatest number."*
*Some philosophers consider the Age of Enlightenment, characterized by human reason, to be the **maximal** period in European culture.*

mayhem—needless, malicious or willful damage or physical injury (ME *maym*, from Anglo-French *mahaim*)

> *The riots in Los Angeles were notorious for looting, **mayhem** and wanton cruelty.*
> *In the suit, the complainant said that the editorial had committed verbal **mayhem** on the candidate.*

megalith—huge prehistoric stone (Gk *megas*, great, strong, large, *lithos*, stone)

> *Each stone at Stonehenge, the eerie monument on Salisbury Plain in England, is a **megalith**.*

melee—brawl, donnybrook, free-for-all (F *mélee*)

> *A bar dispute escalated into a **melee** on the busy street.*
> *Robin Hood's men merrily engaged in a **melee** with the Sheriff of Nottingham.*

mellifluous—honeyed, smooth, sweet (L *mel*, honey, *fluere*, to flow)

> *The **mellifluous** voices of Pavarotti, Domingo and Carreras blended in a magnificent trio from* Turandot.

The feminine name Melissa, as in Mercouri, the famous Greek movie star, is a descendant of the same root.

memento—keepsake, remembrance, souvenir (ME, from L, *memenisse*, to remember)

> ***Mementos** from the past are the heirlooms of the future.*

*Tanya brought back a gold griffin pin from the Louvre as a **memento** for her daughter.*

This word is often misspelled and mispronounced as "momentos."

memoir—report, record, personal narrative (F *mémoire*, from L *memoria*, memory)

*Winston Churchill's **memoirs** make fine reading. Many a movie star wishes another celebrity's **memoir** had gone unpublished.*

mentation—mental activity (L *mens*, mind)

***Mentation** may be difficult after a heavy lunch.*

This word is a synonym for thinking or cerebration.

mercurial—temperamental, uneven, unpredictable, volatile (L *Mercurialis*, of the god or the planet of Mercury)

*Certain ethnic groups or nationalities are falsely stereotyped as **mercurial**.*

No doubt some members of these groups are **mercurial**, but the same could be said of any group.

Mercury, the ancient Roman god of commerce and the messenger of the gods, was noted for his eloquence, shrewdness, and ingenuity.

meretricious—false, pretentious, insincere (L *meretrix*, prostitute)

*Politicians abound in **meretricious** claims and promises.*

*The seemingly cordial relationship between top and middle management was in fact **meretricious**.*

mesmerize—hypnotize, spellbind, fascinate (from Franz Anton Mesmer; see commentary under *charlatan*)

*Even 40 years after Sputnik, the launch of a satellite into outer space is a **mesmerizing** sight.*
*The horseback ride of the nude Lady Godiva **mesmerized** one inhabitant of Coventry.*

This woman's husband promised to repeal his heavy taxes on the city of Coventry if she would ride naked through the city. Lady Godiva, famous in English history, rode through the streets with her nudity partially covered by her ankle-length golden hair. The inhabitants closed their shutters in sympathy with her. According to a later story, one person couldn't help peeking. He is immortalized by the nickname Peeping Tom.

metabolism—process of assimilation and nutrition in the body (G *metabolisch*, from Gk *metabolikos*, changing, from meta, with, after, ballein, throw)

*Nutritionists are concerned with the **metabolism** of certain substances such as iron, calcium and magnesium in the body.*

metaphor—figure of speech implying comparison, analogy or similarity (MF *metaphore*, from Gk *metapharein*, to transfer, change, from *meta*, with, after, *pharein*, to bear)

*Carl Sandburg's best-known **metaphor** is the Chicago fog coming in "on little cat feet."*

---

*Shakespeare used **metaphor** extensively and effectively in his sonnets: "Shall I compare thee to a summer's day?"*

metropolitan—relating to a city (LL, mother city, from Gk *metropolis*, from *metra* or *meter*, mother, *polis*, city)

*Washington, D.C., could be considered the **metropolis** of America.*

*Tokyo and Hong Kong have such a **metropolitan** feeling that the New Yorker felt right at home.*

As a noun, a **metropolitan** is the head of an ecclesiastic district of the Eastern Orthodox Church, especially one headquartered in a large city.

microcosm—miniature universe (ML *microcosmus*, from Gk *mikros kosmos*, small world)

*Aircraft carriers, ocean liners, and nuclear submarines are communities in themselves, **microcosms** of the larger world.*

*Television writers are enthralled by the **microcosmic** nature of medical centers, as can be seen by the spate of series about hospitals and emergency rooms.*

migraine—severe, excruciatingly painful headache (F, from LL *hemicrania*, pain in one side of the head, from Gk *hemi*, half, *kranion*, skull)

***Migraine**, although not life-threatening, is a scourge not confined to people with stressful occupations.*

Migraine cuts across all lines, not respecting age, sex, mental status or physical health. It is often accompanied by nausea and vomiting.

Some **migraineurs** know that a headache is coming on when they experience a familiar aura, with flashing lights before the eyes and other unpleasant symptoms.

milieu—environment, setting, midst (F, from L *medius*, middle, *locus*, place)

Artists are sometimes troubled by the unfamiliar, cold milieu of the business world.

Competition was his milieu, and he thrived on it.

millennium—a thousand years, period free of human imperfections (L *mille*, thousand, *annum*, year)

Controversy swirls around whether the millennium starts in the year 2000 or the year 2001.

Most people think 2000; purists and Stanley Kubrick fans, 2001.

If you have trouble remembering that this word has two *n*'s, think of *annual* and *biennial*.

minimal—the very least possible, extremely minute (L *minimus*, smallest)

If tunnels were built by designers or workers with minimal skills or standards, they would never hold up under the tremendous weight they bear.

misanthrope—one who hates or has contempt for humankind (Gk *misein*, to hate, *anthropos*, man, human being)

> *The rank hypocrisy Gale saw in his profession made him an undiscriminating misanthrope.*
>
> *A man may say he loves humankind, but if he hates his neighbor, he is a true misanthrope.*

misogynist—showing hatred or distrust of women (Gk *miso*, hatred, *gyne*, woman)

> *Many a misogynist has had an unhappy love affair.*
>
> *Andrew's misogyny dissipated as his friendship with Joan grew and he recognized her beauty of spirit.*

The counterpart of misogyny is *misandry* (Gk *mis*, hatred, *andros*, man), hatred or distrust of men.

mnemonic—helping to remember (Gk *mneme*, memory)

> *The mnemonic aid E G B D F, which stands for every good boy does fine, can be used by piano beginners to remember the lines in the G clef. F A C E is a mnemonic to remember the spaces.*
>
> *A checklist is a good mnemonic aid when completing each stage of an important project.*

Here's another **mnemonic** aid that may some day come in handy: Remember *story* for things his*tor*ic and act*ual* for things historic*al*.

The origin of many words containing *mn*, including *amnesty* and *amnesia*, is **Mnemosyne**, the Greek goddess of memory.

modicum—a little bit, limited quantity (L *modicus*, moderate, small)

*A **modicum** of good sense goes a long way in settling a dispute.*
*Their tale of woe hasn't a **modicum** of truth.*

monogamy—one single marriage or mating (LL *monogamus*, marrying once)

*Some societies in the world do not practice **monogamy**. They sanction bigamy (usually two spouses) or polygamy (two or more spouses).*

monolith—a single huge stone or stone structure (Gk *mono*, single, alone, *lithos*, stone)

*Two red granite obelisks from Egypt, nicknamed Cleopatra's Needles, were erected about 1475 BC in Heliopolis ("City of the Sun"). One is the **monolith** on the Thames River in London, and the other is in Central Park in New York City.*

A related word is *aerolithology*, which is the science dealing with meteorites.

monosyllabic—having one syllable, terse, succinct (Gk *mono*, single, alone, *syllabe*, syllable)

*One game that word experts play is to write **monosyllabic** essays, that is, works in which each word contains only one syllable. It's much harder than it sounds.*

*The Red Queen's order was pointedly **monosyllabic**: "Off with their heads!"*

moribund—dying, approaching death, dormant (L *moribundus*, from *mori*, to die

> *Far from being **moribund**, the blacksmithing trade is still lively, especially the horseshoeing part of it.*

> Ask any fan of horse racing.

morphology—the study of structure (Gk *morphe*, form, structure, *logos*, logy)

> ***Morphology*** *includes many kinds of studies, among them the structure of words, cells, anatomy, plants and animals.*

mortify—humiliate, injure, destroy (L *mortificare*, from *mors*, death, *ficare*, to make, form into, make similar to, invest with the attributes of)

> *The flesh can be **mortified** by disease, the spirit by constant humiliation.*
> *In boot camp that day, the drill sergeant managed to **mortify** the entire squad with his brutal language.*

mufti—civilian or street dress, especially when worn by those usually in military uniform (Ar)

> *Ernest was glad to don **mufti** when he was on leave from Okinawa.*

mundane—worldly, relating to human concerns (L *mundus*, world)

> *Astronauts have to contend with such **mundane** things as eating and drinking even as they contend with weightlessness.*
> *The abbot urged the monks to abandon **mundane** thoughts and concentrate on spiritual matters.*

munificent—liberal, exceedingly generous (L *munificus*, generous, from *muni*, service, gift)

> *Many universities and medical centers bear the names of **munificent** donors.*

myopia—nearsightedness, lack of discernment (Gk)

> *Governments are often criticized for their **myopia** in foreign affairs.*
> ***Myopia** can be corrected by the proper eyeglasses.*

N

narcissism—egoism, excessive vanity (from **Narcissus)**

> ***Narcissus** was a handsome youth in Greco-Roman mythology who fell in love with his own reflection in the water, died of unrequited love, and was turned into the flower **narcissus**.*
> *The **narcissistic** impulses of adolescence are ordinarily outgrown in adulthood.*

nascent—being born, beginning to exist (L *nasci*, to be born)

> *In some Pacific islands, industrialization is in a* **nascent** *stage.*
> **Nascent** *stirrings of revolt were seen in the devastated cities.*

nauseous—causing nausea, sickening, disgusting (L *nausea*, seasickness, from Gk *naus*, ship)

> *The odor of sulfur resembles the smell of rotten eggs, and is* **nauseous** *in the extreme.*
> *Half the passengers,* **nauseated** *by the ceaseless rolling of the ship, remained in their cabins for the rest of the voyage.*

> *Things* are **nauseous**, that is, *causing* nausea; *people* are **nauseated**, that is, *feeling* nausea. These words should be carefully differentiated. You wouldn't want to be considered **nauseous**.

negligent—careless, neglectful (L *negligere*, to neglect)

> *Because of the* **negligent** *handling of the dyes, the entire stock of silk had to be discarded.*
> *To forgive* **negligence** *is divine; to sue over it is much more common.*

neologism—new or recent coining, coined word or expression (F *né*, born, *logie*, logy, from L *natus*, born, Gk *neos*, new, recent, *logos*, word)

> *Smog is a* **neologism**, *combining* smoke *and* fog.

Chortle, a combination of *chuckle* and *snort*, is attributed to Lewis Carroll, the author of the witty and delightful children's stories *Alice's Adventures in Wonderland* and *Through the Looking Glass*.

Television has given us many **neologisms**. Some of the best known, including Trekkies (fans) and "beam me up," are from the *Star Trek* series.

Cyberspace, discussed in this book under the *c*'s, is a much used (and overused) **neologism**. Technologic advances bring many **neologisms**.

nepotism—favoritism toward one's family, especially in business or politics (F *népotisme*, from L *nepos*, grandson, nephew)

*"I didn't get this job through **nepotism**," the would-be starlet insisted. "My father hired me."*

*Although his grandfather was the president of the firm, Stewart never took advantage of **nepotism**. He learned the business from the ground up and eventually became a vice president.*

*The citizens' commission sharply criticized the **nepotism** among members of the legislature, who had created lucrative jobs for their relatives.*

noisome—annoying, odorous, harmful, destructive, noxious (ME *noysome*, from *noy*, annoy)

*Smoke from the chemical factory created a **noisome** environment for the nearby inhabitants.*

This word really has nothing to do with noise, except that excessive noise pollution can create a **noisome** neighborhood.

nostalgia—fondness for things past, homesickness (from Gk *nostos*, return home)

*Nguyen confessed to a **nostalgia** for the cooking of her Vietnamese homeland.*

noxious—toxic, harmful, injurious (L *noxa*, damage, offense, from *nocere*, to harm)

***Noxious** influences were thought to be partially responsible for the boy's misdeeds.*

nuance—trace, subtle distinction, slight gradation (from MF, shade of color)

*An expert dyer can distinguish the **nuances** in shades of red or blue.*

*There is more than a **nuance** of difference between acting and emoting.*

numismatist—specialist in coins, coin collector (L *numisma*, money, coin)

*In 1964, when the United States Mint stopped using silver in coins, many **numismatists** grumbled.*

Numismatists are often philatelists as well.

O

obnoxious—offensive, hateful, objectionable (L *ob*, to, toward, *noxius*, harmful)

*Unkind comments are usually **obnoxious**.*

*Extremists' views are **obnoxious** to those who are moderate in their approach.*

obstreperous—loud, unruly, unmanageable, rowdy (L *ob*, to, against, *strepere*, to make noise)

*The party grew so **obstreperous** that the neighbors called police.*

Synonyms for **obstreperous** are *vociferous*, *turbulent* and *clamorous*.

obverse—the front of a coin, currency or medal (L *obvertere*, to turn toward)

*Quarters depict the head of George Washington on the **obverse**.*
***Obverse** you win, reverse you lose.*

octogenarian—person 80 to 89 years of age (L *octogenarius*, consisting of 80)

*Grandma (Anna Mary Robertson) Moses took up painting in her 70s, and continued her art even after she was no longer an **octogenarian**.*

People in their 90s are nonagenarians. On seeing a beautiful young woman passing by, the nonagenarian Oliver Wendell Holmes, Jr. exclaimed, "Oh, to be 70 again!"

octothorp—the symbol # (origin apocryphal; L *octo*, eight)

*The symbol #, the **octothorp,** is called the pound sign when used on the telephone dial.*

This handy, versatile symbol is also the number sign, a sharp in music, and the game tic-tac-toe.

oleaginous—oily (L *olea*, olive or olive tree)

> *The **oleaginous** manner of the snake oil salesman offended the more sophisticated listeners, and even some of the naive.*
>
> *The Valdez accident left an **oleaginous** slick that devastated most of the coastline.*

ombudsman—representative, advocate, proponent (Sw)

> *Consumers can go to an **ombudsman** to hear their complaints and find remedies.*
>
> *College students have access to an **ombudsman** or **ombudswoman** to redress grievances against the administration.*

omnivorous—eating everything (L *omni*, all, *vorare*, to devour)

> ***Omnivorous** readers are usually more successful in their careers and enjoyment of life than nonreaders.*
>
> *Bernard Berenson was an **omnivorous** collector of art and antiques.*

onerous—oppressive, burdensome, heavy (L *onus*, burden)

> *Air traffic controllers have **onerous** jobs.*
>
> "He's not **onerous**. He's my brother."

onomatopoeia—forming words to imitate natural sounds (Gk *onoma*, name, *poila*, make)

Meow, bowwow, tweet, roar, chirp, hiss, buzz *and* zoom *are **onomatopoeic** words.*
*Homer was one of many poets fond of **onomatopoeia**.*

opprobrium—dishonor, contempt, disgraceful or infamous act (L *ob*, to, toward, *probrum*, disgraceful act, reproach)

*Vandals who scrawl graffiti are held up to public **opprobrium**.*
*Embezzlement is **opprobrious**.*

opus—a work, usually of art, as in music (L)

Messiah *was Handel's greatest **opus**.*

The Latin phrase for a great work is **magnum opus**. The plural of **opus** is either **opera** or **opuses**, but the latter word is rarely used.

oral—by mouth, spoken (L *os*, mouth)

*Lawyers tell us that **oral** agreements or contracts are difficult to prove, and they therefore recommend written ones.*
***Oral** medicines are easier to take than injected ones.*

This word can be confused with *aural*, which sounds exactly the same but relates to the ear, not the mouth.

Verbal messages can be either **oral**, that is, spoken, or written. *Verbal* simply means *with words*. Communication can also be nonverbal (without words), for instance, a wink of the eye, a shrug of the shoulders or an uplifted middle finger in traffic.

ordinal—having a specified number or rank in a series (L *ordo*, order)

*First, third, fourth, tenth and twentieth are all **ordinal** numbers.*

The corresponding cardinal numbers are one, three, four, ten, and twenty.

Ordinal numbers are also correctly written as 1st, 3rd, 4th, 20th, and so on, depending on house style.

ornithology—branch of zoology specializing in birds (Gk *ornith*, bird, *logos*, study)

*Cornell University has one of the foremost centers of **ornithology** in the United States.*

*A knowledgeable forest ranger has a wide range of **ornithologic** information.*

ostentatious—showy, flagrant, conspicuous (L *ostendere*, to show)

*Diamond Jim Brady's **ostentation** irritated his fellow financiers.*

James Buchanan Brady was famous for his collection of jewels, especially diamonds (many of which he wore), his enthusiastic participation in Broadway night life, and his enormous appetite. But he was also famous as a philanthropist. Among many other benefactions is a clinic at Johns Hopkins Hospital that bears his name.

ostracize—banish from society (Gk *ostrakon*, oyster, shell, earthen vessel, potsherd)

> *Hester Prynne, the protagonist in Hawthorne's* The Scarlet Letter, *was **ostracized** and forced to wear an "A" for adultery.*

In ancient Greek times, citizens could vote once a year in the *agora* (marketplace) on whether to **ostracize** someone. Political or financial corruption was especially frowned upon. Potsherds were used as ballots. If 6,000 or more votes were cast and a majority voted for **ostracism**, that person was banished from the city temporarily.

otiose—futile, ineffective, idle (L *otium*, ease, leisure)

> *At one time the search for extraterrestrial intelligence was thought to be an **otiose** endeavor.*

overt—open, unconcealed, manifest (MF, from *ovrir*, to open)

> *The faces of the protesters showed **overt** hostility.*
> *The children's **overt** delight as they watched the white lion cubs tumbling was worth the long wait.*

Covert is the opposite of **overt**.

oxymoron—contradiction, paradox, incongruity (Gk *oxymoros*, pointedly foolish, from *oxy*, sharp, keen, *moron*, dull, foolish)

> *The word **oxymoron** is itself an **oxymoron**.*

Examples of **oxymorons** are deafening silence, cruel kindness, jumbo shrimp, mini-supermarket, left-handed compliment, conspicuous absence, critical acclaim, favorite disease and guest host.

Cynics include as **oxymorons** the phrases military intelligence and business ethics.

P

paleography—study of old writings (Gk *palaios*, old, ancient, *graphia*, graphy)

Illuminated manuscripts are a favorite with ***paleographers*** *because of their extraordinary beauty.*

palestra—arena, gymnasium, stadium (Gk, from *palalein*, to wrestle)

Modern gymnasts, wrestlers and other athletes, like their counterparts in ancient Greece and Rome, perform in ***palestras****.*

The University of Pennsylvania basketball team plays in an old arena called the ***Palestra****.*

palimpsest—parchment or manuscript that has been erased and written over more than once (Gk *palin*, again, back, *psestos*, scraped, rubbed)

Previous writings can be discerned on some ancient ***palimpsests****.*

Be careful not to misspell this word "palimpset."

palindrome—word, phrase, number or sentence that reads the same backward and forward (Gk *palindromos,* running back again)

*One of the most famous **palindromes** is the sentence "Able was I ere I saw Elba."*

*Another **palindrome** is "A man, a plan, a canal— Panama."*

Other examples of **palindromes** are the number 2468642, the names *Ada, Anna, Eve, Hannah* and *Lil,* and the words *boob, deed* and *level.*

palpable—touchable, easily discernible, evident (L *palpare,* stroke, caress)

*The hostility between panelists was nearly **palpable.***

*An enlarged liver is **palpable** to the experienced physician.*

The opposite of **palpable** is impalpable.

panacea—remedy, cure for all ills, a cure-all (Gk, *pan,* all, *akeisthai,* to heal)

*A flat tax is no **panacea** for a nation's economic woes.*

*Charlatans have the **panacea** for everything that ails their gullible customers.*

*The nicotine patch is an aid, not a **panacea,** for people trying to quit smoking.*

pandemic—affecting many people over a wide region (Gk *pan*, all, *demos*, populace)

*Malaria is **pandemic** in countries that are afflicted with hordes of mosquitoes.*

An epidemic affects many members of a particular population simultaneously.

pandemonium—a riot, din, uproar, tumult (Gk *pan*, all, *daimon*, spirit, deity)

*President Mandela's entrance into the auditorium created **pandemonium**.*

This word comes from an epic poem by John Milton, *Paradise Lost*, in which he describes **Pandaemonium**, the capital of Hell.

paradigm—model, example, pattern (Gk *paradeiknynai*, to show side by side)

*The genius Mozart is the **paradigm** of musicality.*
*Medical professionals are expanding their **paradigm** of what constitutes health and healing.*

John Simon, a brilliant critic of art and other endeavors, wrote a book titled ***Paradigms** Lost*, in which he reflects on the "decline of literacy."

paradox—person, sentiment, statement or principle that is self-contradictory (Gk *paradoxos*, contrary to expectation)

*"Fighting for peace" is a **paradox**.*

*Jane Eyre was a **paradox**, her modest air belying her spirited actions.*

parameter—statistical or mathematical variable, a value or measure to be sought (Gk *para*, before, ahead, *metron*, measure)

*Many **parameters** must be determined before a population can be called civilized.*

This word should not be used to mean perimeter. See *perimeter*.

paramount—foremost, chief, supreme, preeminent (from OF *par*, through, *mont*, mountain)

*Pete Seeger was the **paramount** folk singer in the middle part of the 20th century.*
*The rescue of victims is always **paramount** in a firefighter's mind.*

paranormal—unusual, supernatural (Gk *para*, beyond, L *norma*, pattern, rule)

*Duke University has studied **paranormal** phenomena such as extrasensory perception (ESP) for many decades.*

parity—equality, equivalence (L *par*, equal)

*There should always be **parity** between power and responsibility.*
***Parity** in intelligence is impossible, but **parity** in opportunity is the goal.*

*To make for competitiveness and fan interest, sports leagues aim for **parity** among teams.*

parsimonious—frugal, excessively thrifty, stingy (L from *parcere*, to spare)

*Ebenezer Scrooge was well known for his **parsimonious**, mean-spirited ways.*

pathology—study of abnormality, especially diseases (Gk *pathos*, experience, emotion, suffering)

***Pathologists** study the changes in tissues of human beings, both in life and in death.*
*Forensic **pathology** is the study of changes in human tissue as they relate to criminal activities.*

Pathology also relates to emotional and mental illnesses.

patina—covering, coloring, film, usually green, on bronze or copper statues or other structures (L, shallow dish)

*Rodin's "The Thinker" is covered with a fine **patina** that enhances its appearance.*
*Her face bore the beautiful **patina** of age and character.*

patrician—noble, aristocratic, relating to gentle breeding (L *patres*, fathers)

*Until about 350 BC, only **patricians**, members of the original citizen families in ancient Rome, could become senators or consuls.*

*Laurence Olivier's **patrician** bearing was used to good advantage in such films as* Hamlet *and* Henry V.

paucity—scarcity, small number, smallness (L *paucus*, little)

*The **paucity** of rain eventually created deserts where once gardens bloomed.*
*Less affluent neighborhoods suffered from the **paucity** of retail establishments, mainly grocery stores.*

pedagogue—teacher, especially of children (Gk *paidagogos*, from *pais*, child, *agogos*, leader, escort, from *agein*, to lead)

*Morris Cogan, a **pedagogue** in the University of Pittsburgh Graduate School of Education, was an experienced teacher of teachers.*
***Pedagogy** is the art or discipline of educating.*

pediatrician—physician specializing in the treatment and care of children (Gk *pais*, child, *iatros*, physician)

*Dr. Benjamin Spock, born in 1903, is a renowned **pediatrician** whose "baby book" has sold in the millions.*

pejorative—derogatory, disparaging (L *pejorare*, to become worse)

*A left-handed compliment seems to be pleasing but is in reality **pejorative**.*

Jargon is not a **pejorative** word, since it merely means a specialized language for insiders. It can, however, be used **pejoratively**.

---

penchant—inclination, leaning (F *pencher*, to incline, bend, from L *pendere*, to weigh)

>*Children have a **penchant** for crayoning on walls.*
>*The amateur collector had a **penchant** for toy mechanical banks.*

penitent—atoning, expressing sorrow for offenses (L *paenitere*, to be sorry)

>*Laura's **penitent** face was all the apology her sister needed.*
>*Joe bought his brother a new Erector set as **penitence** for losing most of the pieces.*

pensive—thoughtful, reflective (F *penser*, to think, from L *pensare*, to weigh, consider, ponder)

>*Aisha was in a **pensive** mood as she sat in the bay window and looked out at the snow-covered hills.*

The pansy (F *pensée*, thought) was given this name because it resembles a face.

penultimate—next to the last in a series (L *pene*, almost, *ultima*, last)

>*The **penultimate** book in the tetralogy was the most successful and widely read.*

A common error is to see only the *ultimate* part of this polysyllabic word and overlook the fact that it means "*next to* the last." Another mistake is to think that **penultimate** means the best or the quintessential. It doesn't.

peregrination—wandering, journey, travel (L *peregrinari*, to travel in foreign lands, from *peregrinus*, pilgrim)

> *Queen Isabella's help made Marco Polo's **peregrinations** financially possible.*
> *Pilgrims to the Holy Land made their **peregrination** a fascinating journey into biblical history.*

perfunctory—routine, mechanical, apathetic, done as a duty (L *per* [completing], *fungi*, to perform)

> *The **perfunctory** manner of the officials at Ellis Island did little to dampen the happiness the Svensens felt on landing in the United States.*
> *Donna's interest in stamping envelopes was **perfunctory**; her real ambition was to be a candidate for city council.*

perimeter—circumference, boundary (F *périmetre*, from Gk *peri*, around, *metron*, measure)

> *Police were stationed on the **perimeter** of the playing field to discourage fans from rioting.*

Be sure to distinguish this word from *parameter* (see entry on page 106).

peripatetic—itinerant, walking or moving from place to place (Gk *peri*, around, *patein*, walk)

> ***Peripatetic** preachers became scarce as the country's population grew and became more prosperous.*

Even today, some clergymen and physicians are **peripatetic**. A physician may serve as a locum tenens, that is, a substitute practitioner for an indefinite time. Should the occasion ever arise, you will know that the plural of the Latin phrase *locum tenens*, which means holding (tenens) the place (locum) of or substituting for, is locum tenentes.

The **peripatetic** "Johnny Appleseed" (John Chapman, 1774-1845), a pioneer who was born in Massachusetts, walked for 40 years through Ohio, Indiana and western Pennsylvania sowing apple seeds. There are many stories about this early environmentalist.

perquisite—privilege, profit (L *per*, thoroughly, *quaerere*, to seek, gain, obtain)

> *One **perquisite** of middle management was the opportunity to buy company stock at a discount.*
>
> *A company car is a **perquisite** of sales representatives in many firms.*

This word is often abbreviated as "perks." It should not be confused with *prerequisite*, which is something required at the outset.

perspicacious—having keen discernment (L *perspicere*, to see through)

> *Anna Quindlen's **perspicacious** commentaries in* The New York Times *earned her a Pulitzer Prize in 1992.*

The noun is **perspicacity**.

phantasmagoria—constantly changing succession of real or imaginary things (F *phantasmagorie*, images that seem to be phantoms)

> *Thomas de Quincey's* Confessions of an English Opium Eater *originated in his own dreadful **phantasmagorias** as an addict.*

phenomenon—fact or event of scientific or cultural interest, extraordinary person (Gk *phanein*, to show)

> *A solar eclipse is a **phenomenon** that can damage the naked eye.*
> *Michael Jordan and Dennis Rodman are basketball **phenomena**; Wilt Chamberlain, Kareem Abdul-Jabbar (formerly Lew Alcindor) and Julius Erving (Dr. J) used to be.*

philately—stamp collection (Gk *philein*, to love, *ateleia*, tax exemption, immunity)

> ***Philately** is a benign obsession unless you bankrupt yourself pursuing it.*
> *Adam's childhood interest in **philately** brought him a huge profit later in life.*

In early times a postage stamp conferred *ateleia*, immunity from public duties, such as the mailing charge or tax.

philology—study of words (F *philologie*, from L *philologia*, love of talk, argument, from Gk *philologos*, love of words and learning)

> *Amateur **philologists** love word puzzles.*

Philology is the study of literature, language as used in literature, and human speech.

pigeonhole—to put into compartments (MF *pijon*, ME, *hole*)

*Politicians are fond of **pigeonholing** their constituents or thinking of them as blocs, but voters continue to cast their ballots as individuals.*

pixel—short for picture element

*A **pixel** is one of a group of small, distinct photographic elements that together make up an image.*
*The number of **pixels** on a monitor determines whether an image will be clear or diffuse.*

The shorthand **pix** (for *pictures*) was used in a memorable headline from *Variety*, the publication of show business: "Hix nix stix pix," which translates from showbiz language into "Country people don't like pictures about country people."

platitude—trite or stale remark (F *plat*, flat)

*Commonplace people are fond of **platitudes**—what others call small talk. "Hot enough for you?"*

Some **platitudes** are cliches.
Even the speech of the bumbler Polonius in *Hamlet* is full of wise, quotable sayings, which we rephrase and now unthinkingly characterize as **platitudes**: "Brevity is the soul of wit." "The apparel oft proclaims the man." "Neither a borrower nor a lender be." "This above all: to

thine own self be true, and it must follow, as the night the day, thou canst not then be false to any man."

pliable—bendable, capable of being molded or changed, flexible (MF *plier*, to bend)

> *Thornton's opinions were as **pliable** as wet clay.*
> *Twine is more **pliable** than vinyl-covered wire.*

Ply, as in three-ply yarn, is from the same root as **pliable**.

poetaster—a failed or would-be poet, versifier (L *poeta*, poet, *aster*, one whose work is inferior)

> *These immature works indicate a **poetaster** rather than a real poet.*

This word is sometimes mispronounced "poet-taster," but the emphasis should be on the *poet* part, with *aster*, denoting lack of art, pronounced like the flower.

pontificate—pronounce pompously, speak as an oracle (L *pontifex*, high priest, pope, literally bridgemaker, from *pons*, bridge, *facere*, to make, do)

> *Heads of state are expected to **pontificate**, and none can resist the temptation.*
> *Celebrities are often asked to **pontificate** on subjects about which they know little.*

In ancient Rome the emperor was the **Pontifex** Maximus. After the ascendancy of Christianity, the pope became the **Pontifex** Maximus or **Pontifex** Summus, the supreme or highest priest.

posthaste—with the greatest speed possible (*post*, courier)

> *When the Maple Leaf defenseman was slashed with a stick across his face, the coach sent **posthaste** for the team physician.*

potency—strength, power (L *potentia*)

> *Antibiotics are tested for **potency** as well as safety.*
> *Never underestimate the **potency** of words.*

potpourri—dried flowers, mixture, medley, unrelated matters (F *pot pourri*, from Sp *olla podrida*, rotten pot)

> *During the shipboard gala, the orchestra was asked to play a **potpourri** of Gershwin tunes.*
> *Barbara's book was a captivating **potpourri** of history, anecdote and fact.*

This word is correctly pronounced *poh-purr-ee*; *pot-purr-ee* is also correct but some consider it substandard.

pragmatic—practical, matter-of-fact (Gk *pragmatikos*, from *pragma*, deed, affair)

> *The **pragmatic** effects of false economy could be seen throughout the pine barrens.*
> *Known for his **pragmatic** bent, Thomas rarely philosophized but instead went about solving problems.*

The noun is **pragmatism**.

precipitate—hasty, premature (L from *praeceps*, headlong)

> *Gabriel tried not to be **precipitate** in his judgment of the facts.*

> Also see *precipitous*.

precipitous—very steep (L *precepitium*, precipice)

> *The **precipitous** descent from Machu Picchu left the climbers dusty and breathless.*
> *Ithaca, New York, has many **precipitous** gorges within the city limits.*

> An advertising executive, who is also a professor of communication at Ithaca College, coined the slogan "Ithaca is gorges."

prehensile—adapted for grasping or seizing (F *préhensile*, from L *prehendere*, to grasp, seize)

> *Monkeys seem to fly because their **prehensile** tails allow them to swing wide distances from tree to tree.*

prerequisite—something required beforehand (L *pre*, before, *requirere*, to need, seek for, inquire after)

> *One **prerequisite** for advanced composition is a working knowledge of style, usage, spelling, grammar and punctuation.*
> *A good memory is a **prerequisite** for actors.*

> **Prerequisites** is sometimes confused with *perquisites*, which is abbreviated "perks" and means privileges.

prestidigitator—magician, sleight-of-hand artist (F *preste*, nimble, quick, L *digitus*, finger)

*Some clowns are also **prestidigitators**, and can find coins in people's ears.*

Harry Houdini was the Great Prestidigitator, and some of his death-defying escape tricks have never been duplicated.

probity—honesty, uprightness, integrity (L *probus*, honest, virtuous)

*Janet was known for her impeccable **probity** in dealing with colleagues.*

***Probity** is the prerequisite for special prosecutors, who have to avoid even the appearance of fault.*

prognosis—outlook, outcome, foreknowledge (Gk)

*The **prognosis** for the nation's economy was good when the period of inflation ended.*

*When the catcher's knee was injured in a collision at home plate, the long-term **prognosis** seemed bleak.*

prognosticate—to foretell, prophesy (ML *prognosticus*)

*Weatherpeople do not **prognosticate**; they simply give you the odds on the weather.*

No one ever hears about the failures of oracles, astrologers and other prognosticators.

Because these **prognosticators** use generalities, some of what they say must be on the mark. The rest is left to the imagination of the audience.

Incidentally, weatherpeople are right 80 percent of the time—not bad.

prolix—talkative, wordy, repetitious (L *prolixus*, extended, protracted)

*Insurance policies, like many other legal documents, seem to be needlessly **prolix**.*

*Anton Bruckner's symphonies are magnificently **prolix**, with the motifs being repeated over and over.*

proprietary—owning privately (L *proprietas*, property)

***Proprietary** drugs are trademarked and are solely owned by the manufacturer.*

*Patent holders have **proprietary** ownership of their inventions for a specified time.*

propriety—decorum, appropriateness (MF *propriété*, personal quality)

*Runnels questioned the **propriety** of searching someone's house without permission.*

*The Three Stooges were known for their slapstick, not their **propriety**.*

prowess—gallantry, bravery, excellence (ME *prouwesse*)

*Audie Murphy was the most decorated American soldier in World War II because of his **prowess** on the battlefield. He also appeared later in Hollywood films about the war.*

prudent—wise, farseeing, frugal (L *prudens*)

> ***Prudent*** *management mandates intelligent and compassionate treatment of its employees as well as its stockholders.*

The noun is **prudence**.

pseudonym—pen name, fictitious name (Gk *pseudes*, false, *onyma*, name)

> *Elia was the* ***pseudonym*** *of the English essayist Charles Lamb.*
> *Mary Ann (or Marian) Evans took the* ***pseudonym*** *George Eliot.*
> *Gypsy Rose Lee, the most famous, and certainly most stylish, stripteaser, was the* ***pseudonym*** *of Rose Louise Hovick. Her sister, the actress June, changed her last name to the* ***pseudonym*** *Havoc when she came to Hollywood.*

A synonym for **pseudonym** that is ordinarily reserved for writers is *nom de plume*.

pterodactyl—extinct flying reptile (Gk *pteron*, feather, wing, *daktylos*, finger, toe)

> *Dinosaur lovers like to build models of* ***pterodactyls***.

punctilious—exact, careful in manners (Sp *puntillo*, small point)

> *In his usual* ***punctilious*** *manner, the host greeted each guest with courtly grace.*

---

pundit—learned person, teacher (Hindi *pandit*, from Skt *pandita*, learned, wise)

*Blackwell is considered the **pundit** of bad taste because of his "Ten Worst-Dressed Actors" list.*

Motilal Nehru, an Indian lawyer and political leader, was called **Pandit** Nehru. He became associated in 1919 with Mohandas (Mahatma, which means *great-souled*) Gandhi in the civil disobedience movement.

Nehru's son, Jawaharlal Nehru, became Gandhi's political heir.

punitive—punishing (L *punire*, to punish)

*The plaintiffs were awarded **punitive** damages in addition to compensatory damages because of the willful and malicious conduct of the defendant.*

*Dissenters were subject to **punitive** measures that included jail time.*

putative—commonly accepted, reputed (L *putare*, to consider, think)

Their **putative** marriage was in fact bigamous.

pyromaniac—arsonist, compulsive firestarter (Gk *pyr*, fire)

*To the community's astonishment, a volunteer firefighter turned out to be a **pyromaniac**.*

Q

quadrilateral—four-sided, four-sided figure with four angles (L *quattuor*, four, *latus*, side)

> *All rectangles are **quadrilateral**, but not all **quadrilaterals** are rectangles.*
>
> *The **quadrilateral** agreement fell apart when the two Eastern countries split with the two Western ones over fishing rights in international waters.*

quash—to suppress, crush, quell (L *cassus*, empty, void, without effect)

> *The district judge denied the defense attorney's motion to **quash** the four-count indictment for embezzling.*
>
> *John Brown's antislavery rebellion was **quashed** when he and his 21 followers were captured at Harpers Ferry by U.S. marines led by Colonel Robert E. Lee.*

querulous—complaining, whining, irritable (L *querulus*, complaining)

> *You can often divert **querulous** children with a shiny toy.*
>
> *Propaganda is sometimes more **querulous** than persuasive.*

quicksilver—mercurial, changeable, quick (ME *quik*, alive, silver, translated from L *argentum vivum*)

> *Roger's **quicksilver** moods were like the northeastern weather—one moment sunny, the next gloomy.*
>
> *The chameleon's movements were like **quicksilver**.*

quintessence—distillation, epitome, the most typical example, purest of its kind (L *quinta*, fifth, *essentia*, essence)

> *Judge Learned Hand's opinions from the United States Court of Appeals were the **quintessence** of reason and compassion.*

> The adjective is **quintessential**.

> *Fred Astaire was the **quintessential** dancer.*

R

ramifications—consequences, subdivisions, developments (L *ramus*, branch, *ificare*, -ify, to make, perform)

> *The **ramifications** of late-night carousing can be disastrous.*

> *Family trees are so **ramified** that it takes an expert or a dedicated amateur to unravel the relationships.*

> *The blood vessels of the heart have innumerable **ramifications**.*

recidivism—relapse into previous behavior (L *recidivus*, falling back, recurring)

> *Unemployment and moral poverty are direct causes of **recidivism** among criminals.*
>
> ***Recidivist** tendencies can be seen in Elizabeth Taylor, Mickey Rooney and others who engage in multiple marriages.*

reciprocal—mutually shared (L *reciprocus*, returning the same way)

> *Some states have **reciprocal** agreements on legal or medical certification and on traffic tickets.*
>
> ***Reciprocity** is the life of trade.*

regime—reigning period, era, social or political system (F *régime*, from L *regimen*)

> *During his 43-year **regime**, Peter the Great established shipbuilding as a prime industry for Russia, encouraged Western influences, and was instrumental in transforming medieval Muscovy into modern Russia.*
>
> *Boss Tweed's **regime** was characterized by greed, corruption, bribery and graft.*

regimen—systematic plan, regulation or treatment (L *regere*, to rule)

> *The antisepsis **regimen** established in the last decades of the 19th century by Semmelweis—requiring frequent washing of hands, especially during childbirth—drastically reduced the mumber of maternal deaths from infectious disease.*

remuneration—payment, reward, gift, recompense (L *munus*, gift)

> *The **remuneration** for a good conscience is, alas, nothing more than a good night's sleep.*
> *Henri's business became more **remunerative** when he acquired the best stylist on Fifth Avenue.*

renascence—rebirth (L *renasci*, to be born again)

> *In middle age the couple had a **renascence** of interest in musical comedy.*

The *Renaissance*, which means exactly the same as **renascence**, usually refers to the transitional period in Europe between the 14th and 17th centuries, which saw the flourishing of literature and the arts and the beginnings of modern science.

repartee—clever retort, witty reply (F *repartie*)

> *Johnny Carson was noted for his **repartee** with* Tonight Show *guests.*

Dorothy Parker, a member of the Algonquin (Hotel) Round Table, was a drama critic as famous for her **repartee** as for her acerbic reviews. Perhaps the best-known review was the one in which she wrote that the actress "ran the whole gamut of emotions from A to B."

reticent—quiet, silent, reserved in speech (L *reticere*, to keep silent)

> *Modesty often goes with **reticence**.*

*Abe Lincoln was by nature **reticent**, but he could be outgoing and jovial when the occasion stirred him.*

retroactive—going back before a specified time (L *retro*, back, *agere*, to drive, act)

*The reinstated workers were entitled to **retroactive** pay to compensate them for time lost when the factory burned down.*

*Because there was no statute of limitations, the business privilege tax could be levied **retroactively**.*

rhinitis—inflammation of the nasal mucous membranes (Gk *rhis*, nose, *itis*, inflammation)

*Seasonal **rhinitis** refers to allergic reactions brought on by pollen and other airborne pollutants.*

The word *rhinoceros* comes from the Greek *rhino*, nose, and *keras*, horn. This well-named, ponderous animal has a horn on its nose.

risible—funny, laughable, laughter-provoking, ridiculous (L *risus*, from *ridere*, to laugh)

The television comedy series Murphy Brown *always tickled his **risible** sense.*

*Life would be dull if it were not for our **risibilities**.*

robot—machine that can duplicate some human activities (Czech *robota*, forced work, labor)

*Today many industries use **robots** or **robotic** machinery to do repetitive, heavy work.*

*Police bomb details use **robots** to retrieve bombs or suspected explosives and to defuse them or blow them up.*

A forerunner of Isaac Asimov's *I, **Robot*** was a famous drama, *R.U.R.*, by the Czechoslovakian humanist and playwright Karel Capek.

R.U.R. stood for Rossum's Universal Robots. Capek's play (1921, translated into English in 1923) introduced the word **robot** into our language.

rote—memorizing (ME *rote,* custom)

> *The entire class had to recite all 52 verses of* The Bells of Atri, *an epic poem, by **rote**.*
>
> *Patriotism cannot be taught—or learned—by **rote**.*

rufous—red, reddish (L *rufus*)

> *The **rufous** plumage and flight of the cardinals delighted the city-dwellers every morning.*
>
> *Thomas Jefferson's **rufous** hair made him conspicuous among the older signers of the Declaration.*

ruthless—merciless, without pity or compassion (ME *rewthe,* pity, *les,* less, without)

> *The **ruthless** onslaught of words was too much for Don's fragile ego.*
>
> *Rare timberland in the Northwest became the target of **ruthless** deforestation.*

S

sadism—gratification from cruelty, excessive mental or physical cruelty (from the Comte [Marquis] de Sade, French author)

> *Sadism is the last refuge of the coward.*
> *The phenomenon of sadism has been studied as a precursor to the teachings of Freud and Nietzsche.*

salutary—wholesome, healthful, curative (L *salus*, health, safety)

> *American Indians were well aware of the salutary effects of certain herbs on disease and injuries.*
> *Improved nutrition is a salutary factor in the education of small children.*

salutatory—welcoming speech (L *salutare*, to salute)

> *To Jonathan's surprise and pleasure, he was chosen to give the salutatory at commencement exercises.*

sanctimonious—hypocritically or falsely pious (L *sanctimonia*, sanctimony, from *sanctus*, holy)

> *Rasputin was a sanctimonious charlatan, a monk without a conscience.*
> *Elmer Gantry's sanctimonious mouthings won him a gullible audience.*

sanction—to ratify, approve, confirm (MF, from L *sancire*, to decree, make sacred)

> *King John, forced by the barons to **sanction** the Magna Carta, signed it at Runnymede.*

> The verb to **sanction** is to approve. Oddly enough, the plural noun **sanctions** means the opposite: coercive measures to punish nations that violate international law, such as trade **sanctions**, which impose an embargo or boycott against a rogue nation.

sanctum—a study, holy or sacred place, refuge, place of retreat or respite (L *sanctus*, holy)

> *The city editor closed the door of his **sanctum** to discourage unwelcome visitors.*

> *Antonia's studio was her **sanctum** sanctorum, her holy of holies, not to be trespassed upon except in a dire emergency.*

sanguinary—bloody, gory, murderous (L *sanguis*, blood)

> *For Americans, the Civil War was the most **sanguinary** conflict of any in United States history, including World War II.*

sanguine—optimistic, confident, cheerful (L *sanguis*, blood)

> *Wilkins Micawber, a character in Dickens's David Copperfield, had a **sanguine** outlook despite his poor financial circumstances. He was eternally certain that "something will turn up."*

satiate—to fill up, satisfy, overfill (L *satis*, enough)

> *Holiday candy can **satiate** the greatest chocolate-lover.*

The noun is **satiety**.

schism—division, gap, separation, discord (Gk *schizein*, to split)

> *When Gordon became head of the national committee, the **schism** over states' rights widened, and the party eventually splintered into two factions.*
> *The **schism** between liberals and conservatives made bitter enemies of former friends.*

Schism is pronounced *siz-im*, as in *scissors*, with the accent on the first syllable.

scintillate—to sparkle (L *scintillare*, to emit sparks)

> *City lights obscure the **scintillating** stars, but they're there just the same.*
> *The **scintillating** wit and humor of the pianist Victor Borge have earned him the nickname the Clown Prince of Denmark.*

In one of his famous monologues, the Great Dane told his audience, "It's a sobering thought that when Mozart was my age, he had been dead 10 years."

scion—descendant, child, shoot of a plant (OHG *chinan*, to sprout)
> *Justice Oliver Wendell Holmes, himself a brilliant writer, was the worthy **scion** of his namesake, who was both a renowned physician and a man of letters.*

scurrilous—vulgar, evil, slanderous (L *scurrilus*, jeering)

>*Too many talk-show hosts are notorious for using **scurrilous** innuendo in their broadcasts.*

segue—(SEG-way) to go from one theme or song to another without pausing (It *seguire*, to follow, from L *sequi*)

>*Talented singers can **segue** from classical to popular music with no trouble at all.*
>*The director **segued** from the scene in the forest to the love scene in the house.*

semiannual—every six months or twice a year (L *semi*, half, *annum*, year)

>*Shoppers flocked to center-city for the **semiannual** sales in the department stores.*
>*Don't forget to go to the doctor for your **semiannual** checkup.*

>*Biannual* also means twice a year, but is seldom used, because it might be confused with *biennial*, which means every two years or every other year.

sempiternal—everlasting, eternal, never-ending (L *sempiternus*, eternal, from *semper*, always)

>*The **sempiternal** redwood trees in California, often towering more than 300 feet, are an awesome sight.*

septuagenarian—person between 70 and 79 years of age (L *septuaginta*, seventy, from *septem*, seven)

>*Many **septuagenarians** frown on retirement, and they continue to work at their occupations indefinitely.*

George Walker, a **septuagenarian**, is the first African American to win a Pulitzer Prize in music. His work *Lilacs* is based on Walt Whitman's *When Lilacs Last in the Dooryard Bloom'd*, an elegy for Lincoln. Walker was also the first African American graduate of the Curtis Institute of Music in Philadelphia.

serendipity—a fortunate or valuable finding by chance

*One of the greatest instances of **serendipity** in all history was the discovery of America by Christopher Columbus, who was looking for the Indies.*

Ceylon (now Sri Lanka) was formerly called **Serendip**. The word **serendipity**, coined by Horace Walpole, stems from a Persian fairy tale about three princes of Serendip who made random discoveries in their travels.

Serendipity played an important role in the discovery of Teflon on April 6, 1938 by Roy Plunkett, a young chemist working for the duPont company, who had received his Ph.D. degree just two years before.

Plunkett and his colleague, Jack Rebok, were experimenting to find a nontoxic refrigerant when they came across an empty tank that wasn't supposed to be empty. On examining the tank, they discovered a waxy white powder that had unexpectedly polymerized and had become polytetrafluoroethylene (Teflon), the material that "nothing will stick to."

The new material was originally used during World War II for gaskets in atom bombs. Today Teflon (*always* use a capital T, or you may get a letter from duPont) is used for everything from frying pans to heart valves and other artificial body parts. It is one of the few prosthetic substances that humans do not ordinarily reject.

Ronald Reagan is often dubbed the "Teflon president."

sesquicentennial—a 150th anniversary (L *sesqui*, one and a half, *centum*, hundred)

> *St. Augustine, Florida, the oldest city in the United States, celebrated the* **sesquicentennial** *of its incorporation in 1974, but it was founded long before that, in 1565.*

sesquipedalian—a very long word (L *sesquipedalis*, a foot and a half long, from *sesqui*, one and a half, *pes*, foot)

> *William F. Buckley is fond of* **sesquipedalian** *words, and uses them constantly in his columns, books and television appearances.*

shalom—hello, goodbye, welcome (Heb, well-being, peace)

> *In Israel and elsewhere in the world,* **shalom** *is like* aloha *in Hawaii—it serves as welcome, farewell and a wish that peace be with you.*

sibling—brother or sister (OE *sibb*, kinship)

> **Sibling** *rivalry is often used as an excuse for lack of civility.*

silicon—nonmetallic element in the earth's crust (from L *silex*, hard stone, flint, *on*, as in *carbon*)

> *Linus Pauling wrote that* **silicon** *plays an important role in the inorganic world, similar to that of carbon in the organic world.*

Silicon is used extensively for parts in computers and other machines. **Silicon** Valley is so called because computer companies are clustered there.

sinecure—easy job, position (ML *sine cura*, without cure [of souls])

> *The idle repairman pictured in the Maytag television commercials has a **sinecure**.*
>
> *Being CEO of a worldwide company, Bill Gates said, is no **sinecure**.*

sinister—on the left side, left, evil, unlucky, inauspicious (L)

> *As Jessica entered the darkened room, she sensed a **sinister** presence near the window.*

In unenlightened times, left-handedness and some things on the left were thought to be abnormal or unlucky. The Latin word *dexter*, meaning right or on the right side, is the antonym or opposite of **sinister**. *Dextrous* (also correctly spelled *dexterous*) means not only right-handed or right-sided but skillful or clever as well.

Sistine—(NL *sixtinus*, from *sextus*, sixth)

The word **Sistine** refers to any of the several popes named Sixtus. The **Sistine** Chapel in the Vatican was built in 1473 for Pope Sixtus IV.

sodality—club, comradeship, association (L *sodalis*, comrade)

> *Many **sodalities** are formed for charitable purposes.*

---

solace—comfort, especially in grief or misfortune (L *solari*, to console, comfort)

> *After the death of his 6-year-old daughter, George found **solace** in working harder than ever.*

solecism—error or absurdity in usage or words, impropriety (Gk *soloikos*, speaking incorrectly)

> *Professor Henry Higgins set about correcting Liza Doolittle's **solecisms** and transforming her into an elegant lady.*

The Greek word *soloikos* originated with the citizens of Soloi, a city in ancient Greece, who were notorious for speaking their language incorrectly. A whole city of Mrs. Malaprops?

soliloquy—monologue, talking to oneself (L *soli*, alone, *loqui*, to speak)

> *Hamlet's **soliloquy** is so familiar and well known that many people can recite parts of it by heart.*

When her friend caught her talking to herself, Gina retorted, "Well, I like an intelligent audience."

solipsism—obsessive or extreme self-centeredness (L *solus*, alone, *ipse*, self)

> *It was evident from her **solipsism** that she felt the universe revolved around her.*

The adjective is **solipsistic**.

solon—lawgiver, legislator (Gk)

> *The Athenian lawgiver **Solon** was called one of the Seven Wise Men of Greece.*
> *Apathetic citizens are often ill served by the **solons** they keep returning to office.*

soporific—sleep-producing, boring (L *sopor*, deep sleep, *ificare*, producing, making)

> *Stale air can be **soporific** for captive listeners.*
> ***Soporific** medications should be taken about an hour before you go to bed.*

sorority—sisterhood (L *soror*, sister)

> ***Sorority** and fraternity chapters are identified by combinations of Greek letters.*

sparse—scarce, thin, scanty (L *sparsus*)

> *Vegetation is usually **sparse** in regions that have little rainfall.*
> *The northwestern mountainous states are **sparsely** populated.*

spatial—relating to space (L *spatium*, space)

> ***Spatial** perception is important for driving skill.*

spurious—false, bogus, fake, counterfeit (LL *spurius*, false)

> *Claims to the gold fields were sometimes **spurious**, but were maintained at gunpoint.*

*In contradistinction to the old Ben Franklins, with their fancy curlicues, the new $100 bills have so much bare space that they look **spurious**.*

stannous—containing or relating to tin (LL *stannum*, tin)

*Pewter is a **stannous** alloy, hardened with antimony and copper, and is used extensively for artware.*

stigma—stain, disgrace, identifying mark (L *stigma*, mark, brand)

*Cain forever bore the **stigma** of his brother Abel's murder.*

The usual plural is **stigmata**, but **stigmas** is also correct.

stygian—gloomy, hellish, infernal (L *stygius*, Gk *stygios*)

*Hansel and Gretel lost their way in the **stygian** darkness of the woods.*

The adjective **stygian** is taken from the Styx, a mythologic river in the subterranean world of the dead.

subliminal—outside ordinary perception, influencing behavior in subconscious ways (L *sub*, under, *limen*, threshold)

*Manufacturers use **subliminal** advertising in persuading consumers to buy their products.*
*The Judas kiss of Terry's sister-in-law sent her an ominous **subliminal** message.*

sublingual—under the tongue (L *sub*, under, *lingua*, tongue)

>*Certain drugs are made to be taken **sublingually** and to melt in the mouth.*

subtle—delicate, elusive, skillful, ingenious (L *subtilis*, finely woven, fine, refined, keen)

>*Manet was skillful in capturing the **subtle** color changes in the landscape at different times of day.*
>*Diplomacy calls for **subtlety** rather than confrontation.*
>*The courtroom image of a prisoner in leg irons and looking disheveled sends a **subtle**, although sometimes incorrect, message to the jury pool.*

succinct—terse, brief, concise (L *succingere*, to bind up)

>*For best effect, most proverbs are **succinct**.*

supercilious—condescending, haughty (L *super*, above, *cilia*, eyebrows)

>*A **supercilious** manner is not conducive to friendly relations.*

supersede—replace, supplant, take the place of (L *super*, above, *sedere* to sit)

>*The railroad and the telegraph **superseded** the short-lived Pony Express, which was gradually discontinued about 1861.*

Note that **supersede** is the only word in the English language with that root that ends in -*sede*. Only three words with that root end in -*ceed*: *exceed*, *proceed* and *succeed*. All other words in the language with that root end in -*cede*, for example, *secede*, *accede* and *intercede*.

surreptitious—secret, stealthy (L *sub*, secretly, under, *rapere*, to seize)

Foreign countries that engage in **surreptitious** *or open pirating of videocassettes may be subject to severe sanctions.*

sybarite—a person who considers pleasure the most important thing in life (from Sybaris, an ancient Greek city in southern Italy)

One day at the spa hardly qualifies Jennifer as a **sybarite**.

The citizens of Sybaris were famous for their love of luxury and pleasure.

Sybarites and hedonists have a common philosophy.

sycophant—scoundrel, talebearer, parasite, yea-sayer, bootlicker (Gk *sykon*, fig, *phainein*, to reveal, show)

The pejorative term **sycophant** *is often applied to yes-men, who laugh at their bosses' jokes and tell tales on their co-workers.*

The fig part of this word's etymology comes from the Greek custom of gesturing with a fig to indicate a scoundrel.

symbiosis—cooperation, living together of two dissimilar entities or organisms (Gk *syn*, together with, with, *bios*, life)

> *The **symbiosis** of volunteerism and philanthropy is beneficial to any community.*
>
> *Remoras and sharks typify underwater **symbiosis**.*

syndrome—concurrence, a group of symptoms or signs, usually relating to diseases or disorders (Gk *syn*, together, with, *dramein*, to run)

> *The Huck Finn **syndrome** includes a child's truancy and a neglect of duties or obligations.*

After decades of working at a difficult or frustrating profession, some people experience the symptoms of burnout **syndrome**, including loss of interest and efficiency, extreme fatigue, impaired appetite and insomnia.

synergy—working together (Gk *syn*, together, with, *ergon*, work)

> *During World War II, government, industry, and labor showed extraordinary **synergy** in turning out products necessary for waging a multicontinental war.*
>
> *Caffeine is a **synergistic** drug that works in harmony with painkillers to relieve severe headache.*

The shoulder and back muscles work **synergistically** in weight-lifting.

T

taciturn—reticent, silent, laconic (F *taciturne*, from L *tacere*, to be silent)

> *A **taciturn** person is more likely to keep secrets than a talkative one.*
> *A **taciturn** master of ceremonies is an oxymoron.*

tantamount—equivalent, amounting to as much (AF *tant amounter*, to amount to as much)

> *Being nominated for office in that Democratic county is **tantamount** to being elected by acclamation.*

tautology—redundancy, repetition (Gk *tautos*, the same, from *to auto*, the same)

> ***Tautology** is hearing the lecturer say, "Before I speak, I'd like to say a few words."*

> Examples of **tautology** are phrases such as "red in color," "oval-shaped," handsome-looking," "basic fundamentals" and "the ultimate in perfection."

temporal—relating to time, fleeting, temporary, earthly (L *tempus*, time, period of time)

> *A clergyman's duty is to deal with spiritual matters, but these often turn out to be intertwined with **temporal** concerns.*
> *The **temporal** life of newspapers is short.*

tendentious—biased, tending or attempting to persuade (from ML *tendentia*, tendency)

> *Propaganda is by definition **tendentious**.*
>
> *Being **tendentious** is an asset for insurance salesmen.*

tendinitis—inflammation of a tendon (L *tendo*, tendon)

> *After years of play, many baseball pitchers and tennis players suffer from **tendinitis** in the elbow.*
>
> ***Tendinitis** in the hands can mean the end of a musician's career.*

Tendonitis is also correct, but the spelling is seldom seen in medical contexts.

tetralogy—group of four connected works or four symptoms in a disorder or disease (Gk *tetra*, four, *logia*, logy)

> *Gloria's autobiography was a **tetralogy**, describing in intimate detail her childhood and adolescence in Illinois, her rise in New York as a dramatic actress, her brilliant career as a star in Hollywood, and her graceful retirement from the screen at age 64 to her home in Connecticut.*
>
> *The **tetralogy** of Fallot, named for the French physician who first described it, includes four main abnormalities of the heart.*
>
> *Botticelli's **tetralogy**, mythologic paintings of exquisite beauty, consists of* Spring (Primavera), The Birth of Venus, Mars and Venus, *and* Pallas Subduing a Centaur.

thespian—actor (from *Thespis*)

> *Drama schools and repertory theaters for aspiring* ***thespians*** *abound in the United States.*

> Thespis was a 6th-century BC Greek poet, who may have originated the actor's role in the theater.

titillate—to please, stimulate, tickle (L *tittilare*, to tickle)

> *Ice-dancing is certain to* ***titillate*** *the spectator with its beauty and grace as well as its athleticism.*
> *True comedy* ***titillates*** *only those with a well-developed sense of humor.*

titular—nominal, in name only, title (from L *titulus*, title)

> *With the election of a hostile legislature, Cheswick became only the* ***titular*** *head of the party.*
> *Steve Martin had the* ***titular*** *role in the movie remake of* Sergeant Bilko.

tortuous—winding, twisted, crooked, devious, circuitous (L *tortuosus*, tortuous, from *torquere*, to twist)

> *Lombard Street is the most* ***tortuous*** *street in San Francisco and perhaps in the United States, but a Cadillac can negotiate the downhill run—carefully, very carefully.*
> *Even philosophy majors can have difficulty following Kant's* ***tortuous*** *reasoning.*

Although **tortuous** and *torturous* are from the same Latin root, keep the two words distinct. *Torturous* means causing torture or extreme pain.

toxic—poisonous, harmful, polluting (L *toxicum*, poison)

> *Tobacco smoke contains carbon monoxide, nicotine, cyanide, nitric oxide, and many more **toxic** or carcinogenic substances.*
> *Psychotherapists see many clients scarred by their upbringing in **toxic** families.*

transcend—to go beyond, exceed, surpass (L *transcendere*, to climb across, surmount, from *trans*, across, beyond, *scandere*, to climb)

> *Civility **transcends** good manners.*
> *Superb acting **transcends** physical likeness and the accurate recitation of lines.*

translucent—transparent, partly transparent, shining through (L *trans*, through, *lucere*, to shine)

> *The turquoise waters of the Caribbean Sea are so **translucent** that you can see the fish swimming below.*
> *In your explanations, strive for **translucency**.*

transvestite—a cross-dresser, one who is addicted to the garb of the opposite sex (L *trans*, across, *vestire*, to clothe)

> ***Transvestites** are in great demand in the theater as female impersonators.*

trauma—a wound, injury, harm, damage (Gk wound)

> *The **trauma** of the Civil War never healed for the Prentiss family, which had lost three sons.*

*Psychologic **traumata** are nearly impossible to eradicate without proper treatment.*

Traumas is also a correct plural.

Trekkie—a fan of the science fiction television series *Star Trek*

*Each year **Trekkies** hold a national convention, at which they enjoy buying memorabilia, meeting Bill Shatner, and even dressing like the* Star Trek *characters.*

triage—selecting, sifting, choosing (F, from *trier*, to sift, pick out).

*Workers in the emergency department acted as a **triage** unit when the accident victims started to flood in, first treating those whose airways were obstructed and then the bleeding patients.*

This word is pronounced *tree-ahjh*, with a slight accent on the second syllable.

triceratops—an herbivorous dinosaur with three horns (L *tri*, three, Gk *keras*, horn, *ops*, eye, face)

*Daniel's favorite dinosaur models were the **triceratops** and the tyrannosaur (*Tyrannosaurus rex, Gk tyrannos, *tyrant*, rex, *king).

trilogy—group of three related things or works (Gk *tri*, three, *logia*, logy)

*Isaac Asimov's landmark science fiction **trilogy**,* The Foundation, *was followed by a fourth work,* Foundation's Edge, *making the body of work a tetralogy.*

trimester—period of three months or thereabouts (L *tri*, three, *mensis*, month)

> *Examinations for certification were traditionally held at the beginning of the third scholastic **trimester**.*
>
> *Most states ban abortions during the third **trimester** of pregnancy.*

triskaidekaphobia—abnormal fear of the number 13 (Gk *triskaideka*, thirteen, *phobia*, fear)

> *Some builders are **triskaidekaphobic**, and therefore omit the 13th floor of buildings, going from the 12th to the 14th in one easy, or uneasy, leap.*

triumvirate—group or association of three persons (from L *trium*, of three, *vir*, man)

> *The best-known **triumvirate** in classical music consists of Bach, Beethoven and Brahms.*
>
> *Violations of constitutional law were heard by a **triumvirate** of learned jurists.*

The word *tribunal* means a group of three persons hearing a case or matter.

truncate—shorten, condense (L *truncare*, to cut off, mutilate)

> *An evening of dancing was **truncated** by the abrupt departure of the band in a huff, 1996 model.*
>
> *In printouts, computer programs often **truncate** long names.*

U

ubiquitous—widespread, universal, being everywhere at the same time (L *ubique*, everywhere)

> *Jean Valjean, the hero of Victor Hugo's* Les Miserables, *was hounded for decades by the seemingly **ubiquitous** detective Javert.*
> *The township contemplated legislation banning the **ubiquitous** highway billboards.*

ultimatum—a final demand or condition (L *ultimas*, last, final)

> *Rejecting the **ultimatum**, the generals foolishly decided that war was the only alternative.*

ultrasound—waves with sound beyond the range of human hearing (L *ultra*, beyond, *sonus*, sound)

> ***Ultrasound** procedures are used extensively in medical practice.*

umbrage—resentment, displeasure (L *umbra*, shade, shadow)

> *Jackie Gleason said you should never take **umbrage** unless you can lick the guy.*

unilateral—one-sided (L *uni*, one, *latus*, side)

> *The lion makes a **unilateral** decision in dividing the prey.*

*Couples in which one spouse or the other makes **unilateral** decisions often wind up in the marriage counselor's office.*

ursine—bearlike (L *ursus*, bear)

*Marty shambled in with his strange, **ursine** walk and went immediately to his place at the dinner table.*

V

vacillate—waver, hesitate (L *vacillare*, to sway, waver)

*Never **vacillate** in your search for the truth.*

The noun is **vacillation**.

vagary—unpredictable, eccentric or capricious action (L *vagus*, wandering)

*Dancing about in the moonlight was only one of the **vagaries** of the Sansouci family.*

Vagaries usually come in bunches. Hardly anyone has just a single **vagary**.

valedictory—farewell speech (L *vale*, farewell, *dicere*, to say)

*President Eisenhower, in his **valedictory**, warned of the military-industrial complex.*

In his ***valedictory*** *speech, usually called his Farewell Address, General Washington said, "I hold the maxim no less applicable to public than to private affairs, that honesty is always the best policy."*

valor—bravery, courage (L *valere*, to be strong)

*The **valor** of Florence Nightingale and her corps of 38 dedicated nurses during the Crimean war is legendary.*

*Discretion is sometimes the better part of **valor**, such as when encountering a jaguar.*

venue—locale of a legal case, sporting event or drama (L *venir*, to come)

*Defense attorneys requested a change in **venue** because of the intensive publicity surrounding the sensational murders.*

*Atlanta was chosen to be the **venue** of the summer Olympic games in 1996.*

verbatim—word for word, following the original exactly (L *verbum*, word)

*Court and hearing stenotypists are **verbatim** reporters, some of whom use both stenotype machines and tape recorders.*

*When quotations are used, they should be either **verbatim** or paraphrased accurately.*

verbose—talkative, wordy, tedious (L *verbosus*, wordy)

*Garmond was as **verbose** in his books as he was laconic in speech.*

*Thalia's **verbosity** in class seemed to encourage the other students to speak up.*

verdant—green, leafy, fresh (MF *verdoyant*, to grow green, from L *viridis*, from *virere*, to be green)

*If you want to see **verdant** life, go to the botanical gardens in any large city.*

*New Jersey is called the "Garden State" because of its **verdant** fields of delicious vegetables.*

versatile—multitalented, flexible, many-sided (L *versari*, to turn, change)

*Plastic is among the most **versatile** of materials for every kind of industry.*

*Because of his legendary **versatility** and originality, as well as his tremendous body of work, Picasso is considered the foremost artist of the 20th century.*

vertigo—dizziness (L *vertere*, to turn)

*The unforgettable motion picture **Vertigo**, starring Jimmy Stewart, depicts in frightening detail the plight of a man who is afflicted with **vertigo** and acrophobia but who risks his life to save another's.*

*During a steep takeoff, a Navy pilot suffered **vertigo** and unknowingly forced his jet into a dive.*

vicarious—substituting, delegated (L *vicarius*, from *vicis*, change)

*Imagination is the most fertile originator of **vicarious** joy or sorrow.*

*Parents take **vicarious** pleasure in the successes of their children.*

viral—relating to or caused by a virus (L *virus*, slimy liquid, poison)

*A wave of **viral** pneumonia swept through the entire hospital.*
*Researchers in genetics and cancer are investigating the composition of **viruses** that cause epidemics.*

virile—male, manly, powerful, forceful, decisive (L *vir*, man)

*He considered it **virile** to run every marathon race in every city on the East Coast.*
*Now in his 60s, Sean Connery is as **virile** as ever.*

The noun is **virility**.

vivacious—lively, sparkling (L *vivere*, to live)

***Vivacious** describes Bonnie's conversation and her outlook on life.*

The noun is **vivacity**.

vocation—calling, profession, inclination (L *vocatio*, summons, bidding)

*Franz Liszt took minor orders in the Roman Catholic Church and could have spent his life as an abbé, but he is better known for his **vocation** as a composer.*

vociferous—vehement, boisterous, raucous (L *vociferari,* to cry out)

> *Most musical comedies were too **vociferous** for Harriet's taste.*
> *The **vociferous** audience intimidated the inexperienced and high-strung cast.*

voluble—talkative, changeable, fluent, glib (L *volvere,* to turn, revolve, roll)

> ***Voluble** people are often hiding something.*
> *Leonhard was so **voluble** that he monopolized eight of every ten conversations.*

The noun is **volubility**.

voracious—all-devouring, all-consuming (L *vorare,* to devour)

> *Joseph Conrad's facility with English stemmed from his **voracious** reading of books in both Polish and English.*
> *Most professional athletes have **voracious** appetites that would make a weight-watcher shudder.*

The noun is **voracity**.

vortex—swirling center of activity (L *vertex, vortex,* whirl, whirlpool)

> *Election headquarters became the **vortex** of enthusiastic volunteers running hither and yon with posters and banners and pamphlets.*
> *A tornado is a violent, destructive whirlwind formed around a **vortex**.*

vulgate—common language, language of the people (L *vulgata*, common, ordinary, from *vulgare*, to make known, publish, from *vulgus*, mob, common people)

>   *Eric Hoffer, a stevedore-turned-author, uses the* ***vulgate*** *in his books like no one else.*
>   *An edition of the Latin Bible used by the Roman Catholic Church is known as the* **Vulgate***.*

vulpine—like a fox, crafty (L *vulpes*, fox)

>   *In* The Pink Panther, *Inspector Clouseau (played by Peter Sellers) thinks he is stalking his prey in a* ***vulpine*** *way, but he succeeds only in being comic.*

W

waive—forsake, abandon, give up (ONF *weyver*, from *waif*, lost, unclaimed)

>   *Johnson* ***waived*** *his right to extradition when it became clear that Florida would insist on trying him for his misdeeds.*

wanton—willful, unrestrained, reckless (ME *wan*, deficient, *towen*, from *teen*, to train, discipline)

>   *Riots marked the* ***wanton*** *disregard of the treaty between the two nations.*
>   ***Wanton*** *spending brought ruin to the family.*

wherewithal—means, money, resources (ME)

> *To be a power in Wall Street, one must have the* ***wherewithal***.
> *Alexander Fleming had the* ***wherewithal*** *to win a Nobel Prize in medicine.*

> This word is not pronounced *wear-with-ALL*. The accent is on the second syllable: *wear-WITH-al*.

whitewash—cover up, gloss over

> *The high officials responsible for the Watergate scandal tried to* ***whitewash*** *the entire affair.*

wittingly—knowingly, deliberately (ME, from *witen*, to know)

> *Forgery is fraud done* ***wittingly***.
> *Laura, with her poor eyesight, had* ***unwittingly*** *snubbed her best friend at a party.*

wreak—to punish, drive out, inflict (ME *wreken*)

> *A diet high in cholesterol can* ***wreak*** *havoc with the health of susceptible people.*
> *Earthquakes, volcanic eruptions, and tidal waves have* ***wreaked*** *catastrophes and killed millions of people over the centuries.*

X

> English words and proper names beginning with *x* are pronounced as if they begin with *z*.

xenophile—one who is attracted to strange or foreign people, customs, manners (Gk *xenos*, stranger, *philos*, loving, dear, beloved)

Xenophiles make the best world travelers.

xenophobia—fear of strangers or foreigners, or of anything strange or foreign (Gk *xenos*, stranger, *phobia*, fear)

Xenophobia is a real handicap in a pluralistic society, because it limits the possibility of learning new things and becoming acquainted with new people.

xerography—dry copying (Gk *xeros*, dry, *graphein*, to write, print)

Before xerography, secretaries made multiple carbon copies of each page; that was B.C. (before computers) and cumbersome.

xylography—wood engraving or printing, woodcut (Gk *xylon*, wood, *graphein*, to write)

Her hobby, xylography, became a lucrative occupation when she branched out into making portraits on wood.

Y

YAG—(yttrium-aluminum-garnet) a synthetic gemstone

YAG is used in laser surgical technology.

The element yttrium is so named from Ytterby, Sweden, where it is found along with other rare-earth elements.

yeoman—characterized by great effort and usefulness (ME *yoman*)

*The ambassadors did a **yeoman** job in completing the delicate negotiations between the two countries.*

Z

zeal—enthusiasm, passion, fervor (Gk *zelos*)

*The chess club spared no effort in its **zeal** to win the national championship.*

*The **zeal** of the Egyptologist Champollion led him and others to decipher the three-language inscription on the Rosetta stone.*

The adjective is **zealous**.

zenith—highest point, peak, summit (ML, from OSp *zenit*)

*Sir Arthur Conan Doyle's reputation as an author reached its **zenith** with the Sherlock Holmes stories.*

Doyle was also an ophthalmologist, but he abandoned his medical practice to devote himself to writing.

zoology—study of animals (Gk *zoion*, animal, *logos*, study)

A current specialty in **zoology** *is genetics.*

Some fans of National Lampoon's Animal House, *the raucous 1978 comedy about college fraternity life starring John Belushi, went on to successful careers in* **zoology***.*

This word, like others with the same root, is pronounced *zoh-OL-ogy*, not *zoo-ol-ogy*.

Word Roots

a, an (not, without)

achromatic	without color
ahistorical	not historical
amoral	without morals
anesthesia	without pain
anhydrous	without water
apathy	without feeling
aplastic	not easily molded
aseptic	sterile, without infection
atheist	godless
atoxic	not poisonous
atrophic	not developing, growing
atypical	not typical

ab (away from, apart, from)

abase	to lower, degrade
abdicate	to surrender, yield
abduct	to carry off
abhor	to loathe, reject
abnormal	not normal
abridge	to abbreviate, shorten
abrogate	to repeal, repudiate
absolve	to release, set free, vindicate, acquit

ac, ad, af, ag, al, ap, as, at (to, toward, adjacent to)

By the process of assimilation, *ad* becomes *ac*, *af*, etc., to conform to the first consonant in the next syllable.

accede	to agree
accelerate	to speed up
accept	to take, receive
acclaim	praise
acclimate	to adjust to climate
accumulate	to gather, collect
adapt	to adjust, accommodate
adept	expert, skilled
adequate	sufficient
adhere	to stick, maintain loyalty
adjacent	near, nearby
adjudicate	to judge, settle finally
admonish	to reprove, chide
affiliate	an associate, subsidiary
affirmation	assertion; declaration
affluent	wealthy, rich
afforestation	replanting, reforestation
agglutinate	to unite, adhere
aggregate	to gather, collect together
allocate	to distribute
allusion	an indirect reference
apportion	to divide in proportion
apposite	highly appropriate

ascribe	to attribute
aspect	phase, appearance
assured	confident
attach	to fasten
attend	to give attention to
attractive	pleasing, personable

alg (pain)

analgesic	painkiller
cephalalgia	headache
nostalgia	homesickness, yearning for times past
podalgia	pain in the foot

ambi (both, around)

ambiguous	unclear, obscure, having two or more meanings
ambilateral	bilateral, affecting both sides
ambivalent	having contradictory feelings

ana (collections of information)

Americana	materials about America
Shaviana	materials about George Bernard Shaw
Darwiniana	materials about Charles Darwin

andr (man, male)

androcentric	stressing male points of view
androgen	male hormone

ante (before, preceding, earlier)

antedate	to precede
antepartum	the period before childbirth
anterior	near the front

anti (against, opposed to, rival)

anticipate	to give early thought
anticlimax	a letdown, disappointing event
antidote	remedy for poisoning
anti-Jacobin	opponent of the Jacobins
antithesis	opposed or contrasting ideas

aqua (water)

aquacade	water extravaganza, spectacle
aquamarine	blue-green, blue-green gemstone
aqueous	watery
aquifer	water-bearing soil

be (on, around, over, thoroughly)

bedeck	to ornament
bedevil	to annoy, pester
befriend	to be kindly to, make a friend
befuddle	to bewilder
berate	to scold, reprimand vigorously

bi (two, twice)

bicameral	having two chambers
bifurcate	to separate into two parts
bilateral	having two sides
bipartisan	composed of two parties
bisect	to divide, cut in two

bio (life, living)

biochemistry	relating to chemical actions in life processes
biology	the science of life
biolith	rock of organic origin

capit (head)

capitation	poll tax
capitulate	to surrender, yield
recapitulate	to sum up

cent (hundred)

century	100 years
bicentennial	200th anniversary
centimeter	1/100th of a meter

circum (around, about)

circumnavigate	to go completely around
circumscribe	to draw a line around
circumvent	to frustrate

col, com, con, cop, cor (with, together, jointly)

By the process of assimilation, *com* becomes *col*, *con*, etc., to conform with the first consonant in the next syllable.

accommodate	to adjust, make fit
collate	to gather in an orderly way
collingual	using the same language
colleague	associate, coworker
commend	entrust, praise
commingle	to mingle or mix together
commiseration	sympathy
concur	to agree, unite
condominium	common ownership
correlate	to establish reciprocal relations
corroborate	to confirm

contra (against, opposed to)

contradict	dispute, disagree
contrary	opposite, opposed, perverse, ornery
contravene	deny, contradict, disregard, dispute

corp (body)

corps	special or elite group
corporal	bodily
corporeal	physical, material, opposed to spiritual
corpus delicti	the body of crime, evidence
habeas corpus	protection against unlawful imprisonment
incorporate	to unit with, combine

crypt (secret, hidden)

cryptic	mysterious, enigmatic
cryptofascist	one having secret fascist sympathies
cryptography	art of reading code messages

de (not, opposite of, reverse)

debase	to degrade, depreciate
deemphasize	to play down, reduce in importance

defuse	to remove the fuse
dehydrate	to remove water or moisture, dry
dejected	dispirited, discouraged
deprecate	to disapprove
desultory	random, intermittent, erratic

derm (skin)

epidermis	outermost layer of skin
dermatology	science dealing with skin and skin disorders
dermatoid	resembling skin
pachydermatous	thick-skinned

dis, dys (not, reverse, deprive of, opposite of)

disconsolate	downcast, dejected
discrete	distinct, separate, detached
disquiet	disturbance
dissuade	to urge or advise against
dysfunction	abnormal or impaired function

e, ex (out of, away, not, missing, absent)

edentate	toothless
elude	escape
ephemeral	fleeting, transient

eviscerate	disembowel
exacerbate	to aggravate, make worse, embitter
exorcise	to drive out
extirpate	to eradicate, exterminate

equi (equal)

equanimity	composure, poise
equidistant	equally distant
equilibrium	balance
equitable	fair, even
equivocation	uncertainty, lie, prevarication

erg (work)

erg	a unit of energy
ergomania	excessive devotion to work
ergophobia	abnormal fear or dislike of work
synergy	cooperation, working together

escent (becoming, beginning)

incandescent	becoming white or hot
nascent	being born
obsolescent	becoming outdated, obsolete
renascent	being reborn

extra (beyond, outside)

extracurricular	outside of regular duties, obligations
extraneous	unrelated, irrelevant
extravagant	excessive

fold (multiplied by, times)

manifold	many, numerous, varied
tenfold	multiplied by ten
twofold	multiplied by two

gyn (woman, feminine)

gynecocentric	centered on women, stressing feminine interests
gynecology	branch of medicine dealing with women
misogyny	hatred or abnormal dislike of women

hex (six)

hexagon	figure with six sides and six angles
hexameter	poetic line of six metrical feet
hexapod	six-footed, an insect
hexasyllabic	having six syllables

hom (same, alike, similar)

homeopathy	system of medical treatment with drugs that can produce, in healthy people, symptoms like those of the disease being treated.
homeostasis	bodily or mental stability
homogenize	to blend, to make consistent
homologous	corresponding
homonym	word sounding like another but different in meaning, homophone

hydr (water)

anhydrous	waterless, devoid of water
dehydrate	to dry completely, remove water or moisture
hydrant	fireplug, faucet
hydraulic	operated by water
hydrophobia	rabies, morbid fear of water
hydrotherapy	treatment by means of water

hyper (super, above, beyond, excessive)

hyperactive	excessively active
hypersensitive	extremely sensitive
hyperventilatation	abnormal respiration

hypo (under, beneath, down, below normal)

hypochondriac	one overly concerned with illness
hypofunction	decreased function
hyposensitize	to reduce sensitivity, especially to allergens
hypotension	abnormally low arterial blood pressure
hypothesize	to make an assumption

iatr (medicine, physician)

geriatrics	study of aging, medical care and treatment of older persons
hydriatics	treatment by means of water, hydrotherapy
iatrogenic	produced by a physician or medicine
pediatrics	study, care and treatment of children

inter (between, among)

inter alia	among other things
intercede	to intervene
intercurrent	intervening
interdict	to forbid
interlingual	existing between two or more languages

internecine	characterized by great slaughter, deadly
intertwine	to entangle, interlace

intra (within, inward, on the inside)

intradermal	between layers of the skin
intraocular	within the eye
intravenous	by way of the veins

leg (law, legal)

legacy	inheritance, heritage
legatee	an inheritor
legislate	to enact laws
legitimize	to legitimate, make legal

less (without, free from, beyond the range of)

ceaseless	without a pause
doubtless	without a doubt
hapless	unfortunate, unlucky
ruthless	pitiless, without compassion
tireless	untiring

log (speech, word, discourse, thought)

logistics   the art or science of being in the right place at the right time

logodaedaly   arbitrary or capricious coinage of words

logomania   extreme talkativeness, logorrhea

magn (great, large)

magnify   to make larger or greater, exalt

magnanimity   generosity, greatness of spirit

magniloquence   highfalutin language, ostentation

mal (bad, evil, inadequate)

maladroit   awkward, clumsy, klutzy

malediction   curse

malefactor   evil person, criminal

malevolent   evil, vicious

malfeasance   misconduct, misbehavior, wrongdoing

malpractice   misfeasance, professional wrongdoing, dereliction of duty

man (hand, by hand)

manual   by or with the hand

manufacture   to make, produce

| manumit | to free from slavery, liberate |
| manuscript | a writing by hand or other means |

mega (large, strong, great)

megabit	one million bits
megabuck	one million dollars
megalopolis	densely populated area comprising several cities or metropolitan areas
megastructure	immense building with many stories

micro (small, enlarging, one-millionth part of)

microbe	extremely small organism
microgram	one millionth of a gram
microphone	device for amplifying or transmitting sound
microtext	text in microform

milli (thousandth)

millennium	a thousand years, era of supreme happiness
milligram	one one-thousandth of a gram
millivolt	a thousandth of a volt

neo (new, recent)

neogenesis	regeneration
neon	an inert gas much used to advertise
neonatal	relating to the newborn

noct (night)

noctambulist	sleepwalker, one who walks at night
noctilucous	shining at night, phosphorescent
nocturne	musical night piece

nomen (name)

cognomen	nickname, surname
nom de guerre	fictitious name
nom de plume	writing pseudonym
nomenclature	collective name, designation
nominal	in name only
nominate	to designate

ose (full of, having the qualities of)

grandiose	full of grandeur
otiose	vain, idle, without effect

paleo (old, ancient, primitive)

paleobotany	science of fossil plants
paleology	study of antiquities
paleotechnic	relating to ancient art or early industrial development

pend (hang)

depend	to rely on, trust
pendant	a hanging object
pendente lite	while litigation is going on
suspend	to hang, delay

peri (around, about, round)

pericardium	membranous sac around the heart
perinatal	occurring around the time of childbirth
peristyle	colonnade surrounding a building
periurban	area surrounding a city

phil (loving)

Anglophile	one who is partial to English ways
bibliophile	lover of books
Francophile	admirer of France or French customs

philanderer	flirt, fickle lover
philhellene	admirer of Greece or Greek culture
verbophile	lover of words

post (after, following)

posterior	toward the back
posthumous	occurring after death
postmillennial	occurring after the millennium
postprandial	occurring after a meal
postwar	occurring after the war

pre (before, preceding)

prejudge	to judge beforehand
preliminary	introductory
prelude	introduction, musical introduction
premeditated	considered, thought of beforehand
pretest	preliminary test

psych (mind, soul, spirit)

psyche	personality, self, soul
psychogenic	originating in the mind or emotions
psychopharmacology	study of effects of drugs on the mind
psychosomatic	relating to interaction between mind and body

quin (five)

quinquennial	occurring every five years, period of five years
quintuple	five times as much
quintuplicate	five identical copies

retro (back, backward)

retrieve	to regain, repossess
retrocede	to cede back
retrogression	movement, development backward

rubi (red)

rubefacient	causing redness
rubella	German measles

sang (blood)

consangineous	being of the same blood, ancestry
sanguinary	bloody, gory, bloodthirsty, murderous
sanguine	confident, optimistic

semi (half)

semiautonomous	mainly self-governing within a larger entity
semidiurnal	occurring twice a day

semimonthly	twice a month
semiprecious	not as valuable as precious gems

sub (under, less than, below)

By the process of assimilation, *sub* sometimes changes to conform to the first consonant in the next syllable.

subacute	between acute and chronic
subcaption	secondary headline
subdivide	to further divide
subjugate	to conquer
sublime	splendid
submerged	hidden, cryptic
subornation	crime of persuading a person to commit perjury
subpoena	summons to appear in court
subservient	servile, subordinate
subtle	delicate, elusive
subvert	to overthrow, destroy, overturn
succinct	terse, brief, concise

super (above, over and above, more than)

insuperable	unsurpassable
superabundant	much more than sufficient, superfluous
superficial	external, shallow, casual
superlatives	exaggerated expression

supersede	take precedence, replace
superstandard	above standard

syn (together)

synarchy	joint rule, sovereignty
synchronous	happening at the same time
syndicate	group of persons or firms
synergic	working together
synopsis	brief outline
synthesis	combination of elements
synthetic	artificially produced, artificial

tachy (rapid, fast, accelerated)

tachycardia	rapid heart action
tachygraphy	rapid or cursive writing, stenography, shorthand
tachymeter	surveying instrument to determine distances quickly

tom (cut)

anatomy	structure of animals or plants
appendectomy	surgical removal of the appendix
microtome	instrument to cut into small sections

| tomography | planar recording of internal body images, body section roentgenography |
| tonsillectomy | surgical removal of the tonsils |

tox (poison)

toxic	poisonous
toxicology	science of poisons and their effects on organisms
toxiferous	conveying or producing poison
toxiphobia	abnormal fear of being poisoned

trans (across, beyond, to the other side, through)

transatlantic	across the Atlantic Ocean
transgress	to sin, trespass
transient	fleeting, temporary, short-lived
translucent	transparent, clear, lucid
transmogrify	to transform
transmute	to transform
transpontine	on the other side of a bridge
traverse	to oppose, go across

ultra (beyond, excessive, hyper, super)

| ulterior | hidden, latent |
| ultimate | extreme, farthest, earliest, utmost, basic, fundamental, last |

ultimatum	final, last word
ultramarine	beyond the sea, vivid blue
ultramontane	beyond the mountain
ultrasonic	beyond the range of human hearing

under (below)

underact	to act with restraint
undercurrent	running under the surface, hidden
underdog	a predicted loser
underpin	to support, substantiate
underscore	to emphasize, stress
understate	to describe with restraint
underwrite	to confirm, guarantee, support

vert (turn)

convertible	changeable
invert	to turn inside out or upside down
perverse	corrupt, wicked, cranky, contrary
reverse	to turn around, revoke
versatile	adaptable, many-talented
versed	practiced, skilled
versicolored	variegated, of many colors
versify	to write poetry, relate or describe in verse or poetry
versus	against

vertex	highest point, acme, peak
vertical	perpendicular
vertiginous	dizzy, giddy, suffering vertigo

xen (strange, foreign)

xenocentric	favoring a culture other than one's own
xenon	an inert gas
xenophile	one fond of foreign things
xenophobe	one abnormally fearful of foreign things and people

xero (dry, arid)

xerography	electrically charged, dry copying
xerophilic	adapted to making do with little moisture
xerostomia	abnormal dryness of the mouth
xeroprinting	dry printing
xerothermic	being hot and dry

zo (animal)

zoic	relating to animals or animal life
zoographic	describing animals
zoomorphic	in the form of an animal
zoophobia	abnormal fear of animals
zoophyte	plant resembling an animal

Word Aerobics No. 1

Match Game

Choose the word or phrase in the right-hand column that best matches the numbered word. The answers are on page 189.

1. ameliorate		a.	without a care
2. circadian		b.	place next to
3. draconian		c.	nerve
4. egregious		d.	outrageous
5. foible		e.	accidental finding
6. germane		f.	boisterous
7. hubris		g.	severe
8. insouciant		h.	improve
9. juxtapose		i.	terse
10. laconic		j.	daily
11. mnemonic		k.	fear of strangers
12. peripatetic		l.	weak point
13. serendipity		m.	relevant
14. vociferous		n.	reminder
15. xenophobia		o.	wandering

Word Aerobics No. 2

Fits and Starts

Choose the word in the right-hand column that most nearly fits the numbered word. The answers are on page 189.

1. mellifluous
   a. handy
   b. talkative
   c. honeyed

2. perquisite
   a. privilege
   b. necessity
   c. requirement

3. querulous
   a. talkative
   b. complaining
   c. nasty

4. reticent
   a. hesitant
   b. silent
   c. demanding

5. munificent
   a. grand
   b. generous
   c. moneyed

6. arcane
   a. secret
   b. cloister
   c. busy

7. flagrant
    a. aromatic
    b. distinguished
    c. notorious

8. honorific
    a. dignified
    b. gentle
    c. title

9. intransigent
    a. stubborn
    b. wandering
    c. official

10. malleable
    a. formidable
    b. hospitable
    c. pliable

11. taciturn
    a. quiet
    b. changeable
    c. talkative

12. torturous
    a. painful
    b. wrongful
    c. winding

13. voracious
    a. truthful
    b. devouring
    c. devious

14. euphonious
    a. tuba
    b. false
    c. tuneful

15. gratuitous
    a. needless
    b. appreciative
    c. hostile

Word Aerobics No. 3

As You Like It

Choose the most suitable word or words to fill in the sentence. The answers are on page 189.

1. These nutritionists require the dieter to adhere to their strict _____ for at least six months.
   a. regime
   b. sports medicine expert
   c. regimen

2. History has bestowed the _____ Father of Medicine on the Greek physician-teacher Hippocrates.
   a. emulation
   b. honorific
   c. honorarium

3. The Rolls-Royce careered down the mountainous, _____ road at breakneck speed.
   a. scenic
   b. tortuous
   c. toll

4. Finishing the Boston Marathon will _____ the average runner.
   a. exhilarate
   b. energize
   c. enervate

5. The pound symbol on a phone is also called a(n) _____.
   a. octothorp
   b. ampersand
   c. chevron

6. When she gave the job to her brother-in-law, the staff regarded it as _____.
   a. negligence
   b. nepotism
   c. sodality

7. The oracle's response was so _____ that no one could understand it.
   a. deleterious
   b. dismal
   c. cryptic

8. Negotiators had a tough job remedying the _____.
   a. panacea
   b. schism
   c. acrophobia

9. Although Beau was not as _____ as his gregarious uncle, he made many friends.
   a. worthy
   b. sanguine
   c. voluble

10. Susan was usually open-minded, but this time she was determined to be _____.
   a. adamant
   b. mercurial
   c. penitent

11. The proofreader was always careful to find any _____ in page proofs of the article.
    a. solace
    b. solecism
    c. iniquity

12. Carrying so many subjects at the same time was too _____ for Tom.
    a. otiose
    b. onerous
    c. versatile

13. The photographers took a _____ route through the jungle to find the birds they had come so far to study.
    a. circadian
    b. blatant
    c. circuitous

14. Differences between them were too _____ to be considered serious.
    a. infinitesimal
    b. impervious
    c. noisome

15. Debates should be lively and adversarial but not _____.
    a. palpable
    b. acrimonious
    c. pragmatic

Word Aerobics No. 4

Roots and Stems

*Using the **Word Roots** list beginning on page 157, choose the proper root to fit the blank spaces and complete the word in each sentence. The answers are on page 189.*

1. Luxurious, high-speed trains take you from Maine to California on a _ _ _ _ _continental journey.

2. Many carpenters and other artisans are _ _ _ _dextrous.

3. Being _ _lingual is a great advantage for people who work in the foreign service.

4. The younger campers sat in a _ _ _ _circle to hear and tell ghost stories.

5. Being of a cheerful and optimistic disposition, Arabella was _ _ _ _uine about the future.

6. Utilizing trash to make energy is con_ _ _ _ing waste into something productive.

7. The _ _ _ _atelist quickly snapped up all the stamps that bore the upside-down design.

8. Syn_ _ _ _ between coach and team members worked successfully for the entire season.

9. Bar_ _ _ _ _ _ is the medical treatment of obesity.

187

10. A host of festivities marked the sesqui_ _ _ennial of the museum.

11. Since the photographs are black and white, they are called _ _chromatic.

12. Bats are _ _ _ _urnal flying mammals that navigate by echolocation, a form of sonar.

13. Some older airplanes are now being _ _ _ _ _fitted with two "black boxes" and other modifications.

14. Montreal, like some other cities in the northern part of the hemisphere, has a bustling _ _ _terranean life, with shops, restaurants, and other comforts during the long, cold winters.

15. Random acts of kindness are _ _ _mendable.

Answers to Word Aerobics No. 1

1. h	9. b
2. j	10. i
3. g	11. n
4. d	12. o
5. l	13. e
6. m	14. f
7. c	15. k
8. a	

Answers to Word Aerobics No. 2

1. c. honeyed	9. a. stubborn
2. a. privilege	10. c. pliable
3. b. complaining	11. a. quiet
4. b. silent	12. a. painful
5. b. generous	13. b. devouring
6. a. secret	14. c. tuneful
7. c. notorious	15. a. needless
8. c. title	

Answers to Word Aerobics No. 3

1. c. regimen	9. c. voluble
2. b. honorific	10. a. adamant
3. b. tortuous	11. b. solecism
4. c. enervate	12. b. onerous
5. a. octothorp	13. c. circuitous
6. b. nepotism	14. a. infinitesimal
7. c. cryptic	15. b. acrimonious
8. b. schism	

Answers to Word Aerobics No. 4

1. transcontinental	9. bariatrics
2. ambidextrous	10. sesquicentennial
3. bilingual	11. bichromatic
4. semicircle	12. nocturnal
5. sanguine	13. retrofitted
6. converting	14. subterranean
7. philatelist	15. commendable
8. synergy	

Better Sentence-Writing In 30 Minutes a Day

By
Dianna Campbell

Contents

Preface

Better Sentence-Writing In 30 Minutes a Day is a workbook for students who have thought seriously about how important it is to improve the technical aspects of their writing. Learning to write well is nothing less than acquiring the power to succeed—in school and in the world that lies beyond school. Developing solid writing skills is not a matter of luck; it's a matter of hard work and practice.

This book features a basic sentence-combining approach, which means that the emphasis is not merely on learning to avoid errors, but also on learning to create good sentences with variety and style. The book also features:

- Clear discussions of rules and strategies for good writing.
- Concise explanations with a minimum of grammatical terms.
- An abundant variety of exercises, from filling-in-the-blank for purposes of identifying the parts of speech to combining short sentences into longer and more graceful combinations.
- An answer key at the end of the book to allow students to work at their own pace and check their work as they go.

Better Sentence-Writing

Students learn best when they are actively engaged in the learning process. They appreciate exercises that teach them the writing skills they need and entertain or inform them at the same time. That is why this book uses a variety of interesting topics in the exercises. Similarly, the instructional material here is brief, but extensive examples and illustrations are provided.

Using *Better Sentence-Writing In 30 Minutes a Day* will help students become skillful and confident writers.

Dianna Campbell

Chapter 1

Introduction to Sentence Structure

1.1 Basic Clause Patterns

•••

Some college students can define a sentence, and some can't, but no doubt you know a sentence when you see one. Read the following choices and circle the letter of the one that is a sentence.

(a) Noses entire people's throughout grow lives their.

(b) Their grow lives throughout people's noses entire

(c) Grow lives their people's entire throughout noses.

(d) People's noses grow throughout their entire lives.

Each of the four sentences contains the same words, but only one makes *sense*—(d). Sequence (d) makes sense because the words in it are arranged in the form of a sentence. Your ability to recognize the sentence shows how natural the sentence pattern is and how much intuitive language skill you already have.

Simple Sentences—Those with One Clause

In order to make good sentences and avoid making errors, we need to develop a basic working definition of a sentence.

Sentences are made up of *clauses*—sometimes one clause, sometimes more than one. This chapter focuses on *simple sentences*—those that contain one clause. Later, you'll work with sentences that contain more than one clause.

A clause is a subject plus a predicate. The *subject* of a clause names something, such as a person, object, place, or idea. The subject is usually one or more nouns or pronouns. The subject might also be a noun substitute.

The *predicate* makes a statement about the subject by telling something about it. The predicate tells one of two things about the subject: It tells that the subject is performing an action, or it states the condition of the subject.

Finding Verbs in Clauses

The easiest way to analyze a clause is to look first at the predicate. The most important part of the predicate is the verb.

1. Action Verbs—Visible and Invisible

You probably know that most verbs show some kind of action. Sometimes this is *visible action*, as in *she swims* or *they kissed.* At other times, it is invisible action, as in *he forgot* or *we decided.*

The verb in our original example sentence shows visible action. Draw a line beneath the verb and write *v* above it.

People's noses grow throughout their entire lives.

If you identified *grow,* you're correct. That's the word that shows the visible action of the subject. What's the subject doing? In this sentence, it's growing.

2. Linking Verbs

Other verbs, such as is and *seem,* don't show an action; instead, they show a subject to be in a certain *condition* or state of being. They do this by *linking* the subject to a word or words in the predicate. These verbs are *linking verbs*.

Let's look at two example sentences:

The woman is an intern.

The students seem confident.

In these sentences, the woman and the students are not performing actions, but they are in a state of being or a condition. We might say that, in the first case, the woman is in the state of being an intern and, in the second case, the students are in the condition of being confident.

There are many linking verbs, such as additional tenses of the verb *to be (am, are, was, were, will be, has been, have been, had been,* and others) and various forms of the verbs *appear, become, feel, look, smell, sound,* and *taste.*

3. The Role of Context

Some verbs are action verbs in one context and linking verbs in another. In sentence (a), is the italicized verb describing an action or a condition?

(a) I *smelled* the familiar fragrance of Chanel No. 5 in the living room.

In (a), the verb from *smelled* is describing an action, the action of the subject (I) smelling. Now notice the very different meaning of the same word in sentence (b).

(b) The rotten chicken *smelled* terrible.

In (b), the subject *(chicken),* is *not* performing an action. The verb in (b) shows that the chicken is in a certain condition—the condition of smelling bad.

Better Sentence-Writing

Finding Subjects in Clauses

Let's return again to our original example sentence:

People's noses grow throughout their entire lives.

To find the subject, simply ask yourself, "What grows?" *Noses.* The word *noses* is the *simple subject* or the *key word* within the complete subject. The complete subject of any sentence is the simple subject or key word plus all the modifiers attached to it.

Throughout our work with clauses, we'll focus on the key word or words within the complete subject because that's what is most directly tied to the predicate. A key word is what the predicate makes a statement about. And, in the present tense, it's the simple subject with which the verb must agree.

Finding Elements That Complete the Verb

In the sentence *People's noses grow throughout their entire lives*, nothing is needed to complete the verb *grow*. Even though four words follow *grow* in the sentence, those words are not needed for sentence structure. They're needed for the writer's meaning, but not for completing the clause. The subject and verb *(noses grow)* make a certain kind of sense and give a feeling of completeness.

But there are other verbs that, by themselves, cannot make a complete structure with a subject. Consider these subject and verb combinations:

they desire

she said

the tree was

people need

Bill kissed

tourists want

4

These sets leave you hanging, wondering: They desire what? She said what? Bill kissed whom? In each case, the verb needs a word or words to complete its meaning. The words that do this job in the predicate of a clause are called *complements* and *objects*. We'll look at their basic types.

1. Subject Complements

One important kind of complement is the subject complement, which follows a linking verb. A subject complement is a noun, pronoun, adjective, or adverb of place that follows a verb in a clause. Here are some sentences in which the subject complements are underlined:

Martha Aliaga is a superb <u>math teacher.</u>

The subject complement answers the question, "Martha Aliaga is what?"

The juniors are our <u>representatives</u> on the committee.

The subject complement answers the question, "The juniors are what?"

James feels <u>wonderful.</u>

The subject complement answers the question, "James feels how?"

2. Direct and Indirect Objects

Direct Objects Linking verbs are not the only kind of verb that needs completion. Another type of verb that needs completion is a kind of action verb called the *transitive verb*. This is a verb that carries or transfers action from the subject before the verb to the object after the verb.

The words that complete the meaning of transitive verbs are called *direct objects*. They follow action verbs and answer the question "What?" or "Whom?" A good example is *I need you. You* is the direct object of the verb *need.*

Do all sentences with action verbs have direct objects? Let's return to the first sentence we considered: *People's noses grow throughout their entire lives.* This sentence has an action verb, but it doesn't have an object. The verb *grow* doesn't need one; *noses grow* has a sense of completeness. Although *grow* shows action, here it is not a transitive verb; it's an *intransitive verb.* It does not move or transport action from the subject to the object. So some action verbs are intransitive, and all linking verbs are intransitive.

So far, we've only looked at linking verbs, because linking verbs are the only kind that are followed by subject complements. In these next sentences, we'll see only action verbs, because action verbs are the kind that take direct objects. We'll label the direct object *do* and underline it:

do

We passed <u>the collection basket</u>.
The direct object answers the question, "We passed what?"

do

Frank paid the <u>money</u>.

The direct object answers the question, "Frank paid what?"

One way to check if a word is a direct object is to try using it as the subject of a passive version of the same sentence. If it *is* a direct object, it will work as the subject. For example, the active sentence *We passed the collection basket* becomes the passive sentence *The collection basket was passed by us.*

If a sentence has a linking verb and a subject complement, you won't be able to transform it from active into passive. This transformation works only with sentences that contain direct objects.

Indirect Objects Sometimes the predicate of a clause also contains a word that is *indirectly* affected by the verb. This word is called the *indirect object,* and it comes before the direct object. The indirect object tells to whom or for whom an action is done. We'll use *IO* as the abbreviation for indirect object.

            io   do

We passed the boy the collection basket.

We passed what? The basket. To whom? To the boy.

            io   do

Francie sent Eduardo the money.

Francie sent what? The money. For whom? For Eduardo.

If you are having difficulty keeping direct and indirect objects straight, reconsider the first sentence. Did we pass the boy from person to person? Or did we pass the collection basket? Which word is *directly* affected by the verb *passed?* It's *basket*—the direct object. The word *boy* is only *indirectly* affected, so it's the indirect object.

Some common verbs that are followed by both indirect and direct objects are the forms of *bring, buy, give, lend, offer, sell, send,* and *write.* Try writing a few simple sentences with these verbs, and you'll probably automatically create clauses with both indirect and direct objects.

3. Object Complements

Some direct objects need a little something extra. They themselves need to be completed by an *object complement.* This word clarifies the meaning of the verb in a sentence or makes the meaning richer. The object complement always follows a direct object, and it helps to complete a direct object by identifying or modifying it.

Object complements are often found in clauses with verbs such as *appoint, choose, consider, elect, make, name,* and *think.* These verbs have one thing in common: They all roughly mean to *make* or *consider.*

We'll use *ob com* as our abbreviation. Here are some examples:

         do ob com
We painted the <u>town</u> <u>red</u>.

Can you see how this sentence means roughly the same as "We *made* the town red"?

         do   ob com
Gerald called his <u>mother</u> <u>a saint</u>.

This sentence is similar to "Gerald *considered* his mother a saint."

Like subject complements, object complements can be nouns or adjectives. Clauses with object complements don't occur as often as the other types of clauses we've examined.

Summary of Basic Clause Types

There are five basic types of clause.

1. subject + verb

        s   v
Example: The children played.

2. subject + linking verb + subject complement

      s   v   sub com
Example: You are beautiful.

3. subject + verb + direct object

       s   v   do
Example: Roosevelt inspired everyone.

4. subject + verb + indirect object + direct object

       s   v   io   do
Example: Samantha sold her friend an antique ruby ring.

5. subject + verb + direct object + object complement

       s   v   do ob com
Example: Marvin called his lab partner a witch.

Exercise 1.1

In the following sentences, label the subject *s*, the verb *v*, the direct object *do*, the indirect object *io*, the subject complement *sub com*, and the object complement *ob com*.

1. His motive was mysterious.

2. I bought the suit.

3. The woman in the second row coughed.

4. Caroline gave Steven a choice.

5. The nectarines feel ripe.

A note on multiple parts: In the remaining exercises, you may find clauses with more than one key word in the subject or more than one verb, complement, or object. In the following sentences, use the blanks provided to identify the multiple parts that appear in italics:

1. *Rose, gray,* and *white* are her favorite colors.

 _____

2. He *loves* and *respects* her. _____

3. The little girl is *curious* and *spunky.* _____

4. I bought *fudge, cashews,* and a *newspaper.* _____

5. The architect gave her *clients* and the entire *audience* a real surprise. _____

6. The release of the movie made him *rich* and *famous.*

 _____

7. The decision *surprised Isaac* and angered *Anna.*

 _____ _____

Item 1 has three key words in the subject. Item 2 has two verbs. Item 3 has two subject complements. Item 4 has three direct objects. Item 5 has two indirect objects. Item 6 has two object complements. Item 7 has two verbs *(surprised* and *angered)* and two direct objects *(Isaac* and *Anna).*

Exercise 1.2

Label the parts of the following simple sentences, using *s* for subject, *v* for verb, *do* for direct object, *io* for indirect object, *sub com* for subject complement, and *ob com* for object complement. Remember: Find the verb first.

1. Serious baseball fans consider Nolan Ryan a superb major league pitcher.

2. According to statistics, the typical major league pitcher shows hitters his best stuff at age thirty.

3. But a recent baseball season was Ryan's twenty-fourth in the big leagues.

4. According to the radar guns, at this point in his long career, his fastballs sometimes reached speeds of one hundred miles per hour.

5. Ryan's amazing fastball made his curveball more effective.

• •

1.2 A Closer Look at Subjects
• •

Let's take a closer look at the subject of the clause. Simple subjects or key words within complete subjects are nouns, pronouns, or noun substitutes. The key word might be a single noun, a single pronoun, or a combination of the two.

Nouns

You might remember that a noun is the name of a person, place, thing, or idea. In this definition, the word *thing* means a concrete noun, something you can touch or experience through one of the senses, and the word *idea* means an abstract noun, something that you can't touch, something intangible.

These nouns are arranged in their respective groups:

Persons	Places	Things	Ideas
accountant	kitchen	butter	success
doctor	city	magazines	memories
mothers	Idaho	toothpaste	cheerfulness
Santa Claus	Disneyworld	Kleenex	Judaism

As you can see, nouns can be singular (one) or plural (more than one). Some are capitalized, and some are not.

1. The Noun-Marker Test

All of the listed nouns, except the capitalized ones, can follow the words *a, an*, or *the*, which are called *noun markers*, because they signal or "mark" the appearance of a noun. For instance, you can say *an accountant, the kitchen, the butter,* and *a success*. But you cannot get the same sense of completeness by saying *a beautiful or the scary*, because *beautiful* and *scary* are adjectives, not nouns.

2. The Subject Test for Nouns

Another way to see if a word is a noun is to try to use it as the subject of a sentence. If a word can be used in this way, it's either a noun or a pronoun.

Let's say, for instance, that we want to see if *decorate* and *decoration* are nouns. We can try each as the subject of a sentence:

(a) The *decorate* lit up the room.

(b) The *decoration* lit up the room.

This test quickly shows us that *decoration* is a noun but *decorate* is not. If you need to practice identifying nouns, try the next exercise.

Exercise 1.3

In each of the following pairs, one word is a noun and one is not. Use the noun-marker test or the subject test to decide which one is the noun. Then circle the noun in each pair.

1. begin, beginning
2. prediction, predict
3. organization, organize
4. liar, lied
5. gently, gentleness

6. decide, decision
7. allow, allowance
8. reliability, rely
9. collection, collect
10. defy, defiance

Most of the nouns in Exercise 1.3 are idea nouns; they're abstract. Notice how often they have the same word endings. Here are five common noun suffixes: *-ance, -ity, -ment, -ness,* and *-tion.*

Pronouns

Pronouns are words that take the place of nouns. We use them to avoid repeating a noun over and over. For example, instead of writing, *"Dancing* is a popular form of exercise. *Dancing* burns up two hundred to four hundred calories per hour," a student might want to change the subject of the second sentence to the pronoun *It,* which, in the context, would clearly mean dancing.

This chapter focuses on the pronoun's ability to function as a subject. But pronouns can do all sorts of other things in sentences, too. Let's look at three groups of pronouns that can be used as subjects of independent clauses. (Pronouns can be subjects of dependent clauses, too.)

Personal	Demonstrative	Indefinite
I	this	anybody
you	that	anyone
he	these	anything
she	those	everybody
it		everyone
we		everything
they		nobody
		no one
		nothing
		somebody
		someone
		something

It's not necessary to memorize these pronouns in their three groups, but it's essential to know that they are pronouns and can be the subjects of sentences.

Noun Substitutes

In addition to nouns and pronouns, other constructions can work as subjects. These are words, phrases, or clauses that perform the same job as a noun. (A *phrase* is any series of two or more words that is less than a clause. A phrase might have a subject-type word or a word from the verb category, but not both.)

Let's look at a few examples of the main types of noun substitutes. In each case, a phrase does the same job a one-word noun could do.

1. Infinitive Verb Phrases

An infinitive verb phrase is any verb preceded by the word to. Examples are *to walk, to sing, to dream.* Look at this sentence:

13

To decide is to take a risk.

Here, the verb phrase to decide works like a noun and acts as the subject of the sentence. You can make a rough equivalent of this sentence by using a conventional noun as the subject:

A *decision* is always a risk.

2. Gerund Phrases

A gerund is a verb that ends in *-ing* and works as a noun. A gerund phrase is simply a gerund plus other words attached to it. Here's an example:

Planning an overseas trip takes a tremendous effort.

You can see that the subject here is roughly equivalent to the noun subject in the sentence:

A *plan for an overseas trip* takes a tremendous effort to create.

3. Prepositional Phrases

Most prepositions are direction or relationship words such as *at, behind, inside,* and *toward.* A prepositional phrase is a preposition plus the noun or pronoun that follows it. Prepositional phrases can also work as subjects:

Before breakfast is a good time for a walk.

Under the boardwalk was the place to be.

4. Clauses

Infinitive verb phrases, gerund phrases, and prepositional phrases are common constructions that can do the job of a noun. Therefore, they can be subjects of clauses. (They can also be objects of verbs.) But these are not the only noun substitutes, just the most common ones. Other constructions can act as nouns. For example, a whole *clause* can act as a subject within a larger clause:

What really gripes me is wilted brown lettuce in a high-priced salad.

Can you see how the subject in this sentence is similar to the noun phrase *My complaint* or *My pet peeve?*
You don't have to be too concerned about the names of these constructions. But it is important to remember:

1. what the job of the subject is (to present a topic for the predicate to make a statement about by showing the subject's action or condition), and

2. that nouns, pronouns, or a variety of other substitutes acting as nouns can do that job.

Exercise 1.4

Find the subject of each sentence. Draw a line under the subject and write s above it. (It will help to find the verb first.) All the subjects here are drawn from the noun substitute category.

1. To work hard today is to believe in tomorrow.

2. What the world needs now is love, sweet love.

3. Tracking students into so-called ability groups often creates great damage of both an intellectual and an emotional nature.

4. Outside that crazy office is where she wanted to be.

5. What a racist or sexist joke reveals about its teller is quite astonishing.

●●

1.3 A Closer Look at Predicates
●●

Now let's look more closely at the part of the sentence that makes a statement about the subject—the predicate.

Verbs

As noted earlier, verbs either show the action—whether visible or invisible—or the condition of a subject. Those that show the condition of the subject do so by linking the subject to a complement that follows the verb.

Another important fact is that verbs change in form to communicate changes in time. These various forms are called a verb's *tenses.* Sometimes forming a verb tense involves nothing more than the addition of an ending; for example, adding a -*d* or -*ed* ending can form the past tense of a regular verb. But other times it involves the addition of a *helping verb*, which is simply a verb that helps another verb form a particular tense or a mood. Helping verbs include forms of the verb *to be* such as *is, are, was, were,* and *will be.* They also include forms of the verb *to have,* such as *has, have,* and *had.*

Other helping verbs are the modal auxiliaries: *can, could, may, might, shall, should, must, will,* and *would.*

There are also helping verbs that give extra emphasis to the predicate: *do, does,* and *did.*

When a verb joins up with a helping verb, it forms a *verb phrase.* For example: *is living, will be reviewed, has answered, could remember, might sing,* and *did pay.* Other verb phrases contain more than one helper. Examples are: *will have been dedicated, should be invited,* and *may have promised.*

Changing Tenses: Regular Verbs versus Irregular Verbs

The past tense of regular verbs is formed by adding -*d* or -*ed.* For example, the present tense *I smile* becomes the past tense *I smiled. They want* becomes they *wanted.* Most verbs are regular verbs.

Irregular verbs do not follow the same pattern. To change the tense of an irregular verb, you do not add *-d* or *-ed.* The base form might not change at all, it might take a spelling change other than the addition of *-d* or *-ed,* or it might change only its pronunciation. See Chapter 6, pages 137-143, for more discussion on regular and irregular verbs and for a list of common irregular verbs.

Exercise 1.5

For the following sentences:

(a) Write *s* over the key word or words in the subject.

(b) Write *v* over the verb or verb phrase. (Create you own marking system to show that an element contains more than one word.)

(c) Label other structurally important elements in the predicate—if there are any—with *sub com, ob com, do,* and *io.*

1. According to a recent study, even mild sleep deprivation can prevent the retention of new and complex knowledge.

2. For centuries, the tongue, with its various colors, textures, and patterns, has given doctors a mirror of the condition of the rest of the body.

3. By November 1964, Malcolm X had made three trips to Africa and had altered his position on the possibility of black and white cooperation and harmony.

4. *Nintendo Power* magazine is published every other month.

5. In his later works, Vincent van Gogh painted his suns a brilliant yellow.

6. *Competition* has been defined as mutually exclusive goal attainment.

7. Perhaps Chester F. Carlson should have named his invention, the copying machine and forerunner of the Xerox machine, after himself.

8. Standard male mannequins wear size 40 regular.

9. Since the beginning of the last Ice Age, the size of human teeth has been decreasing at the rate of one percent every two thousand years.

10. According to experts in nutrition, most people with occasional mood swings should blame their diet, not their ancestry or sheer bad luck.

More About Completing Elements in the Predicate

You have already learned about the different kinds of completing elements that help a verb make a clearer or fuller statement about a subject. You learned that subject complements follow linking verbs; direct objects and indirect objects follow certain action verbs; and object complements follow some direct objects.

The completing elements you worked with earlier were simple—usually a single noun, pronoun, or adjective. Now we'll examine more unusual objects and complements. Three sources of unusual objects and complements are *infinitive verb phrases, prepositional phrases,* and *gerunds and gerund phrases.*

An infinitive verb phrase is any verb in its base form preceded by the word to. Infinitive verb phrases are used to complete verbs here:

(a) He loves to *fly.*

(b) She plans *to compete.*

(c) They want *to surrender.*

These examples show prepositional phrases used as completing elements:

(d) The students went *over the notes.*

(e) He is *without resources.*

(f) The child abuser was *beneath contempt.*

Here gerunds—nouns formed from verbs with *-ing* endings—and gerund phrases serve as completing elements in the predicate:

(g) We attempted *placing the bets.*

(h) I like *playing tennis.*

(i) The director requests loud *singing* on the next number.

1.4 The Modifiers

Up to this point, we have focused on the parts that form the kernal of the clause: the simple subject, the verb, and the completing elements such as complements and objects. These parts can be visualized in another, structural way: They form the skeleton of the clause.

Now we're going to turn our attention to the parts that *modify,* or *describe,* the kernel. These words can be thought of as decorations, because they elaborate on the essential parts of the clause. They add flesh to the skeleton. Sometimes, however, these modifiers are themselves part of the kernel, namely, when they serve as completing elements after verbs.

We'll discuss four types of modifers: *adjectives, adverbs, prepositional phrases,* and *appositives.*

Adjectives

Adjectives, as you know, are words used to describe nouns and pronouns. In English, adjectives usually precede the words they describe. Here are some examples:

(a) This is an *aggressive* team.

(b) She has a *terrific* attitude.

(c) It is a *beautiful* sculpture.

But, as you know, adjectives also can follow the words they describe *if* they are used as complements. For example:

(d) This team is *aggressive*.

(e) Her attitude is *terrific*.

(f) The sculpture is *beautiful*.

Exercise 1.6

Circle the objectives in the sentences below.

1. She sat on the polished oak desk.
2. The biggest problem seemed small.
3. He feared a negative reaction to his best work.
4. I heard a deep, raspy voice.
5. The persistent inflation called for drastic measures.
6. Our supporting evidence was historical.
7. We fished in the crystal waters and hoped for big pike.

8. The tallest man in the group served old-fashioned blackberry pie to the ladies.

9. The final assignment was difficult and challenging.

10. I was struck by the dramatic contrast between her sunburnt arms and pale white face.

You might have noticed how certain words can be adjectives in one context and nouns in another. For example, in Exercise 1.6 the word *blackberry* is an adjective because it describes the pie. But what is the same word in this sentence: "I found only one moldy *blackberry* in the box"? That's right—it's a noun; here, we're talking about an actual blackberry, not something that is described as blackberry in flavor or type.

Adverbs

We usually think of adverbs as words that modify verbs and end in *-ly*. Many adverbs do. But they don't have to end in *-ly,* and they can describe other modifiers—both adjectives and other adverbs. Our focus here is on basic sentence structure, however, so we will discuss only how adverbs modify verbs.

Adverbs can appear almost anywhere in a sentence. In the following sentences, the adverb is italicized, and the verb that the adverb modifies or describes is marked with a *v*:

v
(a) The children sucked their thumbs *loudly.*

v
(b) I tiptoed *quietly* into the corridor.

v
(c) *Eventually* we learned the truth.

v
(d) The doctors *later* spoke to the press.

v
(e) She spends too much time *there.*

21

Some adverbs tell how an action is done: *How* did the children suck their thumbs? *Loudly. How* did I tiptoe into the corridor? *Quietly.*

Another group of adverbs tell *when* an action happens: *When* did we learn the truth? *Eventually.* When did the doctors speak to the press? *Later.*

A third group of adverbs tell *where* an action happens: *Where* does she spend too much time? *There. Where* did the secretary deliver the package? *Here.*

Adverbs don't have a great bearing on sentence structure. However, it is important to realize that adverbs sometimes appear in the *middle* of verb phrases. For example:

Northern Exposure is praised for its quirky, humane portrayal of life in Cicely, Alaska.

Appositives

Appositives are another kind of modifier. They are noun phrases that follow and describe other nouns. Although they can appear after any noun, in this chapter we'll look at how they often follow the simple subject of a clause. Here are some appositives that describe various U.S. presidents:

(a) Calvin Coolidge, *the thirtieth president*, walked a pet raccoon on a leash.

(b) Jimmy Carter, *a former peanut farmer*, was undone by the hostage crisis in Iran.

(c) Andrew Johnson, *a skilled tailor*, made most of his own clothes.

(d) Ronald Reagan, *a former actor*, took the role of president in 1980.

You can see how each appositive is a noun phrase that follows and describes another noun. You also can see that when appositives are used in this position—between the simple subject and the predicate of a clause—they are set off by commas.

Exercise 1.7

The following simple sentences, like the example sentences, contain bits of information about U.S. presidents, and each one has an appositive. For each sentence:

(a) Label the structurally important parts of each clause: the simple subjects *(s)*, verbs *(v)*, complements *(ob com* or *sub com* and direct objects *do)*.

(b) Draw a wavy line under the appositive in each sentence and set it off with beginning and ending commas.

(c) Write the kernel of each clause on the line provided. Remember that the kernel omits all the modifiers and contains only the structural essentials of the clause.

1. George Washington the first president of the United States loved peanut soup.

   Kernel: _____

2. John Quincy Adams the sixth president liked swimming in the nude in the Potomac River every morning at five o'clock.

   Kernel: _____

3. Zachary Taylor a career officer in the army for most of his life voted for the first time at the age of 62.

   Kernel: _____

4. James Buchanan president from 1857 to 1861 was a bachelor throughout his entire life.

   Kernel: _____

5. Abraham Lincoln an extremely persistent individual won the presidency in 1860 after eight election losses in a row.

Kernel: _____

Note: Adjective and adverb phrases also can follow and modify the subject of a clause. Like appositives, these phrases are set off by commas when they appear between the subject and verb of a clause. For example, in this sentence an adjective phrase describes the subject:

The child, *intelligent and strong*, took after her parents.

Here, an adverb phrase is the modifier:

The woman, *cautiously at first*, planted the seeds under a thin layer of reddish dirt.

Prepositional Phrases

Prepositional phrases are probably the most difficult modifiers to learn because there are so many of them. Before we define these phrases, let's look at an example. Underline the modifiers in this phrase:

the high cost of textbooks

The word *high* is obviously a modifier—an adjective, to be precise. But the words *of textbooks* make up another type of modifier—a prepositional phrase. The words *of textbooks* describe the noun *cost* just as surely as the adjective *high* does. We are talking about a high cost, not a low cost. Similarly, we are talking about the cost of textbooks, not the cost of banana splits. So *of textbooks* is a prepositional phrase that works as an adjective.

Here's an example of a prepositional phrase that acts as an adverb:

The boy dialed 911 in a panic.

How did he dial the number? He dialed it *in a panic*, not in a cool, calm frame of mind. In other words, *in a panic* modifies the verb *dialed*.

Prepositional phrases also can describe where an action was done. For example:

The man wrote his novel *at a seaside hotel*.

Or they can describe *when* an action was done. For example:

My mother graduated from law school *in May*.

Most prepositions can be thought of as *direction* or *relationship* words. The noun or pronoun that follows a preposition is called the object of the preposition. Taken together, the preposition and its object form a prepositional phrase. An important thing to know when editing your work is that the subject of a sentence will never be inside a prepositional phrase. Knowing this fact will help to solve problems of subject-verb agreement, a topic we will review later in this book.

Here is a list of common prepositions, each used in the context of a prepositional phrase. The words in italics are the prepositions.

about the introduction	*above* his head
across the border	*after* recess
against his principles	*along* those lines
among ourselves	*around* our city
at the time	*before* the meeting

behind her   *below* the ice

beneath the top layer   *beside* her mother

between two slices   *beyond* tomorrow

by them   *despite* my wishes

down the path   *during* the first minute

except you   *for* my children

from his grandmother   *in* the spirit

inside his mind   *into* the grocery store

like a winner   *near* her heart

of the joke   *off* the top

on the dresser   *onto* the floor

out the door   *outside* the solar system

over the noodles   *past* his house

since her graduation   *through* the middle

throughout the poem   *to* my office

toward the future   *under* it

underneath the books   *until* winter

up the steps   *upon* her entrance

with love   *within* your lifetime

without regrets

There are also *phrasal prepositions*. These are prepositions that are made up of two or more words. Here are a few examples, again given in the context of a prepositional phrase. The phrasal prepositions are in italics:

according to Mark   *along with* fried clams

because of my sister   *except for* him

in addition to the readings   *in case of* emergency

in place of the party   *in spite of* your absence

instead of television   *out of* luck

up to par   *with reference to* the letter

with regard to your request

Exercise 1.8

Use the labels *s, v, sub com, ob com, do* and *io* to mark the key parts of the following simple sentences. Draw a wavy line under appositives and cross out prepositional phrases and other modifiers. Then write the kernel on the line provided.

1. Robin Burns, the highest-paid woman in the United States, is the chief executive officer of Estée Lauder USA.

   Kernel: _____

2. During the early part of his career, Babe Ruth pitched.

   Kernel: _____

3. In 1981, the number of foreign tourists in the United States exceeded the number of American tourists in foreign countries for the first time in the memory of record keepers in the travel industry.

   Kernel: _____

4. For some strange reason, the color of raspberry popsicles has always been blue.

   Kernel: _____

5. The Treasury Department of the United States dry-cleaned soiled money during the administration of President Woodrow Wilson.

   Kernel: _____

6. According to experts in animal behavior, a female tree frog instinctively recognizes the connection between the volume of a male tree frog's song and his physical strength and vigor, prime factors in his desirability as a mate.

   Kernel: _____

7. The headquarters of the McDonald's Corporation in Illinois has a 700-gallon burger-shaped waterbed.

   Kernel: _____

8. The decaying organic matter on the floor of a forest is duff.

   Kernel: _____

9. The average size of the winner of the male division of the Boston Marathon over the years is 5 feet and 7 inches and 135 pounds.

   Kernel: _____

10. Ironically, country singer Hank Williams's last record before his death in 1953 at the young age of 29 was "I'll Never Get Out of this World Alive."

    Kernel: _____

Chapter 2

Sentence Combining: Basic Strategies and Common Problems

2.1 Compound Sentences

One of the easiest ways to combine clauses is to link them with a conjunction. The easiest conjunctions to work with are the *coordinating conjunctions.* Traditionally, seven words are listed in this category:

and	or
but	so
for	yet
nor	

Here are some examples of *compound sentences:*

1. Ernest Lawrence Thayer wrote "Casey at the Bat," **and** the San Francisco *Examiner* first published it on June 3, 1888.

2. Toni Morrison is probably America's finest working novelist, **but** she is also a first-rate essayist and editor.

29

3. According to M. Scott Peck, M.D., in *People of the Lie*, evil people attack others, **yet** they rarely face their own failures as human beings.

Label the subjects, verbs, complements, and objects in the preceding sentences so that you see clearly how each sentence is made up of two clauses. The clauses are *independent,* which means that they can stand on their own. Each one could be written as a simple sentence, which is one independent clause. In a compound sentence, two independent clauses are joined with one of the coordinating conjunctions.

Notice also that a *comma* is used in a compound sentence. It is placed after the first clause, just before the conjunction.

This does not mean that a comma is always used before *and, but, for, nor, or, so,* and *yet.* For example, look at these sentences:

(a) Orange **and** green are two of the secondary colors.

(b) New college graduates are often excited **but** apprehensive about the next phase of their lives.

No comma is used in either sentence because in these cases *and* and *but* are not used to connect clauses.

Exercise 2.1

All of the sentences below are compound sentences. Label both clauses of each sentence, using *s, v, do, io, sub com,* and *ob com.* Circle the conjunction that connects the clauses; then insert a comma before the conjunction.

1. On the average, Mexican-Americans have larger families than any other ethnic group in the United States and they can also claim the lowest divorce rate of all.

2. In the fifteenth century, French gardeners wanted the sweetest possible melons so they watered them with sugar water and honey.

3. Facial tissues are great for cold sufferers but those thin little sheets were actually invented for the removal of cold cream.

4. Both Bill Wilson, a New York stockbroker, and Robert H. Smith, an Ohio surgeon, had a drinking problem so they joined forces and started Alcoholics Anonymous in 1935.

5. Most people keep their New Year's resolutions for no more than a few weeks or they don't make them in the first place.

Important Note: As you've learned, the coordinating conjunctions are usually used to connect two independent clauses, but they can also be used to connect more than two clauses within one sentence. Analyze and punctuate the following example. Circle the conjunctions that connect the clauses and insert a comma before each:

At the age of 23, Frank Church of Idaho learned of his incurable cancer but he lived another 36 years and in that time he became one of the century's most powerful and effective U.S. senators

You can see that *three* independent clauses have been connected by coordinating conjunctions in the sentence about Senator Frank Church. This is a useful option for combining clauses, but, of course, you should not overuse it because you know that variety in sentence structure is a mark of good, lively writing. Three or four clauses combined with coordinating conjunctions would probably be the limit within one sentence. Keep in mind that the standard and most common use of the coordinating conjunction is simply to bring together two clauses.

2.2 Complex Sentences

Complex sentences are another easy technique of sentence combination, and they provide even more variety in your writing because most of them can be presented in two different sequences. In a complex sentence, the conjunction can be placed between the clauses, just as in a compound sentence. For example:

(a) The mandrill of Western Africa is often called the most colorful mammal in the world **because** it has a brilliant crimson nose and bright blue cheeks.

Or the conjunction (the word because) can be placed before the first clause in a complex sentence. For example:

(b) **Because** it has a brilliant crimson nose and bright blue cheeks, the mandrill of western Africa is often called the most colorful mammal in the world.

In both the (a) and (b) sentences, the clause that comes right after the conjunction is called the *dependent clause*. It's called dependent because it depends upon more information. It can't stand alone. *Because it has a brilliant crimson nose and bright blue cheeks* doesn't make sense by itself. It needs something else, namely an independent clause. Once it is attached to an independent clause, such as *the mandrill of western Africa is often called the most colorful mammal in the world*, the two clauses work together to make a perfectly good sentence—a *complex* sentence.

A Note on Punctuation

If you're especially observant, you may already have noticed that a comma is used in the preceding examples only when the conjunction appears at the start of the first clause; then a comma is placed between the dependent clause and the independent clause. A comma is not generally used in a complex sentence when the conjunction appears before the second clause; in other words, you don't use a comma when the conjunction is in the middle of a complex sentence. Here is another way to say this:

dependent clause first → comma between clauses

independent clause first → no comma

There are exceptions to this rule, and later you might want to learn about them and about some other fine points, but in this book, we are concerned with the basics, and this punctuation rule is correct for the vast majority of complex sentences that you will write.

Subordinating Conjunctions

So far, we've looked at just one of the *subordinating conjunctions*, that are used to make complex sentences, but there are others. These are the most commonly used:

after	because	that	whenever
although	before	though	where
as	if	unless	wherever
as long as	since	until	while
as soon as	so that	when	why

You need to be able to recognize both coordinating and subordinating conjunctions when you see them in sentences.

Exercise 2.2

Label the two clauses in each complex sentence. Circle the conjunction that connects the clauses. Then follow the punctuation rules for complex sentences.

1. When you lick a postage stamp you consume one-tenth of one calorie.

2. The birth of the Dionne quintuplets in 1934 created an enormous sensation because no other set of identical quintuplets had ever survived.

3. Although Pretty Boy Floyd was originally known for his string of bank robberies he gained even greater fame for his uncanny knack of avoiding police traps.

4. Eight thousand people must live in a community before the U.S. government calls it a city.

5. If F. Scott Fitzgerald had completed *The Last Tycoon* before his death in 1940 at the age of 44 it might have been a major American novel.

A Final Note

You may have noticed that some of the subordinating conjunctions were listed earlier as prepositions. Don't let this confuse you. Some words can be used as both subordinating conjunctions and prepositions, depending on how they are used.

1. (a) Wendy went to the Halloween party *after* school.
   (b) She had to go back for her broom *after* she left the party.

2. (a) I'd like to see you *before* the spring break starts on Monday.
   (b) I'd like to see you *before* the spring break.

3. (a) Daniel wasn't completely at home in Detroit *until* his third year there.
   (b) *Until* Daniel had been in Detroit for three years, he wasn't completely at home in the city.

• •

2.3 Embedded Sentences

• •

Another very valuable strategy for combining sentences is *embedding*. At first this might seem less familiar to you than the process by which you form compound and complex sentences. But if you look at a large sampling of your own writing, you're sure to find examples of embedded sentences. You are already creating them, so it's just a matter of becoming more conscious of how the process works and learning the fine points of punctuation.

This process does not involve conjunctions. It involves *relative pronouns*, and these are the most important ones:

who

whose

which

(The word *that* can also be used for embedding, but we'll deal with it in Chapter 3 because it involves a different punctuation rule.)

Let's say that you wanted to combine these two sentences:

(a) Eudora Welty is a major Southern writer.

(b) She was born in Mississippi in 1909.

If you try to combine clauses (a) and (b) to make a compound or a complex sentence, you'll find that none of the conjunctions seems quite right. Sure, you could probably say, "Eudora Welty is a major Southern writer, and she was born in Mississippi in 1909," but doesn't that sentence have a weak, flat sound to it?

Better Sentence-Writing

The process of embedding, on the other hand, works well with clauses (a) and (b). The first thing we have to do is change the subject of the second clause to a relative pronoun. Here's what we do:

who
(b) She was born in Mississippi in 1909.

Then we insert the new clause (b) between the subject and predicate of the (a) clause. Now this is what we have:

Eudora Welty **who was born in Mississippi in 1909** is a major Southern writer.

As a finishing touch, we'll add two commas—one before and one after the clause we have embedded. And here's our final product, an embedded sentence:

Eudora Welty, who was born in Mississippi in 1909, is a major Southern writer.

The commas set the *embedded clause* off from the *main clause*, making the whole sentence much easier to read.

Exercise 2.3

Combine these sets of sentences by using the embedding process. Remember to insert commas around the embedded clause. (Again, the relative pronouns we are using are *which, who,* and *whose.*)

1. (a) Thomas Jefferson was broke when he died.
   (b) He was certainly one of America's most brilliant presidents.

_____

_____

_____

2. (a) Monrovia was founded in 1822 and named after President James Monroe.
   (b) It is the capital of the West African nation of Liberia.

   _____

   _____

   _____

3. (a) Herbert Hoover was supposedly worried that King Tut was becoming too attached to other people.
   (b) He once gave an order that no White House staffers were to pet his dog.

   _____

   _____

   _____

4. (a) James Buchanan was the only president to remain a bachelor.
   (b) His 23-year-old fiancé broke off their engagement and died mysteriously a short time later.

   _____

   _____

   _____

5. (a) Grover Cleveland's duties as a sheriff in New York State resulted in his participation in the execution of two convicted murderers.
   (b) They included serving as one county's official hangman.

   _____

   _____

   _____

Two Variations of Embedded Sentences

Some of the embedded sentences that are made with the words who and which can be reworked in two ways. Knowing how to create these two variations will give you a little more flexibility in your writing.

Look at this example. First, we will combine two sentences by embedding, just as you did in the last exercise. We'll use these two simple sentences:

(a) Flashlight fish blink their lights to attract their prey.

(b) They are equipped with glowing pockets of bacteria beneath each eye.

When they are combined by embedding, we have:

1. Flashlight fish, which are equipped with glowing pockets of bacteria beneath each eye, blink their lights to attract their prey.

Sentence 1 is the type of sentence you were creating in the last exercise, but we're going to start calling it a "full embedding" or a "fully embedded" sentence.

Now we're going to make the first variation. We simply drop the relative pronoun *(which)* and the helping or linking verb *(are)*. With what we have left, we make a "reduced embedding":

2. Flashlight fish, *equipped with glowing pockets of bacteria beneath each eye*, blink their lights to attract their prey.

Now we're going to try the other variation. All we do is take the words that appear between the commas in sentence 2 and use them as an introductory phrase. Now we have:

3. **Equipped with glowing pockets of bacteria beneath each eye**, flashlight fish blink their lights to attract their prey.

Sentence 3 is the "moved embedding." Notice that we haven't changed any wording when we went from 2 to 3. All we did was change the order of the words. Also notice that the reduced embedding takes two commas. The moved variation takes only one.

Exercise 2.4

Here are five fully embedded sentences. Practice working out the two variations for each.

1. A quetzal, which is unable to take off into the air like other birds, has to jump off a tree branch backward to avoid snagging its 24-inch tail.

    Reduced: _____

    _____

    _____

    Moved: _____

    _____

    _____

2. Male narwhals, which are nicknamed "unicorns of the sea," sport a single nine-foot-long tusk.

    Reduced: _____

    _____

    _____

    Moved: _____

    _____

    _____

3. Some biologists, who are puzzled by the hump on the back of the thorny devil, speculate that the lizard can push the hump up to create the illusion of a second head when it wants to confuse its enemies.

Reduced: _____

_____

_____

Moved: _____

_____

_____

4. A sloth, which is blessed with three very efficient curved claws on each foot, normally hangs from a tree for its daily 18-hour snooze.

Reduced: _____

_____

_____

Moved: _____

_____

_____

5. One scientist, who was curious about the basic color of the zebra, conducted a study and concluded that zebras are actually black with white stripes, not white with black stripes.

Reduced: _____

_____

_____

Moved: _____

_____

_____

2.4 A Sentence-Combining Approach to the Problem of Run-ons and Comma Splices

Up to this point, you have been working with various methods of combining sentences. Now we're going to turn our attention to two different types of errors that can easily occur during the process of sentence combining.

The first is the problem of *run-ons*. If run-ons have always been a problem in your writing, now you have some good sentence-combining techniques to use in solving them. In later chapters, you'll learn even more techniques.

What exactly is a run-on? It's actually a very simple sentence structure error. A run-on is a series of two or more unconnected independent clauses. Here is an example:

The Daughters of St. Crispin was founded in 1869 in Lynn,

Massachusetts it was the first national organization of trade

union women.

Label the key structural components example so that you can clearly see the two clauses. Then write *RO* where one sentence "runs on" into the other.

When teachers see this kind of sentence in a student's writing, they know that the student is attempting to combine clauses. They know it from the placement of the two clauses between one capital letter and period. But the two clauses are *not* combined or connected. Instead, they are running into one another.

How can you solve the run-on? A comma after the word *Massachusetts* cannot join the clauses. That "solution" would simply create another error—a comma splice. You *can* solve the run-on in a number of ways, using the techniques you've learned in this chapter. The following are four solutions. Notice that the solutions are compound, complex, and embedded sentences. In other words, the solutions are types of sentence combinations you have been studying in the preceding units. Here are the four possible solutions for the run-on:

(a) The Daughters of St. Crispin, which was the first national organization of trade union women, was rounded in 1869 in Lynn, Massachusetts.

(b) The Daughters of St. Crispin was rounded in 1869 in Lynn, Massachusetts, and it was the first national organization of trade union women.

(c) When the Daughters of St. Crispin was founded in 1869 in Lynn, Massachusetts, it was the first national organization of trade union women.

(d) Founded in 1869 in Lynn, Massachusetts, the Daughters of St. Crispin was the first national organization of trade union women.

As you can see, (a) is a fully embedded sentence, (b) is compound, (c) is complex, and (d) is a variation of an embedded and reduced sentence that was produced after juggling the parts of the sentence a bit. These are all good techniques for solving run-ons, and you'll learn more strategies later.

Combining, Not Breaking Up

Notice that we did not solve the run-on about the Daughters of St. Crispin by breaking apart the two clauses and making two separate sentences, each with its own capital letter and period. Breaking run-ons up into separate sentences is a good technique to use in the early grades, but for adult writers, it is usually inappropriate. You *should* be combining clauses, but you have to do it correctly. Use a period and a capital letter when your run-on or comma splice is long enough that it might be difficult for your reader to follow your writing, or when you want to write a short, perhaps choppy sentence for a strong, simple, or dramatic effect. But for most students, those two cases are the exception. In the great majority of cases, run-ons and comma splices should be corrected by combining clauses, not by separating them.

Three Things to Realize About Run-ons and Comma Splices

There are three important things to remember about run-ons. First of all, they aren't necessarily long. These are all run-ons:

(a) He walked she ran.

(b) The vegetables were fresh they were great.

(c) Dogs bark cats meow.

(d) Nancy loved antiques, she disliked most modern things.

(e) The picnic was postponed, it rained.

(f) The first semester was hard, the second one was a little better.

Notice that the first three examples do not contain a comma between the clauses, and the last three examples do. Examples (d) through (f) are technically called *comma splices*, but they are a sentence structure error so similar to run-ons that both types of mistakes are frequently just called *run-ons* to keep things simple. Try to solve each of the six errors above, using the sentence-combining techniques that you know.

The second important fact about run-ons and comma splices is that the second clause often begins with a pronoun. Go back and see how many examples in our discussion show this pattern. If you watch for this tendency in your own writing, you'll prevent a lot of problems. Let's suppose you wrote,

"Christopher wants to eat, he is starved." When you wrote "he is starved," you produced an independent clause, which must be connected to the clause before it. The fact that *he* refers to *Christopher* in the first clause does not mean that the two clauses are already connected.

Here's the third point. The word *that* can attach one clause to another clause as a complement. So the following examples are *not* run-ons. They are perfectly acceptable sentences because the word *that* makes the second clause the complement of the first clause. The clauses are connected by the word *that*.

(a) Charlene knew that Mike was right.

(b) The managers of both stores thought that they could solve their problems alone.

(c) Mary Ann and Bobby hoped that their baby would be on time.

Exercise 2.5

Label each sentence *OK, CS,* or *RO*. Mark the spot where one sentence runs on or splices into the other. Then rewrite the problem sentences, using sentence-combining techniques where possible. Please use your own paper for the rewrites for this exercise and all the other exercises in this unit.

1. _____ Diamonds have a certain mystique about them this has been true for over 2,700 years.

2. _____ The first diamonds were discovered along riverbeds in south central India, they were found about 800 B.C.

3. _____ South central India was the primary source of diamonds for about two thousand years, then South America became the major source, later South Africa did.

4. _____ Although South Africa is the location of the best diamond mines in the world, diamonds are also found in many other places, including other parts of Africa, Australia, Russia, and the United States.

5. _____ In the United States, there are 19 diamond mines, most are around the border between Colorado and Wyoming.

Exercise 2.6

Label each sentence OK, CS, or RO. Mark the spot where one sentence runs on or splices into the other. Then rewrite problem sentences, using sentence-combining techniques where possible.

1. _____ How do you know a good diamond when you see one?

2. _____ Diamonds are judged on the basis of the three Cs, the three Cs are carats, cut, and clarity.

3. _____ The word *carat* comes from the Greek word *keration,* which means "carob seed" carob seeds were used to measure the weight of diamonds long ago in India.

4. _____ In the modern world of diamond dealing, a carat is a more standard measure it represents $1/142$ of an ounce.

5. _____ The largest diamond ever found was 3,106 carats, that equals about 1.3 pounds.

2.5 A Sentence-Combining Approach to the Problem of Fragments

Another problem that can be solved by sentence combining is that of *fragments*. In the last unit, you learned that run-ons and comma splices are not always long, and in this unit, you'll learn that fragments are not always short.

What is a fragment? As you might expect from the name, it is a *piece* or a *part* of something. A fragment is only part of a sentence, but it's "pretending" to be a whole sentence. In what way does it pretend to be a sentence? It does this by starting out with a capital letter and ending with a period. A fragment is a group of words that is set up between a capital letter and a period even though it does not meet all three of the requirements of a sentence. To be a sentence, a group of words must have three things:

1. a subject

2. a predicate

3. a sense of independence

In other words, a fragment might have one or two of these ingredients, but it doesn't have all three. If it did, it would be a sentence, not just part of one.

The problem of fragments is not one that all students have. In fact, many more students have a problem with run-ons and comma splices. But when adult writers do have a hard time with fragments, their fragments usually take a number of different forms, and that fact, of course, makes working with fragments a bit of a challenge. We're going to take a look at the four types of fragments that appear most often in the work of college students.

Type 1: Dependent Clause Set Up as a Sentence

A type 1 fragment is the simplest type of fragment, and it should be especially easy to spot now that you've worked with complex sentences. This fragment has a subject and a predicate, but it does not have a sense of independence. It lacks that because a conjunction has been attached to it. When we say that it lacks a sense of independence, we mean that it can't stand on its own as a unit of communication. The conjunction makes the reader expect to be told more than the information in the dependent clause. Here are some examples of dependent clause fragments:

(a) **Because** goldfish were supposed to bring love and harmony to an Egyptian household in ancient times.

(b) **If** the color red really does scare witches away.

(c) **Although** the word *bride* comes from an Old English word for "cook."

Items (a), (b), and (c) are perfectly good clauses, but they are not whole sentences. That's why they cannot be set up between a capital letter and a period. Once you add a subordinating conjunction to the beginning of a clause, that clause has been "marked" for combination with another clause. Then you have two choices: You can combine the dependent clause with an independent one, which will give the sentence its sense of independence, or you can remove the conjunction and make the clause a simple sentence. Here are possible revisions:

(a) Goldfish were supposed to bring love and harmony to an Egyptian household in ancient times.

(b) The color red really does scare witches away.

(c) Not all newlywed brides are talented in the kitchen, although the word *bride* comes from an Old English word for "cook."

Better Sentence-Writing

Special note: Whenever you start a sentence with one of the subordinating conjunctions, you can be sure that if the sentence has only one clause, you've got a fragment. But you do not always have a fragment if you start a simple sentence with one of the coordinating conjunctions. Sometimes those seven— *and, but, for, nor, or, so,* and *yet*—are used as transitions at the beginning of a simple sentence.

For instance, there's no fragment here: "I told him never to come here again. *And* I meant it." *And I meant it* has been written as a separate sentence to give it strong emphasis, and that's fine. If the writer did not want the emphasis that comes from a new sentence, he or she could have written, "I told him never to come here again, *and* I meant it." Either way is acceptable.

Type 2: Fragment Involving an *-ing* Verb

A type 2 fragment may look less familiar, but it's not difficult to understand. This type also has a subject and a predicate and lacks a sense of independence. But this time there is no conjunction involved. Here the problem is an *-ing* verb used alone in a sentence of one clause. For example:

1. Many African-Americans joyfully **celebrating** Kwanzaa each winter.

2. The tradition of Easter eggs **having** its roots in early Germanic custom.

3. The pearl **being** an essential ingredient in many love potions.

Each of these three fragments has a subject and a predicate, but the *-ing* verb used alone robs each one of its sense of independence.

To solve this type of fragment, you can use three different approaches. One is to add a helping verb. For example:

1. (a) Many African-Americans **are** joyfully **celebrating** Kwanzaa each winter.

We added the helping verb *are*.
Another method is to change the *-ing* verb to a different verb form. For example:

2. (a) The tradition of Easter eggs **had** its roots in early Germanic custom.

We changed *having* to *had*.
A third solution calls for treating the *-ing* verb and the words after it as a phrase that describes the subject. Then you add an entirely new predicate to the sentence. For example:

3. (a) The pearl, being an essential ingredient in many love potions, **was highly valued by superstitious romantics.**

We added the predicate *was highly valued by superstitious romantics.*
A note about being: The word *being* is often the culprit in this type of fragment. *Being* is a form of the verb *to be*. So *being* should be changed to another form of the verb *to be*—a word such as *is, am, are, were,* or *will be.*

Type 3: Fragment Related to Embedding

Another type of fragment comes from a slipup in the embedding process. Here are three examples:

(a) The superstition **that** amethysts prevented drunkenness. Was widely believed by people in ancient times.

(b) A person **who** spills pepper. Is probably going to get into an argument with a good friend.

(c) Tattoos, **which** some sailors considered protection against drowning. At one time were also thought to prevent smallpox.

49

After all the work you've done with embedding, the problem with these fragments should be clear. Each lettered item really contains two fragments. Each contains a subject that is set up as a full sentence and a predicate that is set up as a full sentence. To correct them, all you have to do is change capitalization and punctuation.

Another kind of fragment is a variation of this type. It begins with a relative pronoun, and it describes a noun or pronoun at the end of the sentence before it. For example:

The pepper was spilled by Pat. **Who any minute might find himself in an argument with his best friend John**.

To solve the fragment, change the period to a comma and make the capital *W* on *Who* lowercase.

Another way to avoid fragments that involve relative pronouns is simply to keep this rule in mind: *The only sentences that can begin with relative pronouns are questions*. These, for example, are perfectly fine. They're not fragments:

Who wrote *Jitterbug Perfume?*

Whose size 13 shoes are these?

Which pasta recipe works best?

Type 4: Cutoff Modifier

The last type of fragment involves a modifying phrase that is cut off from the sentence it describes. Here are some examples:

(a) **Used to cure headaches and insomnia**. Opium was extracted from poppies in Persia and Asia Minor for centuries before it was discovered in other parts of the world.

(b) **Hoping to keep a friendship from breaking up**. Some people whisper "bread and butter" whenever anything, such as another person, a tree, or a child on a bike, momentarily separates two friends out for a stroll.

(c) The ancient Greeks valued thyme highly. **Believing that the herb's fragrance restored one's energy.**

Again, you can see how easily these would be solved. Once more, it is just a matter of changing the period to a comma and making the following letter lowercase.

Exercise 2.7

Label each item *OK* or *F.* Then rewrite the fragments, using a variety of sentence-combining techniques. Please do the rewrites on your own paper.

1. _____ *The Statistical Abstract*, which is produced annually by the U.S. Commerce Department. Fills almost 1,000 pages.

2. _____ In one recent year, *The Statistical Abstract* offered a number of interesting tidbits of information about the 50 states in the union.

3. _____ Massachusetts, for example, being the state with the highest number of doctors per 100,000 people.

4. _____ The fact that New York has more lawyers per person than any other state.

5. _____ The state with the highest percentage of people over the age of 65 is, not surprisingly, Florida.

Exercise 2.8

Label each item *OK* or *F.* Then rewrite the fragments, using a variety of techniques.

1. _____ *Cross Your Fingers, Spit in Your Hat,* which is a book about superstitions and folklore.

2. _____ The most interesting superstitions being the ones about love and marriage.

3. _____ Here are two especially quirky ones.

4. _____ If you pull a hair from the head of someone you love, he or she will love you back and love you deeply.

5. _____ The object of your desire will also love you if you give him or her a bowl of soup. Which is flavored with three drops of your blood.

Chapter 3

Punctuating Sentence Combinations

3.1 Using Commas in Compound and Complex Sentences (A Review)

. . . .

As you know, one use of the comma is to punctuate compound and complex sentences. In the last chapter, you worked with compound and complex sentences, but there we were primarily interested in the structure of those sentence forms. Here our emphasis is on the punctuation of compound and complex sentences.

Compound Sentences

Here again are the coordinating conjunctions:

and   nor   so

but   or   yet

for

The basic rule is this: *In a compound sentence, you insert a comma before the conjunction that joins two clauses.* Your writing teacher might tell you that sometimes it's okay to omit the comma if the clauses in a compound sentence are short and if there's no chance of confusion. That's true. But for the purpose of simplicity and for reinforcement of your knowledge of the basic rule, you should *insert a comma in all compound sentences in this chapter*. This is also the simplest rule to remember and use in your own writing.

Also remember that you don't put a comma before every and or but you see in a sentence. Make sure there's actually a clause both before and after the conjunction.

Complex Sentences

By now you know that these are the most important subordinating conjunctions.

after	because	that	whenever
although	before	though	where
as	if	unless	wherever
as long as	since	until	while
as soon as	so that	when	why

Remember that a subordinating conjunction can join clauses in two different ways: The conjunction can be placed before the first clause or before the second clause. When the conjunction is placed before the first clause, you use a comma between the clauses. When the conjunction is placed before the second clause, you normally don't use a comma between the clauses. Another way to say this is:

dependent clause first → comma between clauses

independent clause first → no comma

Here's a review exercise on recognizing and punctuating compound and complex sentences.

Exercise 3.1

Some of these sentences are compound, and others are complex. Please do the following: (1) Label each sentence *compound* or *complex*. (2) Circle the conjunction that joins the two clauses in each sentence. (3) Insert a comma if it is needed because a sentence is compound or because a sentence is complex with the dependent clause first. (Label subjects, verbs, complements, and objects if that helps you to see the two clauses in each sentence.)

1. _____ When it introduced box lunches on a flight to Paris in 1919 Handley Page Transport of England became the first airline to serve meals in flight.

2. _____ No one was surprised when Wilma P. Mankiller became the principal chief of the 72,000-member Cherokee nation.

3. _____ Most beer drinkers now buy their beer in cans but for 35 years bottled beer outsold canned beer.

4. _____ England's Queen Victoria wore mostly black for the remaining 39 years of her life after she lost her beloved husband Albert.

5. _____ Since Kahlil Gibran, the author of *The Prophet* and many other works, died in 1931 at the age of 48 the royalties from all posthumous sales have helped to the people of his impoverished native village of Bsharri in Lebanon.

Compound/Complex Sentences

Before we move on to other punctuation rules, we want to point out that some sentences are both compound and complex. They're called, not surprisingly, *compound/complex sentences*. You'll see that in such a sentence a writer uses a coordinating conjunction and a subordinating conjunction. Here are two examples.

(a) Because Jesus Christ died on the cross, many Christians assume that the symbol originated with Christ's death, but actually the cross had been used as a religious emblem for centuries before the crucifixion.

(b) This was the favorite saying of the great American actor Spencer Tracy: "You only live once, and if you work it right, once is enough."

3.2 Using Commas in Embedded Sentences

Like the unit you have just completed, this unit is partly a review of what you already know from your work in Chapter 2, but it also introduces a new idea.

Earlier we were interested primarily in how to make embedded sentences. Now let's look at how to punctuate them.

Example (a) is typical of the kind of embedded sentence you've already been dealing with. Please punctuate it.

(a) Pierre-Auguste Renoir who was born in 1841 never wanted to be known as a painter of modern life.

If you set off *who was born in 1841* with two commas, you're correct. This is the classic embedded sentence. In sentences like example (a) you have a clear subject—*Pierre-Auguste Renoir*— that is easily understood by the reader without the embedded information. In other words, *who was born in 1841* is extra information. It's interesting perhaps, but you don't need it in order to know what the subject of the sentence is; it's clear that the subject is *Pierre-Auguste Renoir*. When you have embedded information that is extra, meaning that you don't need it in order to identify the subject of the sentence, then you always set off that extra embedded information with two commas.

But there's another kind of sentence in which the embedded information is necessary to identify the subject. Look at this example and draw a wavy line under the embedded clause:

> (b) All men who are irrationally and excessively submissive to their wives can be described as uxorious.

If you want to figure out if the embedded information is merely extra and not needed to identify the subject of the sentence, just omit it for a moment. Then you'll have: *All men can be described as uxorious*. That's not true, is it? If this rather odd and interesting word *uxorious* means "irrationally and excessively submissive to one's wife," then certainly you can't describe "all men" as uxorious.

In other words, the subject in (b) is not simply *All men*. The subject is really *All men who are irrationally and excessively submissive to their wives*. It's a particular kind of man the writer is talking about. The embedded words are not extra information added as an interesting aside after the subject. The embedded clause is so important that it can be considered part of the subject itself. Because of that, it should not be set off with two commas.

Here's another way to say this: If the subject of the main clause is clear and easy to identify without the embedded information, surround the embedded clause with two commas. If the embedded information is needed to make sense of the subject of the main clause, don't use any commas.

Let's look at a few more examples before you do the exercises. Make a decision about each of the following sentences. Two commas or none? Take your time.

> (a) My parents who are worried about everything going just right should start planning their trip abroad as early as possible.

(b) Travelers who are worried about everything going just right should start planning their trip abroad as early as possible.

(c) My very best friend who loves to find old dishes at bargain prices would really go for this store.

(d) Anyone who loves to find old dishes at bargain prices would really go for this store.

Examples (a) and (c) each require two commas. Examples (b) and (d) should have no commas. It's important to realize that in (a) and (c) you're not using the embedded information to identify the subject of the main clause. In other words, it's not as if you have two or more sets of parents and you want to be sure that the reader knows you're referring to the particular set of parents who are going on a trip soon. The same goes for (c): No matter what he or she loves to find at bargain prices, you have only one very best friend. The subjects *My parents* and *My very best friend* are clear and specific without the embedded information that follows them.

An Important Reminder

Remember, when you drop out the embedded information, you are trying to see whether it is needed or not needed in order to make sense of the subject. You are not trying to see how important the embedded clause is in relationship to the overall meaning of the sentence. Keep your eyes on the *subject* of the main clause!

Exercise 3.2

Draw a wavy line below the embedded clause in each sentence and write *s* over the subject of the main clause. Then make your decision to insert either *two commas* or *none*.

1. St. Nicholas who was a fourth-century bishop in Asia Minor is the patron saint of children and sailors.

2. The dog who guarded the gates of Hades in ancient mythology was the three-headed Cerberus.

3. Janet Reno who became U.S. Attorney General shortly before the cult-related tragedy in Texas was praised for her wilingness to take responsibility for her decisions.

4. The person who wrote the Oz books probably remains unknown even to many of the biggest fans of his work. (The Oz series was written by L. Frank Baum.)

5. The average child who is between two and three years of age does not really know how to play with other children.

The Difference between *Which* and *That*

When a sentence contains an embedded clause beginning with *which,* it usually calls for two commas because *which* is normally used with extra information that is not needed to make the subject clear and specific.

When an embedded clause begins with *that,* the information in the clause is usually needed to understand the subject, so no commas are used. Study these examples:

(a) Neverland, **which is often mistakenly called "Never-Never Land,"** is the place where the children in *Peter Pan* met mermaids, pirates, and Indians.

(b) The lines **that connect points of equal barometric pressure** on a map are isobars.

The Relative Pronoun *Whose*

The relative pronoun *whose* works the same way as *who;* in other words, whose is sometimes used with two commas and sometimes with none. It all depends upon whether or not the embedded clause is needed to make sense of the subject of the main clause.

Better Sentence-Writing

In the previous exercise, you worked only with the embedding word *who.* Now you'll begin to analyze sentences that have been made with *who, whose, which,* and *that.*

Exercise 3.3

Draw a wavy line below the embedded clause in each sentence and write *s* over the subject of the main clause. Then make your decision to insert either *two commas* or *none.* (Remember to think about how important the embedded information is in relation to the *subject of the main clause*—not in relation to the whole sentence.)

1. A person who was born under the sign of Taurus is supposedly stubborn and independent.

2. The person who founded Vassar College was a brewer. (It was Matthew Vassar.)

3. The U.S. Senate which has been called "the most exclusive club in the world" is never open to more than 100 members.

4. The grape that makes California's most successful white wine is the Chardonnay.

5. The abbreviation *lb.* which means pound comes from the Latin word *libra,* meaning "scales."

Exercise 3.4

Here are five pairs of sentences about figures in the history of popular music. Take each pair and embed the (b) sentence into the (a) sentence. (You learned to do this in Chapter 2.) After you have combined the sentences by embedding, decide whether to add *two commas* or *none*. You will choose from the relative pronouns *who, whose, which,* and *that.*

1. (a) Chubby Checker worked as a chicken plucker in a poultry shop before he became famous for doing "The Twist."
   (b) His real name was Ernest Evans.

_____

_____

_____

2. (a) Neil Sedaka made a comeback in the 1970s with the help of Elton John.
   (b) He had enjoyed a great deal of success as a songwriter and singer in the 1950s.

_____

_____

_____

3. (a) Critic Jon Landau is responsible for the line "I saw rock 'n' roll's future, and its name is Bruce Springsteen."
   (b) He wrote a rave review after seeing "the Boss" in concert in 1974.

_____

_____

_____

4. (a) Annie Mae Bullock changed her name to Tina Turner.
   (b) She married Ike Turner in 1958.

_____

_____

_____

5. (a) The heart attack occurred while the famous soul singer was performing on stage in Cherry Hill, New Jersey, on September 25, 1975.
   (b) It left Jackie Wilson in a coma for the rest of his life.

_____

_____

_____

3.3 Using Commas to Set Off Phrases

To understand the punctuation featured in Unit 3, you need to know the difference between a *clause* and a *phrase*. Remember that a clause has both a subject and a verb. A phrase, on the other hand, is a sequence of words that has some sort of meaning but does not have both a subject and a predicate. A phrase might have a noun or a pronoun, or it might have a verb, but it will not have a subject and a verb working together. A phrase might be short or long, but it does less grammatically than a clause.

Label each sentence of words *cl* (for clause) or *p* (for phrase):

1. _____ this man loved his child

2. _____ loving his child

3. _____ the water is deep

4. _____ in a certain depth of water

5. _____ closing the store soon

6. _____ devoted to the exploration of space

7. _____ if we expect to continue the quest

8. _____ expecting to continue the quest

The clauses are items 1, 3 and 7. The phrases are items 2, 4, 5, 6 and 8.

Introductory Phrases

Read this sentence aloud:

Not leaving a thing to chance one cookbook says that Grandma's "pinch" is really one-eighth of a teaspoon.

If you're like most readers, this sentence cannot be read easily without a very short pause and a slight shift in vocal pitch after the word *chance*. Insert a comma after *chance* and read the sentence aloud again. It's clearer with the comma, isn't it?

Most writers would insert a comma after *chance* even if they know very little about the formal rules of punctuation. You might say it's a commonsense comma. The reason it's so helpful is that it separates what is called an *introductory phrase* from the independent clause that follows it. Go back to the sentence and draw a bracket over *Not leaving a thing to chance;* then write *introductory phrase* above the bracket. Finally, mark the main parts of the sentence's independent clause.

End Phrases

Now read this sentence aloud:

Kurt Vonnegut has written some of the funniest and saddest books of the twentieth century repeatedly lamenting the exchange of kindness and love for progress and technology.

Go back and insert a comma after the word *century;* then read the sentence aloud once more. Again, it's easier to handle with the comma, isn't it? With the Kurt Vonnegut sentence, we have an example of an *end phrase*. In this kind of sentence, we have the independent clause first. For the convenience of your reader, the end phrase that follows the clause should be set off with a comma. Bracket and label the end phrase in the example sentence and mark the key parts of the independent clause.

Better Sentence-Writing

Notes to Remember

Sometimes it's a matter of your own judgment whether or not to set off an introductory phrase or an end phrase from an independent clause. You'll do fine as long as you use this question as your guideline: *What will make my sentence easier to read?* That, of course, is the whole purpose of punctuation—making your writing easier for your reader to understand.

When a single word or a very short phrase appears before an independent clause, you can *usually* go either way. For example, you can insert a comma after the introductory phrase in each of these sentences, or you can leave it out:

(a) In a minute she'll be ready.

(b) Later he'll stop at the library.

(c) Actually I don't know what to do.

But there are times when you should definitely use a comma even though you might have only *one word* before the start of the independent clause. *Yes, No, First, Second,* and *Third* are good examples of single words that should be set off with a comma when they appear as the first word in a sentence. Another example is a person's name when you are addressing that person in a sentence. Add commas to these sentences:

1. No he isn't scheduled to play tonight.

2. Yes she seems to be the front-runner.

3. First you must have the desire to write well.

4. Second a certain amount of time must be set aside for the effort.

5. Ann come here for a minute.

6. George do you think we'll have time for a short drive?

When in doubt, try reading aloud and let your reader's need for a pause be your guide.

Exercise 3.5

Add commas to set off phrases where doing so makes the sentence easier to read. (You might want to label the key structural components of the clauses to make your decisions easier.)

1. In the lingo of the racetrack a maiden is a horse that has not yet won its first race.

2. First awarded in the American Revolution the Purple Heart is bestowed upon soldiers who are wounded in the line of duty.

3. The city of St. Petersburg has undergone something of an identity crisis through the years having been known both as Petrograd and Leningrad.

4. England adopted a national policy of women's suffrage in 1918 followed by the United States in 1920.

5. The word *khaki* comes from the Persian word *khak* meaning "dust."

Mid Phrases

We've been working with phrases that come before or after an independent clause, but a phrase can also appear in the middle of a clause. When it does, again you have to use your judgment to decide if it should be set off with commas. If you think that a pause and a shift in vocal pitch are required, then use *two commas*—one before and one after the phrase. Read these sentences aloud and notice how helpful the sets of commas are.

(a) The new shopping district, in spite of careful planning by the town council, did not turn out to be much of a success.

(b) Your cousin, with or without his Doberman pinscher, is not welcome here today.

(c) The real reason for her actions will, however, become obvious by the end of the story.

(d) The hospital, surprising everyone, became the center for heart transplant surgery in the region.

3.4 Using Commas in a Series

One of the most natural uses of the comma is for separating items in a series. The items might be three or more of almost anything—nouns, adjectives, verbs, prepositional phrases, or practically any other grammatical unit.

The comma before the *and* that joins the last two items in a series is optional, but it often makes a sentence easier to read if you put it in.

Exercise 3.6

Add commas where they are necessary or helpful for separating items in a series. (Commas that are necessary for other reasons have already been added for you.)

1. Animals that form monogamous bonds between males and females include ducks swans geese eagles foxes wolves and mountain lions.

2. *Fly patterns flares bombs safety blitzes* and *flea flickers* are all part of the lingo known only to the true football fan.

3. The Arc de Triomphe in Paris is 164 feet high 148 feet wide and 72 feet thick.

4. In one of the many works written about him, the famous Faust exchanged his soul for 24 years of wisdom wealth power and pleasure.

5. Until recently, Ariel Miranda Oberon Titania and Umbriel were thought to be the only moons that revolved around the planet Uranus.

Commas in Adjective Pairs

A related rule concerns the use of a comma between two adjectives that describe the same noun. Sometimes you insert a comma, and sometimes you don't. What's the rule? It's really very simple. Just ask yourself if you could put the word *and* between the two adjectives. If you could, then insert the comma. If the word *and* would sound odd between the adjectives, then leave out the comma.

With this guideline in mind, put a comma between the adjectives in one of these two sentences:

1. Peter is a **happy young** man.

2. Peter is an **enthusiastic energetic** man.

The comma should be inserted in sentence 2, right? You know that it's 2 because you might easily say, "Peter is an enthusiastic and energetic man," but you would never say, "Peter is a happy and young man."

This rule can be explained in another way, which you might find useful. Normally, if you can switch the order of the adjectives, then you put in the comma. If you can't switch the order, then you omit the comma. See if this rule works by rewriting sentences 1 and 2, switching the order of *happy* and *young* in sentence 1 and *enthusiastic* and *energetic* in sentence 2:

1. _____

2. _____

When the adjectives in sentence 1 are switched, the sentence—*Peter is a young happy man*—sounds odd, doesn't it? It's not a sentence you'd be likely to write. That tells you to leave out the comma. When the adjectives in sentence 2 are switched, the sentence sounds fine; that tells you to put in the comma.

Exercise 3.7

Underline the adjectives in each sentence. Then insert a comma between them where one is needed. In each set of sentences, one adjective pair will call for a comma, and one will not. Use one or both of the methods just described to help you.

1. (a) She was known for her quick little smile.
   (b) She was known for her generous good-hearted smile.

2. (a) This is a serious military affair.
   (b) This is a ridiculous tragic affair.

3. (a) The garden was bordered with perfect tea roses.
   (b) The garden was bordered with delicate delightful roses.

4. (a) A creamy buttery soup was served in the cafeteria.
   (b) A delicious bean soup was served in the cafeteria.

5. (a) He was a skillful thoughtful sculptor.
   (b) He was a thoughtful Italian sculptor.

3.5 Cumulative Review of Commas

This unit simply allows you to practice all the different comma rules you've learned in this chapter. But before beginning the exercise, please study these two additional rules.

Commas to Set Off City from State

You normally use one comma between the name of a city and a state and another comma after the state. For example:

1. (a) The authors of *The Best* insist that **New York, New York,** is home to the best hamburgers in America.

2. (a) **New Haven, Connecticut,** is the city where they found the best pizza.

The only exception is when the city and state come right before another punctuation mark, such as a period or a semicolon. In these examples, you use only the comma between city and state:

1. (b) The authors of *The Best* insist that the best hamburgers in America are served at the Campus Dining Room Restaurant and Bar in **New York, New York.**

2. (b) Peter Passell and Leonard Ross really liked the pizza at The Spot in **New Haven, Connecticut;** in fact, they called it the best pizza in the United States.

Commas in Dates

The rule for punctuating dates is similar. You use one comma between the day of the month and the year and another comma after the year. In other words, you normally set off the year with two commas, just as you usually set off the state with two commas. For example:

(a) The first use of videotape on television was on **October 23, 1956,** on "The Jonathan Winters Show."

(b) **December 25, 1968,** was the day when the *Apollo 8* astronauts became the first human beings to see the far side of the moon.

The same exception that applies to city and state applies here; in other words, you use no comma after the year if another punctuation mark is used in that position.

Exercise 3.8

Add commas where they are necessary or helpful, according to the guidelines of this chapter.

1. If you ever really want to go to Timbuktu you'll have to head out for Mali in northwest Africa. Timbuktu which was a famous center for trading in gold was settled by the Tuaregs in 1087.

2. The ice-cream sundae now a classic American treat was supposedly created in a Wisconsin ice-cream parlor and originally it was served only on Sundays.

3. On October 25 1940 Col. B.O. Davis became the first African-American to attain the rank of brigader general in U.S. military history.

4. For concocting the original Coca-Cola in 1886 John Styth Pemberton an Atlanta pharmacist will always be remembered and appreciated.

5. When fireflies light up they send sexual signals to one another. According to the experts male and female fireflies identify themselves and indicate sexual interest by the frequency and intensity of their flashes.

6. King Louis XIV of France who was a ballet dancer from the time he was 13 years old is credited with founding the Royal Ballet Company.

7. A desert rose is not a rose at all. It's a rock that is made up of fused eroded grains of sand. Desert roses which are "flowers" carved by the elements are not difficult to find in the Sahara.

8. The first person to be called the "father" of his country was Cicero not George Washington.

9. Totally unrelated to either sweets or bread a sweetbread is actually the thymus gland of an animal.

10. The longest heaviest snake in the world is the South American anaconda or python a typical specimen measuring 30 feet or more.

3.6 Using Semicolons

The basic function of the semicolon (;) is simple. A semicolon is used where you could use a capital letter and a period, but you'd rather not have such a strong break between your clauses. It's good for spots where you want to bring clauses together, but you don't want to use a conjunction.

In other words, a semicolon is used between independent clauses that are not linked by a conjunction. A semicolon is used when the information in the independent clauses is related or balanced. Here are five good examples for you to study:

1. Children between the ages of one and three need about 25 grams of protein a day; adults need 55 to 75 grams a day.

2. The red parts of poinsettias are not flowers; the red parts are actually leaves.

3. A female has two X chromosomes; a male has one X chromosome and one Y chromosome.

---

4. The first president who didn't go to college was George Washington; the last was Harry Truman.

5. It is against federal law to impersonate a 4-H Club member; it is also a federal offense to misuse the 4-H symbol in a fraudulent manner.

Label the kernels of the clauses in examples (1) through (5) if that helps you see that each sentence is made up of two independent clauses. Note that the first word after the semicolon is not capitalized unless it is a proper noun.

Exercise 3.9

Insert one semicolon into each sentence. Label the key parts of the clauses if you need to. (In this exercise and in other exercises in this unit, any punctuation that is not related to the use of the semicolon is already supplied. See sentence 4, for example.)

1. Mildred "Babe" Didrikson was voted the woman athlete of the year in 1932 for her accomplishments in track she received the honor for her achievements in golf in 1954.

2. The Eiffel Tower was not intended as a permanent structure it was built as a temporary attraction for the Paris Exposition in 1889.

3. The skeletons of sharks are not composed of bone they are made up entirely of cartilage.

4. According to one national survey by *American Demographics,* high school boys expected a starting salary of $18,500 for their first full-time job high school girls expected a starting salary of only $14,700.

5. In the 1870s the most admired American sports heroes were riflemen oarsmen were almost as popular with the U.S. public.

An Introductory Word or Phrase for the Clause After the Semicolon

You know that semicolons are used when a writer wants to show a relationship between two independent clauses. (Sometimes it's actually independent *combinations* of clauses; for example, you might have a complex sentence on one side of a semicolon and a compound sentence on the other side.) Often a writer uses an introductory word or phrase at the beginning of the clause that follows the semicolon. *This word or phrase does not connect the clauses. The semicolon does that.* The introductory word or phrase simply makes the relationship between the clauses clearer and more explicit.

Here's a list of words and phrases that are often used in this way. They're divided into groups on the basis of having similar or closely related meanings:

for example	therefore
for instance	consequently
however	as a result
on the other hand	in fact
nevertheless	as a matter of fact
also	actually
furthermore	then
in addition	now
in other words	later

Here's a sample sentence:

> According to one national survey by *American Demographics,* high school boys expected a starting salary of $18,500 for their first full-time job; high school girls expected a starting salary of only $14,700.

The sentence is perfectly fine the way it is. But it can be revised in a very small way so that the contrast it describes is more obvious. To see how this works, fill in the blank with an introductory word or phrase from the list above:

> According to one national survey by *American Demographics,* high school boys expected a starting salary of $18,500 for their first full-time job; _____, high school girls expected a starting salary of only $14,700.

If you chose *however* or *on the other hand,* you're correct. Either one helps to make the contrast between the clauses more apparent.

Notice that a comma is used after the introductory word or phrase. This is the normal procedure: Use a semicolon before the introductory word or phrase and a comma after it.

Other Introductory Words and Phrases

The list we have given you is certainly not complete, but it's a good basic list of introductory words that can be used in creating this particular sentence structure. But there are many other expressions that can serve as introductory words and phrases before a clause. You'll probably come up with a variety in your own writing. Look at these two examples:

(a) The manager of a professional baseball team can visit the pitcher on the mound only once; *after that,* he can't go out again unless he's going to call in a reliever.

(b) There are many legends about the Canary Islands; *according to one*, the islands are really the highest peaks of Atlantis, the lost continent.

Exercise 3.10

Punctuate these sentences with semicolons and commas. Some sentences call for a semicolon only, and others call for a semicolon and a comma. (Label the key parts of clauses if you need to.)

1. The largest lake or inland sea in the world is the Caspian Sea however the biggest freshwater lake is Lake Superior.

2. The familiar word *oriental* refers to the people and culture of the East the less familiar word *occidental* refers to the people and culture of the West.

3. Fyodor Dostoyevsky wrote a novel called *The Gambler* in fact the great Russian literary figure was himself a compulsive gambler.

4. North America is slowly moving westward at an annual rate of about three inches consequently the Atlantic Ocean is now about 20 feet wider than it was when Columbus crossed it.

5. During the ninth-century reign of Alfred, King of the West Saxons, there was a specific punishment for practically every bodily injury for example if a person's thigh were pierced, he or she could collect a fine of 30 shillings from the injuring party.

6. A copyright stays in effect for the lifetime of the creator of the copyrighted work in fact it is valid for his or her lifetime plus 50 years.

7. In O. Henry's "The Gift of the Magi," a husband sells his watch in order to buy his wife a pair of combs for her beautiful hair the wife cuts off her long hair and sells it in order to buy her husband a fob chain for his watch.

8. Much of Humphrey Bogart's mystique came as a result of his wonderful performance in *Casablanca* however few people know that Ronald Reagan was originally cast as Rick, the main character.

9. An amulet is an object that supposedly protects a person against bad luck a talisman is something that is thought to attract good luck.

10. A wolf's eye, a stone with a hole in it, and a horseshoe are examples of amulets a four-leaf clover and a rabbit's foot are examples of talismans.

A Note of Caution

There's one bad habit that some writers fall into. They begin to assume that the introductory words and phrases listed earlier are always used with semicolons and are never used in any other ways in a sentence. Of course, that's not true. These words and phrases are not used with a semicolon unless an independent clause (or an independent combination of clauses) appears both before and after the semicolon. All these words and phrases can be used with semicolons, but they can all be used in other spots in sentences, too. Study these correct examples and then complete Exercise 3.11:

1. (a) Craig always has something to complain about; *for instance,* he might be upset about lumpy mashed potatoes one night and the growing national debt the next.
   (b) Craig's complaints, *for instance,* cover everything from lumpy mashed potatoes to the growing national debt.

2. (a) The doctor predicted a good outcome for the operation; *as a matter of fact,* she almost guaranteed
total recovery.
   (b) The doctor's prediction, *as a matter of fact,* was
almost totally optimistic.

Remember, there are no words or phrases that are always
used with semicolons. All of these introductory words and
phrases, can be used in other ways in sentences. They don't
always signal the need for a semicolon.

Exercise 3.11

Punctuate the following sentences. Some sentences call for
no additional punctuation, some for commas only, and some for
a semicolon and a comma.

1. (a) Robert had a great idea.
   (b) His idea however was not immediately accepted by
the group.
   (c) Robert had a great idea however it was not immediately accepted by the group.

2. (a) Christina was more than a passing acquaintance of
Ben's in fact she was his closest friend.
   (b) Christina was very close to Ben.
   (c) She was in fact his best friend in the world.

3. (a) Mitchell wants to graduate with a degree in
mechanical engineering at the end of his college
days.
   (b) This highly motivated young man is therefore going
to have to work hard and play little during the next
four years.
   (c) Mitchell wants to graduate from college with a
degree in mechanical engineering therefore he is
going to have to work and play little during the next
four years.

4. (a) The exact time that language skills emerge in children varies greatly among individuals.
   (b) Language skills emerge at greatly varying times in the development of children for example some toddlers begin talking in short sentences around the age of two.
   (c) Other completely normal youngsters for example speak very little until they're three.

5. (a) John and Marsha are debating whether they should go with periwinkle blue or China red for their new carpet.
   (b) Marsha thinks periwinkle blue would be an elegant choice on the other hand John is afraid that blue might make the room seem cold.
   (c) John on the other hand thinks that China red would be warm and lively.

3.7 Using Colons

Occasionally, you might want to use a colon (:) to set up a list. In order to do this, you need to create a complete sentence, usually one that ends with a subject complement or a direct object.

Don't do this:

The four major reasons for the landslide victory *were:* the candidate's personal popularity, the enthusiastic support of his party, his stand on budget issues, and the general mood of the nation.

What's wrong with it? The problem is that the colon follows a verb—in this sentence, the verb *were.* You might see this type of sentence in a newspaper or a popular magazine, but it's not accepted in academic writing by most college teachers.

In academic writing, it is normally expected that a subject complement or a direct object should appear before the colon. Label the complement in this example:

The four major reasons for the landslide victory were obvious: the candidate's personal popularity, the enthusiastic support of his party, his stand on budget issues, and the general mood of the nation.

If you identified the word *obvious* as the subject complement, you're correct. The addition of *obvious* in the second sentence corrects the problem that exists in the first sentence. A colon should not follow a verb.

An Important Note

Sometimes you'll use a word that isn't a complement or a direct object but that still gives the sentence a sense of completion before the items in the list begin. For example, let's look at this correct sentence:

The strange coincidences happened during each of these years: 1921, 1937, 1952, 1964, and 1986.

You know that the word *years* is not the complement of the verb *happened*. If something happened, it happened. We don't ask a question such as "It happened what?" So strictly speaking, *happened* is a verb that doesn't take a complement.

The word *years* is not a complement or a direct object, but it does help to give the first part of the sentence a sense of completion—a sense that now we've finished the setup, and we're ready to present the items in the list.

To keep things simple, we'll refer to this kind of word as the *complement of the setup.* In the majority of sentences—your own and ours—you'll be working with a true complement anyway, so this won't often be an issue.

The important thing is this: You need a feeling of completeness in the setup, the part of the sentence that precedes the colon. That sense of wholeness in the setup can be produced by using a *true complement or a complement-type word.*

Exercise 3.12

Punctuate the following sentences with colons and commas. Some sentences might call for commas only. Label the subject complement *sub com* and the direct object *do* to help you see if a sentence has the setup needed for a colon. (Punctuation not related to this unit has already been supplied.)

1. In *The Misunderstood Child,* Dr. Larry B. Silver says that the human brain goes through major growth spurts during five time periods. Those periods are the following between three and ten months between two and four years between six and eight years between 10 and 12 years and between 14 and 16 years.

2. Santa's eight tiny reindeer are Dasher Dancer Prancer Vixen Comet Cupid Donner and Blitzen.

3. These are the seven wonders of the ancient world the Great Pyramid of Cheops the Hanging Gardens of Babylon the Tomb of King Mausolus at Halicarnassus the Temple of Artemis the Colossus of Rhodes the Statue of Zeus at Olympia and the lighthouse on the Isle of Pharos.

4 Most of us would probably call a flock of birds a flock of birds. But those who want to be more precise might use one of these terms a bevy of quail a muster of peacocks a charm of finches or an exaltation of larks.

5. Charles Blondin, the French acrobat and tightrope walker, crossed Niagara Falls in 1855 1859 and 1860.

A Common Error

One very common error is to use a colon after the word *including* or after *such as.* These situations, however, do not call for colons. The word *including* or the expression *such as* is really better viewed as the start of an "end phrase" or, in other words, a phrase following a clause. Look at these correct examples:

(a) J.B. Rhine of Duke University has conducted scientific studies of various aspects of parapsychology, **including** clairvoyance, extrasensory perception, psychokinesis, and telepathy.

(b) J.B. Rhine of Duke University has conducted scientific studies of various aspects of parapsychology, **such as** clairvoyance, extrasensory perception, psychokinesis, and telepathy.

You should *not* use a colon in (a) and (b). Try rewriting the sentence about J.B. Rhine so that a colon is appropriate. Then punctuate sentences 1 through 4:

1. These are the seven deadly sins anger covetousness envy gluttony lust pride and sloth.

2. He committed each and every one of the seven deadly sins anger covetousness envy gluttony lust pride and sloth.

3. She committed a number of the seven deadly sins including anger envy lust and sloth.

4. Of the seven deadly sins, they had their own personal favorites such as gluttony lust and sloth.

1. sins: anger, covetousness, envy, gluttony, lust, pride, and sloth; 2. sins: anger, covetousness, envy, gluttony, lust, pride, and sloth; 3. sins, including anger, envy, lust, and sloth; 4. favorites, such as gluttony, lust, and sloth.

Another Use for the Colon

There is another way to use the colon, but if you still have difficulty with *any* of the other rules of punctuation, you should skip this brief section. This is a low priority compared with the other rules, and it will *not* be included in the cumulative exercises in the next unit. But for many writers, it is a valuable sentence-combining technique, so that is way we are presenting it here.

The colon can be used in this way:

Carol Tavris's *The Measure of Women* has an interesting

subtitle: *Why Women Are Not the Better Sex, the Inferior*

Sex, or the Opposite Sex.

Mark the key parts of the clause before the colon. You see that we do have a complement—*subtitle*—just as we always have a complement when we are using the colon before a list. But here we're not setting up for a list; we're setting up for an *explanation of the word in the subject complement or direct object position.* The word *subtitle* is explained by the words that follow the colon.

When you make this kind of a sentence, you can capitalize the first word after the colon if the explanation is a full sentence. If you use the capitalization option, be consistent within a piece of writing.

3.8 Cumulative Review of Commas, Semicolons, and Colons

This unit contains exercises that ask you to use all the information you've learned and all the skills you've acquired in Chapter 3.

A Few Important Words About the Exercises

In these exercises, you will be using *commas, colons,* and *semicolons.* Commas, of course, will be used most frequently because the comma has so many different functions. But not every exercise will call for all three punctuation marks. And some sentences will call for no additional punctuation.

Furthermore, some sentences will lend themselves to more than one interpretation or more than one method of punctuation.

If punctuation is needed to introduce a direct quote, it will be supplied for you. You'll learn how to punctuate quotes in the next chapter.

Label the key parts of clauses if that practice is helpful to you.

Finally, *mark up the book!* Most often, if you take a look at the books of students who are really improving in their writing, you find that those books are completely marked up with notes, labels, underlinings, and symbols. The marks give testimony to a lot of hard work and show that those students are making the information their own. Develop a system— whether it's circling conjunctions, drawing wavy lines under embedded clauses, or whatever—and use it. And when you're stuck on a particular sentence, if you can't figure it out, put a question mark in the margin and move on. You can come back to it later.

Exercise 3.13

Insert commas, semicolons, and colons where they are needed.

1. *Sea of Slaughter* which was published by Atlantic Monthly Press was written by Farley Mowat.

2. Mowat who is a Canadian is a naturalist and a writer.

3. Focusing on the northern part of the Atlantic seaboard Mowat examines the history of man's relationship with wildlife since the first Europeans arrived on this continent.

4. Although Farley Mowat's research is limited to one geographical area his conclusions can be said to hold true for the entire continent of North America.

5. According to the author human beings have meant almost nothing but death for the mammals birds and fish of North America in fact Mowat estimates that the entire "biomass" has been reduced by perhaps as much as 95 percent through human destruction.

6. Animals have been "overkilled" basically for three reasons economic recreational and scientific.

7. Economic reasons include the killing of animals for meat hides and fur.

8. Some species have survived but they have survived only with great difficulty for example the wolf the Plains buffalo and the grizzly bear were depleted by the millions because of wanton slaughter by human beings.

9. Other animals such as the passenger pigeon the sea mink and the Eastern buffalo are gone forever driven into extinction by the planet's supposedly most intelligent creatures.

10. These are harsh tragic realities and they are not only a matter of history animals continue to die for sport for fashion for food and for experimentation.

Exercise 3.14

Insert commas, semicolons, and colons where they are needed.

1. *Sea of Slaughter* a substantial book of more than 400 pages points out that human beings destroy their own rich history when they destroy any part of the natural world.

2. Many people for example believe that the great auk was only a myth.

3. Farley Mowat assures us that this fascinating bird which could dive to a depth of 300 feet and stay underwater for a quarter of an hour did exist.

4. While the great auk once numbered 100 million its natural enemies numbered only one.

5. That enemy of course was deadly it was man.

6. Mowat also reminds us that the whale once one of the most stable of all life forms is now in danger of disappearing from the planet.

7. The author sees only one animal that has succeeded in thriving against all odds the coyote.

8. Mowat credits the coyote for being adaptable and just plain smart.

9. Lamenting man's role as a predator Mowat concludes that there is some hope for the future but the best hope lies with aware and sensitive individuals not with massive organizations.

10. Although books like *Sea of Slaughter* are rare they can make important headway in forming sensitive aware human beings. As Robert W. Smith said in a review of Mowat's publication it "deserves to stand with Rachel Carson's *Silent Spring* as an outstanding indictment of man's stupidity in alienating himself from nature."

Chapter **4**

Revising Sentences

4.1 Dangling Modifiers

In Chapter 3, you learned to punctuate sentences that have *introductory phrases*. In this unit, you'll learn to make sure that the introductory phrase that you set off with a comma really describes what it's supposed to describe—the subject of the main clause or the action of the subject. If the introductory phrase modifies some other word in the sentence (or a word that doesn't even appear in the sentence), then the introductory phrase is called a *dangling modifier*. A sentence that has a dangling modifier is a weak, awkward, illogical-sounding sentence.

Here's an example:

1. **Employed as a weekend weatherman on an Indianapolis TV** station, hailstones as big as canned hams were once predicted by David Letterman.

The subject of the sentence is the word *hailstones*. Whatever introductory phrase is attached to the sentence before the subject must describe the subject or the action of the subject. But the modifier in sentence 1 obviously is supposed to describe

David Letterman, not hailstones or anything that hailstones could do. To see if an introductory phrase is well attached or if it's dangling, ask yourself a question like this: Can the word *hailstones* (your subject) be described as *employed as a weekend weatherman on an Indianapolis TV station* (your introductory phrase)? If it can, then you're okay. If it can't, then you have a dangling modifier.

Once you know you have a dangling modifier, there is usually more than one good way of revising it. Here are some possible correct rewrites for sentence 1:

(a) Employed as a weekend weatherman on an Indianapolis TV station, David Letterman once predicted hailstones as big as canned hams.

(b) David Letterman, who once worked as a weekend weatherman on an Indianapolis TV station, predicted hailstones as big as canned hams.

(c) Hailstones as big as canned hams were once predicted by an Indianapolis TV station's weekend weatherman, who was none other than David Letterman.

Exercise 4.1

Label each item *OK* or *DM* (dangling modifier). Underline the introductory modifier and label the subject *S* before you make your decision. Then rewrite the sentences that contain dangling modifiers; try to use a variety of sentence-combining techniques as you do your rewrites. Use your own paper, please. (The information here is found in *Life-spans, Or, How Long Things Last,* by Frank Kendig and Richard Hutton.)

1. _____ Refrigerated at the proper temperature, beer can be stored a maximum of three months; after that, it often has a buttery or papery taste.

2. _____ Wrapped individually in plastic or foil, hard candies and caramels can last anywhere from three to twelve months at room temperature.

3. _____ Cared for properly, the U.S. Army estimates that an M-1 rifle should last 10,000 rounds.

4. _____ Currently about four to five billion years old, scientists believe that the sun has a life span of 10 billion years.

5. _____ Performed upon average skin, plastic surgeons estimate that a successful face lift should last from six to 10 years.

Exercise 4.2

Label each item *OK* or *DM*. Underline introductory modifiers and label subjects. Rewrite problem sentences on your own paper. (These tidbits are from *Joan Embery's Collection of Amazing Animal Facts.*)

1. _____ Weighing up to 32 ounces, Southeast Asia is the home of the world's largest bat, whose wingspan has been measured at five feet, seven inches.

2. _____ Having no bark at all, the basenji dog of Africa makes the perfect hunting dog.

3. _____ Extremely long-lived, it is known that swans can survive up to one hundred years.

4. _____ Thought to be the heaviest insect in the world, the goliath beetle, which can weigh almost a quarter of a pound, has been observed peeling a banana while in captivity.

5. _____ Lacking the tiger's usual reddish orange coloring, some zoos have black and white Bengal tigers, all

of whom are descendants of a single white male tiger named Bohan, who was found in a jungle in India around the middle of this century.

4.2 Faulty Parallelism

If you've ever been told that your writing is sometimes awkward in spots, one problem might be *faulty parallelism.* Usually when you're writing about a series of things within one sentence, each item in the series should be in the same form as the other items. If the items are in the same form, you have parallelism in your writing. If they are not in the same form, you have faulty parallelism, and that's the problem we're going to work on in this unit.

When we talk about items being in the same form, we're talking about grammatical forms, such as nouns, verbs, adjectives, adverbs, prepositional phrases, and clauses. Here is an example of faulty parallelism in which it is easy to see that the writer is switching grammatical forms:

(a) In order to be classified as great, a baseball player must hit with power, a high lifetime batting average is necessary, to field well, be a fast runner, and throwing with strength and precision.

After you read (a) aloud, do the same with (b), which is a good example of parallelism:

(b) In order to be classified as great, a baseball player must hit with power, achieve a high lifetime batting average, field well, run fast, and throw with strength and precision.

Just by reading it aloud, you can tell that (b) has a nice sound, a flow, a repeated pattern that (a) lacks. By analyzing the structure of (b), you can see that the sentence has those good features because all the parts match in form and because all of them can be read with what we call a "setup." The setup in (b) is *a baseball player must.* Notice that each of the five items can be read fluently with *a baseball player must.* Read aloud each of the following items with this setup:

a baseball player must:

1. hit with power

2. achieve a high lifetime batting average

3. field well

4. run fast

5. throw with strength and precision

In other words, each item in the series (1 through 5) can be read individually with the setup, which in this case is *a baseball player must.* In sentence (b) the setup is the subject plus a helping verb, and the items all begin with base verbs *(hit, achieve, field, run, and throw).*

In your rewrite of sentence (a), what if you had repeated the word must five times? Then you'd have this: *In order to be classified as great, a baseball player must hit with power, must achieve a high lifetime batting average, must field well, must run fast, and must throw with strength and precision.* It sounds a little stiff and wordy, doesn't it? It shows one of the problems you might encounter in your rewrites. Your revisions of sentences that contain faulty parallelism should normally cut down on wordiness, not add to it. Therefore, you should use a word like *must* only once—in the setup—if you can, and that way you'll avoid awkward, pointless repetition. Use repetition only if you have a special reason for doing so; one valid reason is to give extra emphasis. But this will be the rare case, not the norm.

You should also realize, however, that sentence (b) is not the only possible revision of the faulty parallelism in sentence (a). Here is another, quite different rewrite that is also good:

(c) In order to be classified as great, baseball players have to be more than power hitters with a high lifetime batting average; they must also excel at running, fielding, and throwing.

Notice how sentence (c) has parallel structure by using the parallel verbs *running, fielding,* and *throwing.*

Important Notes on Creating Strong Parallelism

When you try to correct faulty parallelism and to create good parallelism, you'll sometimes find that there's no way you can construct one setup that will work with all your items. That's no problem. In that situation, just create two setups. For instance, you might have written a list of qualities that a person should have to become a good doctor, but mixed in it are a number of observations about characteristics that probably do not predict success in medical practice. What are you going to do? You might unravel your items and create one setup for the "dos," or the *assets,* as you might call them, and another setup for the "don'ts," or the *liabilities.*

Sometimes it's not a matter of creating two setups; rather it is a matter of removing one stubborn item and making it into a separate sentence. That is another good solution for faulty parallelism.

Exercise 4.3

In each of the following items, underline the part that is an example of faulty parallelism. Then rewrite that section, correcting the problem. (You don't have to rewrite the entire item, just the part that needs to be revised.) Try to use a good setup that you can read with all the parts that follow it. Read your revision aloud.

1. One key factor in the effort to revitalize our national system of education is the need to raise the minimum grade point average required for entrance into a college

or university teacher-training program. In addition, if the teachers of the future are to come from the best class of students, they will need higher salaries, the issue of greater professional status being important, and if they have more opportunities for advancement.

_____

_____

_____

2. Some transcontinental travelers have found ways of minimizing their great curse—jet lag. If you're flying from the United States to Europe, for instance, there is no way to avoid this phenomenon because traveling such a long distance in such a short time will inevitably disrupt the body's rhythms. But there are things you can do to adjust as quickly as possible. Seasoned travelers suggest that you take a daytime flight, should eat as little as possible on the plane, and napping as much as you can in the air. Then when you reach your destination, whatever you do, don't go to sleep until the sun sets.

_____

_____

_____

3. Many parents find it difficult to know if a child is ready to start kindergarten. According to Louise Bates Ames and Frances L. Ilg of the Gesell Institute of Child Development, it's not just a matter of chronological age. Not all five-year-olds are ready to benefit from being in an organized school setting. Ames and Ilg suggest that before the child begins, parents should make sure he or she already has certain skills. The child who is ready for kindergarten should be able to name at least three or four colors, drawing or copying a square should be a simple matter, repeat a series of four numbers without practicing them, the ability to tell the

right hand from the left, and if the child can identify what things such as cars, chairs, and shoes are made of. The authors suggest, by the way, that most little ones are not ready for kindergarten until they're five and a half.

_____

_____

_____

• •

4.3 Passive Sentences
• •

Like faulty parallelism, unnecessary passive sentences are a source of awkwardness in the writing of many students.

You know that the word _passive_ ordinarily means inactive. People are called passive if they wait for things to happen instead of making them happen. Passive sentences are somewhat similar. A passive sentence is not technically wrong like a run-on or a fragment, but it's relatively weak, flat, and dead. The subject of a passive sentence does not act; it is acted upon.

Here is an example:

1. (a) The position of poet laureate of the United States is currently held by Rita Dove.

Doesn't that sentence sound awkward? Why use the word _position_ as the subject? Wouldn't _Rita Dove_ be a more natural choice for a subject? After all, she is the one who is doing something. Here's an _active_ rewrite of the sentence:

1. (b) Rita Dove currently holds the position of poet laureate of the United States.

Here's another passive sentence:

2. (a) In some of Sir Arthur Conan Doyle's stories, the violin is occasionally played by Sherlock Holmes.

An active rewrite is this:

2. (b) Sherlock Holmes occasionally plays the violin in some of Sir Arthur Conan Doyle's stories.

Acceptable Passive Sentences

Sometimes passive sentences are all right. For instance, it's fine to use a passive sentence if you don't know who did a certain action. For example, it would be perfectly logical to write, "The music was written in the seventeenth century" if you didn't know who composed the piece. Passive sentences might also be written about an anonymous poem, a purse stolen by an unidentified person, and so forth.

Another valid reason for using a passive sentence is the writer's desire to place emphasis on a certain area. For example, look at these sentences, each of which is passive for a good reason:

(a) The pterodactyl, a flying dinosaur, was discovered by O.C. Marsh in 1871.

(b) The ancient city of Troy, which for centuries was thought to be purely mythical, was discovered by Heinrich Schliemann.

In each example, the writer might have thought that the thing discovered—in one case, the pterodactyl and in the other, the city of Troy—was of greater historical importance than the person who discovered it. That value judgment then would have led the writer to put the discovery rather than the discoverer in the subject position. Certainly, another writer, perhaps with a different emphasis in mind, could have made *O.C.*

Marsh and *Heinrich Schliemann* the subjects. The point is that it's all right to use a passive sentence if you have a valid reason for it.

Here is one more example of an acceptable passive sentence:

(c) The water in and around Minamata, Japan, had been completely contaminated, and many children from the area were born with severe birth defects as a result of the mercury their mothers had ingested.

The first clause—*The water in and around Minamata, Japan, had been completely contaminated*—is passive, but there may be a good reason for this construction. Perhaps the writer is not concerned at this point with the question of *who* contaminated the water, and wants instead to emphasize the simple fact that the water was contaminated.

Important Notes About Passive Sentences

Before you do the exercises in this unit, you need to realize that the "by so and so" phrase does not always appear in a passive sentence; sometimes it is only implied. Such a sentence might still be in need of a good rewrite.

Sometimes when you are changing a sentence from passive to active, you'll find other opportunities to make it crisper and less wordy.

And sometimes you'll find a sentence that is passive in more than one clause. Make sure you change each passive clause when you revise it.

Finally, you'll notice that all passive sentences are not alike. Read them aloud, and you'll hear that some sound horrible, whereas others barely need to be rewritten or, perhaps, in some cases don't need to be rewritten at all.

The important thing is to eliminate unnecessary passive sentences and to make your writing as active and lively as possible.

Exercise 4.4

Rewrite these passive sentences, making them active. Please use your own paper.

1. Approximately 200 pounds are gained per day by the baby calf of a blue whale.
2. An age of over 80 years has been reached by goldfish in captivity.
3. The practice of monogamy is observed by storks.
4. Its tail is used effectively as a whip by an iguana when it is threatened.
5. One-third of the total amount of canned fish in the United States is eaten by cats.

Exercise 4.5

Rewrite these passive sentences, making them active. Please use our own paper.

1. Their physical senses can be developed by human beings to a much higher degree than most people realize.
2. Enough examples from everyday life can be found by anyone to determine that this is true.
3. For example, the amount of alcohol or acid in a particular wine can be tasted by an experienced vintner to within one percent.
4. Differences between certain shades of red that are indistinguishable to the layperson can be seen by expert color technicians.
5. Just by its feel, the moisture content of bread dough can be measured by some professional bakers to within two percent of accuracy when the dough is being kneaded by them.

●●

4.4 Direct and Indirect Quotes

●●

There are many times, especially in college-level writing, when you work with the words of others. There are two basic ways that you can present what others have said: (1) You can quote a person *directly,* using his. or her exact words, or (2) you can quote *indirectly,* expressing the person's thoughts in your own words. An indirect quote is also called a paraphrase.

A direct quote is a presentation of the exact words that someone used. An indirect quote is a description of what was said.

Here is an example of a *direct quote:*

(a) In a review of Woody Allen's *Hannah and Her Sisters,* critic David Ansen said, "Anyone bemoaning the disappearance of adult matter from the movies need look no farther."

In (a), the writer is choosing to use the exact words that Ansen used in his review. To show that, the writer must enclose what Ansen said within a set of double quotation marks ("). Notice that the word *Anyone* is capitalized. The first word of a direct quote is usually capitalized. (We'll discuss an exception later.)

Below, the writer is choosing to quote Ansen *indirectly:*

(b) In a review of *Hannah and Her Sisters,* critic David Ansen said that anyone who's complaining that adult subject matter has disappeared from the movies doesn't have to look beyond this Woody Allen movie.

Sentence (b) contains an indirect quote, which is also called a paraphrase. In (b), the writer does not use Ansen's exact words but does communicate Ansen's point. When you quote someone indirectly, remember that you still must give the person credit. That's why Ansen's name is used in (b) just as it was in (a).

Punctuating Direct Quotes

In addition to using double quotation marks before and after a person's exact words, you also have to learn to use the correct punctuation to set off the attribution part of the sentence. This is the part that tells who said it; for instance, *he said* and *she remarked* are attributions. Often you use a comma to set off an attribution, sometimes you use a colon, and occasionally you use no punctuation at all.

1. Using a Comma

If the attribution is simply a subject and a verb or verb phrase, use a comma after it. Study these correct examples, in which only a subject and verb appear in each attribution.

She said, "_____."

He commented, "_____."

They insisted, "_____."

An s-v attribution can also appear at the end of the sentence; in other words, it may follow the direct quote. When the attribution is in this position, use a comma before it. Look at these correct examples:

"_____," said Barbara.

"_____," commented the captain.

"_____," they insisted.

When it's appropriate, an attribution can even interrupt a direct quote. For instance, a writer might choose to structure a sentence this way:

"Just once this week," James suggested, "let's try to get through an entire evening without turning on the television."

In such sentences, the attribution is set off with two commas. Make sure to enclose each part of the quote within a set of double quotation marks. Use a period and a capital letter only if each of the two sections is a full sentence. This is a correct example:

"He doesn't know what to do," my mother said. "He's completely confused."

2. Using a Colon

If the attribution contains a subject complement or a direct object, use a colon after it. Study these examples and label each with *s, v, sub com,* and *do.*

The waiter gave us some advice: "_____."

She said only three words: "_____."

The lawyer issued one warning: "_____."

3. Using No Punctuation

Occasionally, no punctuation is used directly before a direct quote. Here are two correct examples:

Jack Kroll, the well-known critic, called Henry Fonda, Gary Cooper, Spencer Tracy, and Jimmy Stewart a "celluloid Mount Rushmore of American icons."

A *Washington Post* reviewer once wrote that novelist Gloria Naylor's talent "glows like beaten copper."

Because of the way the quoted material is worked into the sentence, the first word of the direct quote is not capitalized, nor is the quote set off with a comma or colon.

One Last Note

Don't double your punctuation when the attribution comes after a direct quote. In other words, if a direct quote ends with a question mark or an exclamation point, omit the comma. These examples are correct:

"Who's watching the store?" she asked.

"Throw the ball!" they yelled.

Exercise 4.6

Make the necessary changes wherever you find direct quotes. Your changes may involve quotation marks, commas, colons, and capitalization. Some sentences might not contain direct quotes; those sentences should not be changed.

1. Zsa Zsa Gabor once said I'm a wonderful housekeeper. Every time I get a divorce, I keep the house.

2. In 1787, the United States minted a copper coin with a simple motto mind your business.

3. *The Outer Limits*, a science fiction TV series, always opened with the same line there is nothing wrong with your set.

4. Assassination is the extreme form of censorship claimed George Bernard Shaw, the famous playwright.

5. George Gallup, the nationally known pollster, once said that he could prove the existence of God statistically.

Chapter 5

Free Exercises in Sentence Combining

This is an important chapter for everyone, no matter what your strengths and weaknesses are. The exercises in Chapter 5 will help you reinforce the skills you've learned to this point and assist you in gaining greater flexibility and variety in your sentence structure.

The chapter contains a series of sentence-combining exercises to do on your own paper. In terms of sentence structure, sentence combining is a great finishing touch. You've learned a lot of dos and don'ts, and this is an excellent way of reviewing and exercising them. If you've had a hard time with run-ons or comma splices, for example, this chapter will give you another opportunity to work on correcting them. You'll also get more practice reworking sentences with fragments, dangling modifiers, and faulty parallelism. After all, these errors are nothing more than missteps in the process of sentence combining. And if you've had any difficulty making compound, complex, or embedded sentences, or remembering the rules for punctuating them correctly, the exercises in this chapter will help you. If you need more work on semicolons and colons, try to use them whenever you think they're appropriate.

Now let's examine how free sentence-combining exercises work. Please read the following series of sentences carefully.

Better Sentence-Writing

Agatha Christie disappeared in 1924.

She was a famous English mystery writer.

She was missing for 10 days.

Her disappearance made headlines in the British newspapers.

It made the front page.

If these five sentences appeared consecutively in a college student's paper, they would be judged to have a choppy, overly simple sound. On the other hand, if they appeared in the writing of a 10-year-old, they probably would be regarded quite favorably. Adult writers generally use short, unconnected sentences infrequently, and when they do, it's for a dramatic effect. Normally, adult writers are interested in showing relationships between facts, and that's why they automatically combine clauses most of the time. Here are some of the ways that the series of sentences can be combined:

(a) Agatha Christie, a famous English mystery writer, was missing for 10 days in 1924, and her disappearance made front-page headlines in the British newspapers.

(b) The 10-day disappearance of Agatha Christie, a famous English mystery writer, made front-page headlines in the British newspapers in 1924.

(c) When Agatha Christie dropped out of sight for 10 days in 1924, British newspapers featured the disappearance of the great English mystery writer in front-page headlines.

(d) In 1924, banner headlines in British newspapers announced the 10-day disappearance of the famous English mystery writer, Agatha Christie.

(e) Agatha Christie, an Englishwoman who was already famous for her "whodunits," became front-page news in the British press when she disappeared for 10 days in 1924.

Notice that the meaning of each sentence in the original series is preserved in every variation, (a) through (e). In sentence combining, the wording and the order of information can change, but the meaning stays basically the same.

Notes on the Exercises

Some students love sentence combining; others find it monotonous. For most people, the trick is to work on the exercises in chunks of not more than 20 or 30 minutes. If you try to do two or three hours' worth of sentence combining in one sitting, you're probably going to get very little out of the experience. If it starts to seem like busywork, take a break and come back fresh.

Once in a great while, you might find a group of sentences for which you can make only one satisfactory combination. However, for most groups, you'll be able to combine the sentences in a variety of ways. Make at least one combination for each group.

If a numbered "group" actually consists of only one sentence, it's a transitional sentence or a sentence that is short for some other intended effect. This kind of sentence should not be combined with anything else or rephrased.

Sometimes you'll see items that should be put into parallel form. The natural parallelism of some listed items has been altered in order to give you a little challenge here and there.

Exercise 5.1 Odd Moments in the World of Sports

This exercise consists of 10 short items (A-J) based on sports oddities described in *The Great American Sports Book* by George Gipe.

Better Sentence-Writing

A. 1. Two football teams were practicing before a game. The teams were from King's Island, Alaska.
They were getting ready for the 1938 New Year's Day Ice Bowl game.
   2. They had been practicing on an ice floe.
The ice floe was huge.
It was flat.
It was near their village.
   3. They went out to practice.
The date was December 18, 1937.
They couldn't find their practice field.
Gale-force winds had blown it away.
B. 1. The French Boxing Federation made a decision.
It made the decision in 1924.
   2. The federation issued an official ban.
It was a ban against fighters kissing each other.
Fighters had traditionally kissed each other at the end of each bout.
C. 1. How slow can you go and still win?
   2. The slowest time for a winning racehorse was set in 1945. It was set during a steeplechase.
   3. The horse was named Never Mind II.
Never Mind II refused a jump.
His jockey gave up.
He returned the horse to the paddock.
   4. When the jockey arrived at the paddock, he learned that all the other horses had met one of two fates.
Some of the horses had fallen.
The rest had been disqualified.
   5. So he jumped onto Never Mind II.
He rode him back onto the track.
   6. Never Mind II won the race.
The race was two miles.
His winning time was 11 minutes and 28 seconds.
The race is normally finished in four minutes.

D. 1. Here's another odd bit of trivia.
   It is from the world of horseracing.
   2. A jockey had just won the first race of his career.
   His name was Hayes.
   The date was June 4, 1923.
   After his victory, he immediately dropped dead.
E. 1. The first official baseball game played in the United States took place on June 19, 1846.
   It was between the "New York Nine" and the Knickerbockers.
   2. During the game, a New York player swore at the umpire.
   He started a baseball tradition by doing so.
   The tradition is long.
   The tradition is rich.
   3. The New York player was named Davis.
   He was fined for his outburst.
   The fine was six cents.
F. 1. Hockey is known for its violence.
   Most of it seems to be intentional.
   2. But one hockey game was marked by a very unusual incident.
   It was an incident of unintentional violence.
   It happened in 1930.
   The game was in Quebec.
   It was a junior amateur game.
   3. A puck was lined at the goalie.
   The goalie was Able Goldberry.
   The puck struck a pack of matches.
   The matches were in Goldberry's pocket.
   His uniform caught on fire.
   4. The fire was put out.
   It was put out by players and spectators.
   Abie Goldberry was badly burned in the bizarre incident.

G. 1. During a basketball game at St. Peter's High School, all of the players on one team, with one exception, fouled out. The game was between sophomores and seniors. The game was played on March 16, 1937. The high school was in Fairmount, Virginia. The exception was Pat McGee.

   2. When all the others fouled out, the game was tied.
The score was 32-32.
There were four minutes left to play.

   3. It didn't look good for McGee's team.

   4. But McGee faced the five players on the opposing team.
He scored a goal. He made a foul shot.
He defended his team's basket.
He prevented his opponents from scoring.

   5. McGee won the game for his team.
He did it single-handedly.
The final score was 35-32.

H. 1. In 1958, Robert F. Legge swam the Panama Canal.
Legge was a U.S. Navy doctor.
He was 53 years old.
The canal was 28.5 miles long.
His time was 21 hours and 54 minutes.

   2. During the swim, he encountered only two living creatures.
One was a boa constrictor.
The other was an iguana.

   3. At times, progress was difficult.
He had to contend with occasional swells.
The swells were a result of the heavy traffic of ships.

   4. When he arrived at Balboa, he was met by a greeting party. It consisted of several hundred well-wishers. It also included a toll collector.
The toll collector charged Legge 72 cents.
That was the minimum fee for a one-ton vessel in ballast.

I. 1. In 1890, a postseason baseball series was played.
It was a best-of-seven series.

It was between New York of the National League and St. Louis of the American Association.

2. New York had won three games.

St. Louis had won two.

Then the St. Louis Browns won their third game.

The series was all tied up. It was three games apiece.

3. After they evened up the series, the Browns stayed out all night.

They were celebrating.

The next day, they claimed to be "too tuckered out" to take the field.

As a consequence, the final game was canceled.

The best-of-seven series still stands as "tied 3-3" in the record books today.

J. 1. In 1865, Louis Fox was playing John Deery in Rochester, New York.

They were playing pool.

They were playing for a $1,000 purse.

2. Louis Fox was a billiard champion.

He was enjoying a very comfortable lead.

Suddenly, a fly landed on the cue ball.

3. The problem was how to get the fly to move without moving the cue ball.

4. Those who were present tried everything.

The fly would not budge.

It didn't matter what anyone did.

5. Fox was more than bugged by the presence of the fly.

He became completely rattled.

6. He miscued.

He lost the match with Deery.

He rushed out of the pool hall.

He was angry.

7. Several days later, his body was found.

It was floating in the river.

The river was near the pool hall.

Many people assumed that Fox committed suicide after his strange loss.

Exercise 5.2 Sweet Dreams

A. 1. Several years ago, the editors of *Psychology Today* asked their readers a question.
   They asked readers if they remembered their dreams.

2. More than 1,000 of the magazine's readers responded.
   Approximately 95 percent of the readers reported that they do remember at least some of their dreams.
   About 68 percent claimed to have a recurring dream.

3. Two different themes were represented most frequently in the recurring dreams.
   One was the experience of being chased.
   The other was the sensation of falling.

4. The readers reported other recurring themes.
   Those themes included flying.
   They included appearing naked or almost naked in a public place.
   Another one was being unprepared to take a test.
   One was the act of returning to the dreamer's childhood home.

5. About 45 percent of the readers said that they sometimes dream about celebrities.
   The celebrities that were noted most frequently were sex symbols and rock stars.

6. After sex symbols and rock stars, people most often reported dreaming about politicians and historical figures.
   One such historical figure was Abraham Lincoln.

7. Lincoln himself put a lot of stock in dreams.
   He believed that one dream had forewarned him of his own assassination.

8. Of those who responded to the *Psychology Today* survey, 28 percent had seen themselves die in a dream.

That sounds very ominous.

Most experts say a dream of one's own death should not be at all frightening.

B. 1. Ann Faraday is a psychologist.
     She is the author of *The Dream Game*.
     She says that a dream about one's death often indicates something far different from what you might expect.

   2. She says it usually symbolizes the death of a self-image. The self-image is obsolete.
      She says it signals an opportunity to move to a higher state of self-definition.

   3. The interpretation of dreams in general is a highly controversial area.

   4. There are those who follow Sigmund Freud.
      They believe that dreams are the key to the unconscious.

   5. Then there are those who follow the thinking of Francis Crick. He is a Nobel laureate.
      He believes that dreams are a garbage disposal for the mind.

   6. Their function is to clear out a certain type of information. That information is useless.
      It interferes with rational thought.
      It interferes with memory.
      This is what Crick believes.

   7. Then there is a third school of thought.
      It consists of psychologists who believe that dreams are not important in themselves.
      They believe that dreams become important because people think they are important.

   8. These psychologists believe that people give dreams meaning.
      People give them influence.
      They give them power.

Exercise 5.3 A Giant of a Man

A. 1. *The People's Almanac #3* includes a cautionary tale.
The almanac is the work of David Wallechinsky and Irving Wallace.
The tale is for anyone who has ever daydreamed about what it would be like to be a giant.

2. It is not a tall tale.
It is a true story.
It is the story of Robert Wadlow.
He was probably the tallest person who has ever lived.

3. Wadlow was born in Alton, Illinois.
He was born on February 22, 1918.
His weight at birth was nothing unusual.
He was eight-and-a-half pounds.

4. His family's medical history was normal.
There were no unusually tall members in his family.

5. But he grew rapidly.
He grew steadily.
This was true from birth.
It didn't stop until his death.

6. He was weighed at six months.
He was 30 pounds.
The average six-month-old baby weighs from 15 to 17 pounds.

7. He was weighed again at 18 months. His weight was 62 pounds.
The average toddler at that age weighs 24 or 25 pounds.

8. He underwent his first thorough examination at the age of 5. He was five feet, four inches tall. He weighed 105 pounds.

9. He started school when he was five and a half.
He was wearing clothes made for 17-year-olds.

10. He was measured again at the age of 8. He had reached a height of six feet. His father was Robert Wadlow, Sr. His father started wearing hand-me-downs. The hand-me-downs came from his son.

B. 1. When Robert Wadlow was 12, his rapid growth was finally diagnosed.
The diagnosis was excessive pituitary gland secretion.
After that, careful records of his growth were kept.
They were kept at Washington University.
Washington University is in St. Louis, Missouri.

2. He grew an average of three inches a year.
This rate of growth continued throughout his entire life.
At his death, his height was eight feet, eleven inches.
He died on July 15, 1940.

3. His early death was not surprising.

4. Pituitary giants usually die before middle age.
Their organs outgrow the ability to function correctly.

5. Physical coordination becomes difficult for a giant.
As a result, a giant usually has many more accidents than a normal-sized person has.

6. A giant's accidents also tend to result in more serious injuries.
This problem is compounded by the fact that a giant's body heals more slowly.

7. Wadlow in particular had more than his share of physical problems.
They began with an operation for a double hernia.
The operation took place when he was 2 years old.

8. Everything he encountered in this world was on the wrong scale.
School desks were too small.
Doorways were too low.
Beds were too short.
Chairs were too tiny.

9. He had terrible problems with his feet.

    10. Doctors advised Wadlow to walk as much as possible.
Walking was supposed to build up the strength in his feet.
It did not.
It damaged his arches even more severely.

    11. For a while, he attended Shurtleff College.
He wanted to become a lawyer.
He had to drop out.
The reason was that it was too difficult for him to walk from classroom to classroom.

C. 1. Robert Wadlow's life was marked by tragedy.
His life was not completely tragic.

    2. He was intelligent.
He was charming.
He had good parents.
They tried to make his life as normal as possible.
They tried to make it as full as possible.

    3. His boyhood days were filled with typical things.
They were filled with hobbies.
They were filled with sports.
He belonged to the Boy Scouts.
He loved to read.

    4. But his life was also filled with things that were not so typical.

    5. The more unusual aspects of Wadlow's story started when he was discovered by the media.
That discovery happened when he was 9 years old.

    6. It happened when the Associated Press came across a photograph.
The Associated Press circulated it in newspapers all across the nation.

    7. That's when Robert Wadlow became a public person.

    8. From that time on, he had to deal with a steady stream of people.
Some were reporters.

Some were medical researchers.
Some were curiosity seekers.
Some were entrepreneurs.

9. Theatrical agents pressured him to perform.
They made very attractive offers.
They wanted his services.

10. His parents rejected all opportunities to make money from his misfortune.

11. He did, however, make appearances for the Peters Shoe Company.
They were paid appearances.
The Peters Shoe Company was in St. Louis.

12. This endorsement arrangement was appropriate.
Wadlow had to have specially made shoes.
He often outgrew new shoes even before they were delivered.

13. Robert Wadlow also worked for the Ringling Brothers Circus.
He worked for Ringling Brothers in New York and Boston.
He did so for a short time.
This was in 1937.
There were strict conditions in his contract with the circus.

14. These were the conditions of the contract.
He would make only three-minute appearances.
He would make them in the center ring.
He would not make them in the sideshow.
He would wear ordinary street clothes for these appearances.

15. Wadlow occasionally made appearances for churches.
He also helped to raise funds for charities.
He accepted no pay for these activities.

D. 1. In 1936, Robert Wadlow had a visit from a doctor.
He was a doctor from a small town in Missouri.

The doctor was interested in studying giantism.

2. He happened to catch Wadlow on a bad day.
Bad days were relatively rare for Wadlow.

3. The doctor later wrote an article about Wadlow.
The article was published in the *Journal of the American Medical Association*.
The article described Wadlow as dull.
It described him as surly.

4. According to information cited in *The People's Almanac #3*, this characterization is generally true of most pathological giants.
It was not true of Robert Wadlow.
He was truly an exceptional human being.

5. The unflattering description in the medical journal hurt Wadlow deeply.
It disillusioned him.
It did so for two reasons.

6. For one thing, all his life he had put up with medical researchers.
The medical researchers had invaded his privacy.
They had taken up his time.
He always had done so voluntarily.
He usually had done so graciously.

7. For another thing, the article was based on the doctor's impressions.
Those impressions were made very quickly.
The doctor's only visit with Wadlow had lasted less than an hour.

8. Wadlow wanted his character vindicated.
His family did, too.
They took legal action against the doctor.
They also took legal action against the American Medical Association (AMA).

9. The AMA strongly defended the doctor.
The litigation dragged on and on.

The matter was not resolved when Wadlow died.
He died at the age of 22.

10. Robert Wadlow stipulated that after his death he wanted his body to be kept out of the hands of medical researchers.
His stipulation was partly the result of this episode.

11. In accordance with his wishes, there was no examination of his body after his death.

12. He was buried in a custom-built casket.
The casket was 10 feet long.
The casket was placed inside a tomb.
The tomb was almost impregnable.
The tomb was in his hometown.

13. More than 46,000 people came to the funeral home in Alton, Illinois.
They paid their last respects to Robert Wadlow.

Exercise 5.4 *Control and Well-being*

A. 1. Judith Rodin is a psychology professor.
She teaches at Yale University.
She has been involved in important studies on a number of topics.
One topic is bystander intervention.
One is learned helplessness.
One is obesity.
One is aging.

2. She is interested in relationships.
One that especially interests her is the relationship between the mind and the body.
Another one is the relationship between biology and environment.

3. Older people, in particular, have benefitted from Rodin's research.

4. In fact, it's been said that it's not easy for her to find places in Connecticut where she can continue to study the problems of older people in nursing homes.

   This is because so many positive changes already have been made in the state's nursing homes as a result of her work.

5. Rodin conducted a study on perceived choice among residents of nursing homes.

   She did this at one point in her career.

   She did this with psychologist Ellen Langer. The study was fascinating.

   It was described in an issue of *Psychology Today*.

6. Perceived choice is the amount of control that a person believes he or she has over events.

7. Rodin already knew that the degree to which people feel they can exert control in important areas of their lives influences three things.

   It influences their happiness.

   It influences their ability to perform.

   It influences their sense of well-being.

   She knew this on the basis of laboratory studies.

B. 1. Judith Rodin and Ellen Langer wanted to investigate perceived choice or control in a real-life setting.

   The real-life setting they chose was a nursing home.

2. They were especially interested in one relationship.

   It was the relationship between the degree of control that the nursing home residents thought they had and the residents' health and happiness.

3. Rodin and Langer believed that a nursing home might be a place where the effects of increased control could show up dramatically.

   Improvements in well-being could be quite obvious.

   They would show up in people who were already sick or frail.

4. It would be more difficult to show the positive benefits of an increased sense of control in people who were younger and healthier.
   In those people, any benefits would more likely be in the form of prevention rather than improvement.
5. The results of the study were indeed dramatic.
6. Nursing home residents in the study were given new choices. These were in areas in which they previously had no choice.
   Many of the new choices seemed quite trivial.
7. For example, residents were allowed to choose when they could see a movie.
   They were allowed to arrange their rooms as they wished.

C. 1. The choices may have been trivial.
   The results were not.
2. The researchers used a variety of methods to measure the effects of the residents' new sense of control.
   The researchers discovered that the residents' new sense of control had a number of effects.
   One effect was an improvement in their health.
   One effect was an improvement in their overall mental state.
   One effect was a drop in the death rate at the nursing home.
3. Why would having new choices in trivial areas of life produce such profound effects?
4. Rodin explains that the choices seem trivial only to people who have a broad range of choices in their lives.
   To those who have little or no choice, any choice at all has great impact.
5. A sense of control or perceived choice created a profound psychological state.
   It is a state in which the residents felt better about themselves.
6. They felt a sense of power.

That sense of power caused them to respond more positively to family members.

It caused them to respond more positively to other residents.

It caused them to respond more positively to nurses and doctors.

In turn, everyone in their lives responded more positively toward them.

7. Choosing when to see a movie or where to put a picture on a wall might seem trivial.

But Rodin says that small bit of control can have an energizing effect. It can have that effect on every aspect of an older person's life.

Exercise 5.5 Mabel K. Staupers and Black Nurses in the Military

A. 1. Mabel Keaton Staupers was one of the outstanding women of the twentieth century.

She was a black woman.

She was fast-talking.

She was energetic.

2. She broke a link in a chain.

She did it almost single-handedly.

It was a chain that had kept many black women from using their talents and skills.

It was a chain that had denied them their full rights as American citizens.

3. Her story is fascinating.

It is inspiring.

It is a classic David and Goliath tale.

It is told in *Black Leaders of the Twentieth Century*.

4. It is the story of a battle between one woman and two branches of the American military.

The woman was the executive secretary of the National Association of Colored Graduate Nurses (NACGN).

The branches of the military were the U.S. Army and the Navy.

5. Mabel K. Staupers's accomplishment must be viewed within the context of a certain period in American history if it is to be fully appreciated.

6. It was around the time that the United States entered into World War II.

   American blacks recently had become much less accepting of the racial status quo.

   There were many reasons for this.

   One was the anti-Nazi mood of the nation.

7. For many blacks, their unequal treatment in their own country was highlighted in an ironic way by America's opposition to Nazi Germany.

8. In opposing the philosophy and actions of Germany's Nazis, the U.S. government did a lot of talking.

   So did many members of the press.

   So did much of the general public.

   They all talked a lot about the ideals upon which America had been founded.

9. They contrasted Germany to an America that was pure in the realization of its democratic ideals.

   They spoke of an America that was just in its treatment of people of different backgrounds.

   The differences might be in religion, ethnicity, or race.

10. Such statements about this country struck some Americans as hypocritical.

    They struck some Americans as ironic.

    Some of those Americans were black.

    Some were white.

11. One person summed this up the situation well.

    He was Walter White.

    He wrote, "World War II has immeasurably magnified the Negro's awareness of the disparity between the American profession and practice of democracy."

B. 1. It was during this time and in this context that Mabel K. Staupers began her long fight.

Her fight was for the rights of black nurses.

She used patience.

She used persistence.

She used a great deal of political savvy.

2. Staupers was born in Barbados, West Indies.

She was born in 1890.

She came to New York with her parents.

They came to New York in 1903.

3. She graduated from Freedmen's Hospital School of Nursing.

It was in Washington, D.C.

She graduated in 1917.

Then she began her career.

Her first position was as a private nurse in New York City.

4. She played an important role in establishing the Booker T. Washington Sanatorium.

The Booker T. Washington Sanatorium was in Harlem.

It was the first facility in the area where black doctors could treat patients.

5. Then she worked as the executive secretary for the Harlem Committee of the New York Tuberculosis and Health Association.

She did that for 12 years.

6. Finally, Staupers was appointed executive secretary of the NACGN.

That was in 1934.

In her new position, she focused on one main goal.

That goal was to help black nurses become fully integrated into the mainstream of American health care.

7. Then the United States entered World War II.

It was 1941.

8. Mabel K. Staupers had a perfect opportunity to realize her goal.

The war created a great demand for nurses to care for the wounded.

9. That demand could result in the acceptance of black nurses into the Army and Navy Nurse Corps.

That acceptance could be a vehicle.

It could be a vehicle for the full inclusion of blacks into the profession of nursing in America.

C. 1. Staupers knew that black nurses had suffered great discrimination in World War I.

She vowed that would not happen again if she could help it.

2. So Staupers fought her own battle.

She fought it throughout the years of the American war effort.

She fought it on various fronts.

3. First, she fought the exclusion of black women from the Army and Navy Nurse Corps.

4. Then the Army established a quota system for black nurses.

She fought the quota system.

She fought it because it implied that black nurses were inferior to other nurses.

5. At one point, she fought another policy of the military.

It was the policy of having black nurses care for black soldiers and no others.

6. Later, she discovered the Army was finally assigning black nurses to care for white soldiers.

But those white soldiers included no Americans.

The white soldiers were German prisoners of war.

She fought that practice, too.

D. 1. These were tough battles.

Staupers eventually found a powerful ally.

That ally was First Lady Eleanor Roosevelt.

2. Eleanor Roosevelt began lobbying for black nurses.

3. She talked to Norman T. Kirk.

He was the surgeon general of the U.S. Army.

She talked to W.J.C. Agnew.

He was a rear admiral in the U.S. Navy.

Most of all, she talked to her husband.

Her husband was Franklin D. Roosevelt.

4. Meanwhile, Staupers staged a public confrontation with Norman T. Kirk.

   It was a confrontation that received a good deal of coverage in the press.

5. Kirk described the dire shortage of nurses in the Army.

   He predicted that a draft for nurses might be necessary.

   He made his prediction in a speech at the Hotel Pierre.

   The Hotel Pierre is in New York.

6. Staupers was in Kirk's audience.

   The audience was made up of about 300 people.

   The audience included nurses.

   It included politicians.

   It included private citizens.

7. She rose to her feet.

   She asked the surgeon general, "If nurses are needed so desperately, why isn't the Army using colored nurses?"

8. She explained to the entire audience that there were 9,000 registered black nurses in the United States.

   The Army had taken 247.

   The Navy had taken none.

9. Kirk was visibly uncomfortable, according to newspaper reports.

   He did not have much of an answer for Staupers.

E. 1. At about the same time, President Roosevelt announced his desire to amend the Selective Service Act of 1940.

   He wanted it amended so that nurses could be drafted.

   He made his desire known in a radio address.

   The address was broadcast on January 6, 1945.

2. The public reaction was tremendous.

   The irony of calling for a general draft while at the same time discriminating against black nurses was obvious to almost everyone.

3. Staupers showed a lot of political savvy in the way she handled the public's dissatisfaction with the plans of the top brass.
4. She gave speeches.
   She issued press releases.
   She urged people to send telegrams to President Roosevelt.
5. The groups that sent messages of protest to the White House included the National Association for the Advancement of Colored People (NAACP).
   They included the Congress of Industrial Organizations.
   They included the American Federation of Labor.
   They included the United Council of Church Women.
   They included the Catholic Interracial Council.
   They included the Alpha Kappa Alpha Sorority.
   They included the New York Citizens' Committee of the Upper West Side.
6. The great wave of public protest had an effect.
   The policies of exclusion, segregation, and quota systems for black nurses were ended.
   They were dropped by the Army.
   They were dropped by the Navy.
   They were dropped by the War Department.
7. A few weeks later, a black woman was the first to break the color barrier in the U.S. Navy Nurse Corps.
   She was Phyllis Dailey.
8. The Army also began to accept black nurses with no restrictions.
9. Most of the credit goes to one woman.
   It goes to one woman alone.
   It goes to Mabel K. Staupers.

Chapter **6**
Revising at the Word Level

●●●

6.1 Subject-Verb Agreement
●●●

We all follow a system of subject-verb agreement, even if we can't define what subject-verb agreement is. If you listen to your speech and the speech of your family and friends, you'll find that most people follow a fairly consistent pattern. For instance, you probably say *she smiles* and *he laughs*. In other words, you have your own unconscious rules about adding *-s* or *-es* on a verb when it's in the present tense. But if your system differs from the one that is considered standard, you may want to make an adjustment in your writing.

The Standard Rules

Basically, subject-verb agreement is a problem only in the present tense. Here are the standard rules:

1. If the Subject Is Singular, Add -S or -Es to Your Verb

For example:

        s   v

(a) One teenage *suicide occurs* every 90 minutes in the United States.

127

The subject *suicide* is singular (one), so we added an *-s* to the verb *occur* and produced *occurs*. Now we'll make the subject plural (more than one) and see how the verb changes to agree with it:

s   v
(b) Teenage *suicides occur* at the rate of one every ninety minutes in the United States.

The rule shown in (b) is this:

2. If the Subject Is Plural, Use the Base Verb

The word *suicides* is plural, so we used the base verb occur to agree with it. By *base verb* we mean a verb with no ending B no *-s* or *-es,* no *-d* or *-ed,* no *-ing* or any other ending.

Label the subject in each example below and fill in the standard form of the verb, choosing from *live* and *lives:*

1. The pint-sized sand cat _____ on the extremely hot sand dunes of African, Asian, and Arabian deserts.

2. Pint-sized sand cats _____ on the extremely hot sand dunes of African, Asian, and Arabian deserts.

If you used an -s in sentence 1 and the base verb in sentence 2, you're on the right track.

Study these correct examples and read them aloud several times before you do the first exercise:

(a) a steak sizzles	(d) the roof leaks	(f) a balloon pops
steaks sizzle	roofs often leak	balloons pop
(b) the horse prances	(e) the girl stretches	(g) the group decides
horses prance	the girls stretch	the groups decide
(c) one light flickers		
five lights flicker		

Exercise 6.1

Fill in each blank with the form of verb at right that agrees with the subject. Use the base verb or add *-s* or *-es*. For example:

    the plan   succeeds   (succeed)
    the plans   succeed

1. a carpenter _____ (build)
   carpenters _____

2. one star _____ (shine)
   all the stars _____

3. the golfer _____ (putt)
   golfers _____

4. roses _____ (grow)
   a rose _____

5. the chimneys _____ (smoke)
   the chimney _____

6. a pitcher _____ (pitch)
   pitchers _____

7. one loaf _____ (rise)
   the loaves _____

8. bombs _____ (explode)
   a bomb _____

9. the popside _____ (melt)
   popsicles _____

10. last-minute shoppers _____ (rush)
    a last-minute shopper _____

A Note on Spelling

In the next exercise, you'll notice that sometimes a small spelling change is necessary before you add an *-s* or *-es* to a

Better Sentence-Writing

base verb. For example, with a word that ends in -*y*, such as *fry,* you change the *y* to *i* before you add -*es*. So *fry* becomes *fries.*

Exercise 6.2

Fill in each blank with the form of verb at right that agrees with the subject. Use the base verb or add -*s* or -*es*. Make other spelling changes where necessary.

1. the article _____ (explain)
   the articles _____

2. one baby _____ (cry)
   all the babies _____

3. one player _____ (win)
   four players _____

4. the team _____ (perform)
   the teams _____

5. the ink spots _____ (dry)
   an ink spot _____

6. the soldiers _____ (march)
   a soldier _____

7. the telephone _____ (ring)
   telephones _____

8. ideas _____ (form)
   an idea _____

9. chickens _____ (hatch)
   a chicken _____

10. a peacemaker _____ (pacify)
    peacemakers _____

Two Important Exceptions

There are two important exceptions to the standard rules described here. One involves the word *I*, and the other involves the word *you*. When *I* and *you* are used as subjects, they always appear with the base verb. These are correct examples: *I want, I sing,* and *I give; you want, you sing,* and *you give.* Even though *I* is singular and *you* can be singular or plural in its meaning, each pronoun—*I* and *you*—agrees with a base verb.

The Verbs *To Be* and *To Have*

Here's an easy way to approach subject-verb agreement when the verb is a form of *to be* or *to have.* Just as with regular verbs, the correct form to match a singular subject will end in *-s.* The correct form to match a plural subject will not end in *-s.* Study these correct examples:

Singular Subject	Plural Subject
The dessert *is* delicious.	The desserts *are* delicious.
The dessert *was* delicious.	The desserts *were* delicious.
The dessert *has* pizzazz.	The desserts *have* pizzazz.

Notice that all the words that agree with the singular subject *dessert* end in *-s: is, was,* and *has.* Also notice that the verbs that agree with the plural subject *desserts* do not end in *-s.* They are *are, were,* and *have.*

Exercise 6.3

Fill in each blank with the verb that agrees with the subject. Remember: A singular subject agrees with a verb that ends in *-s*—with the exceptions of *I* and *you,* which are treated as plural subjects.

1. A Steven Spielberg movie _____ *(has / have)* certain characteristics.

Steven Spielberg movies _____ *(has/have)* certain characteristics.

2. Her attitude _____ *(is/are)* wonderful.
Their attitudes _____ *(is/are)* wonderful.

3. The mail carriers _____ *(was/were)* late.
The mail carrier _____ *(was/were)* late.

4. Soft pretzels _____ *(is/are)* one of life's little necessities.
A soft pretzel _____ *(is/are)* one of life's little necessities.

5. One fingernail _____ *(was/were)* polished with jade green lacquer.
Her fingernails _____ *(was/were)* polished with jade green lacquer.

Three Important Points

There are three important points about subject-verb agreement that everyone should know. We'll look at each one before you begin the more difficult exercises.

1. Using *And and* Or *between Key Words in the Subject*

You probably already know that two singular words joined with and form a plural subject. But you should also know that two singular words joined with or form a singular subject. Study these correct examples:

(a) A magazine <u>subscription</u> **and** a book club <u>membership</u> <u>make</u> good gifts for the person who has everything.

(b) A magazine <u>subscription</u> **or** a book club <u>membership</u> <u>makes</u> a good gift for the person who has everything.

2. Using Prepositional Phrases in the Subject

Remember when you worked with prepositional phrases in Chapter 1? The key word in the subject is never within a prepositional phrase, and the key word in the subject is, of course, the word with which the verb must agree. So you have to be careful to set off any prepositional phrases that appear within the complete subject of a sentence.

Study these correct examples:

         s   v

(a) Rock and roll <u>festivals</u> <u>are</u> a common feature of summertime entertainment.

    s   v

(b) Any <u>history</u> (of rock and roll festivals) <u>is</u> sure to begin with the concert at Woodstock.

In (a), the word *festivals* is the key word in the subject, and because it is plural, it agrees with *are*. But in (b), the word *festivals* is not the key word in thesubject. Why not? It's not the key word because it's in a prepositional phrase—*of rock and roll festivals.* (The preposition is *of.*) A prepositional phrase modifies the subject, but it never contains the subject.

In (b), the key word in the subject is *history,* and because *history* is a singular word, it agrees with the verb *is.*

3. Using Delayed Subjects

There are two kinds of sentences that have delayed subjects. A subject is called "delayed" when it follows the verb.

One kind of sentence with a delayed subject begins with the word *there* or *here.* If a sentence begins with either word, you have to look beyond the verb to find the real subject—the word with which the verb must agree. Study these correct examples:

           v   s

1. (a) There <u>was</u> one bad <u>joke</u> in the middle of the script.

133

       v   s

(b) There were several bad jokes in the middle of the script.

          v   s

2. (a) Here is the best play of the day.

          v   s

(b) Here are the two best plays of the day.

Think of the words *there* and *here* as empty sentence starters. They're not the subjects in any of the preceding four sentences. They're sort of placeholders that indicate where the subject word would normally be.

The other kind of sentence with a delayed subject is a question. In the following sentences, the question word acts in the same way as *there* or *here*. Study these correct examples:

         v   s

3. (a) What is your plan?

         v   s

(b) What are your plans?

         v   s

4. (a) Where was his new shirt?

         v   s

(b) Where were his new shirts?

Important Note on the Exercises

The next two exercises involve all the points covered in this unit. If you need to review, please do so before you proceed.

In the exercises, when the directions ask you to label the subject, please understand that you're really being asked to mark the *key word or words* within the complete subject.

Exercise 6.4

Write *s* over the subject of each clause. Then fill in the blank with the form of the verb that agrees with the subject.

1. According to the latest records kept by the U.S. Agriculture Department, 1,431 pounds of food _____ *(are / is)* consumed by the average American in one year. Twenty years ago, the average intake of food per person _____ *(was / were)* 1,381 pounds. Forecasters in the department's Economic Research Service *(say / says)* that increases in the consumption of chicken, fish, vegetables, and vegetable oil _____ *(are / is)* expected. Meat and fruit _____ *(appear / appears)* to be on the decline.

2. The correct term for American buffaloes _____ *(are / is)* American bison.

3. Only the true fan among fans _____ *(care / cares)* enough about sports trivia to know that the real names of "the Georgia Peach" and "the Galloping Ghost" _____ *(was / were)* Ty Cobb and Red Grange.

4. According to chiropractors, poor posture habits in a child usually _____ *(begin / begins)* around age eight.

5. *Final Payments* and *The Company of Women* _____ *(are / is)* excellent novels by Mary Gordon. *Men and Angels* _____ *(are / is)* another of her books.

135

Exercise 6.5

Write *s* over the subject of each clause. Then fill in the blank with the verb that agrees with the subject. This collection of strange facts *(are / is)* based on information in *Life-spans, Or, How Long Things Last*.

1. One of every seven pennies in circulation eventually _____ *(end / ends)* up out of circulation. This _____ *(happen / happens)* because the penny's owner _____ *(plunk / plunks)* it into a piggy bank or _____ *(force / forces)* it into early retirement in the bottom of a dresser drawer or in an inner compartment of an old purse. One of every 14 nickels _____*(share / shares)* a similar fate.

2. Most nuts _____ *(stay / stays)* fresh for one year if they _____ *(remain / remains)* in the shell. However, pecans and Brazil nuts_____ *(keep / keeps)* for only six months unless you _____ *(store / stores)* them in the refrigerator.

3. Moonbeams, which _____ *(are / is)* rays of light from the sun reflected off the moon, _____ *(take / takes)* 1.3 seconds to travel from the moon to the earth.

4. The life span of a deck of cards _____ *(depend / depends)* upon a number of factors. The moisture in the hands of the card players_____ *(are / is)* one important factor because the moisture and oil in human skin definitely _____ *(affect / affects)* the cards' longevity. The condition of any and all playing surfaces on which the cards (are/is) used _____ *(are / is)* also significant. For some people a deck of cards _____ *(last / lasts)* a lifetime. For professional gamblers, the average pack _____ *(has / have)* outgrown its usefulness

after two to five hours of playing time. After that, the cards usually _____ *(show / shows)* enough wear and tear that they _____ *(slow / slows)* down the dealer if they _____ *(are / is)* not replaced with a fresh pack.

5. A series of elastic waves, most often caused by the earth's rupture along a fault, _____ *(are / is)* better known as an earthquake. The length of most earthquakes _____ *(are / is)* not more than a few seconds, but major earthquakes, such as the one in Lisbon, Portugal, in 1975, _____ *(has / have)* been clocked at over five minutes. Certainly one of the most devastating earthquakes in recent times _____ *(was / were)* the one to hit Mexico City in September 1985.

•••

6.2 *-Ed* Endings
•••

The purpose of this unit is to help students who sometimes drop the *-d* or *-ed* endings on regular verbs and the adjectives made from them.

First you need to be able to distinguish between *regular* and *irregular* verbs. If a verb is regular, its past tense and past participle are formed by adding *-d* or *-ed* to the base verb. For example:

Base Verb	Past Tense	Past Participle
ask	asked	have asked

If a verb is irregular (in other words, not regular), it does not follow this nice, easy pattern of adding *-d* or *-ed*. For example, *give* is an irregular verb. Here are its three main forms:

Base Verb	Past Tense	Past Participle
give	gave	have given

You're already familiar with base verbs and past tenses, but the term *past participle* might be new to you. What does it mean? The *past participle* is the form of a verb that is used with helping verbs such as *have, has,* or a form of the verb *to be* when it is used to make the passive voice. (See Chapter 4 if you need to review the definition of *passive voice*). These examples show how the presence of a helping verb signals the need for a *-d* to be added to the regular verb purchase:

(a) *I have purchased* the suit.

(b) She *has purchased* the apartment building.

(c) He *had purchased* the license only thirty minutes before the wedding.

(d) The tainted medicine *was purchased* in a drug store two miles from the victim's home.

(e) Fourteen square acres in the middle of the city *were purchased* by an international corporation.

The Three Trouble Spots

When writers drop *-d* and *-ed* endings, they drop them on *past tense verbs, past participles,* and *adjectives that are derived from verbs.* Of these three trouble spots, the first—past tense—is the easiest to catch. The other two are more challenging. Study these correct examples:

(a) Yesterday the doctor *prescribed* a basic blood pressure medicine for Carl. (past tense)

(b) Another specialist *has prescribed* treatment for him on several occasions. (past participle)

(c) The *prescribed* pills were very effective. (adjective derived from a verb)

You can probably see why most students would have the least difficulty with (a). The word *Yesterday* is a context clue for the past tense, and that helps the writer remember to add the *-d* to *prescribe*.

In (b) and (c), there are no obvious context clues for the past tense, but there are other clues for the student who's wondering whether to use a *-d*. The clue in (b) is the helping verb *has*. And sometimes, as you'll see in the exercises, a sentence contains more than one helping verb. For example, you'll see sentences with longer verb phrases, such as this one:

A third doctor *might have prescribed* something else.

In (c) the clue is the noun *pills*. Someone did the act of prescribing the pills, and now they can be described as *prescribed*. Adjectives that are made from regular verbs end in *-d* or *-ed*.

In this set of three examples, add *-d* where it belongs and, each time, make a note of why you added it:

1. Sharon had change tremendously since high school.

2. After the birth of his first child, Gregory was a change man.

3. We change our phone number after a few crank calls.

1. verb phrase; 2. adjective; 3. past tense

Two Notes on Spelling

There are two spelling rules that you need to remember.

1. With a verb that ends in *y,* you usually change the *y* to *i* before you add *-ed*. For example: fry → fried; satisfy → satisfied

2. With a verb that ends in a consonant preceded by a short vowel, you usually double the consonant before you add *-ed*. For example: trip → tripped; wrap → wrapped

Better Sentence-Writing

Some Common Errors

There are a few common errors that many students make. They involve *used to, supposed to, old-fashioned,* and *prejudiced.* Add *-d* or *-ed* where they are needed in these sentences:

1. I use to be afraid of the dark.

2. Jane is really an old-fashion girl.

3. We are suppose to be home by midnight.

4. That was a prejudice remark if I ever heard one.

5. Do you suppose we can get some ice cream?

6. Prejudice is the act of prejudging.

7. The thing that use to drive me crazy was his gum chewing.

8. They were suppose to preregister to vote.

9. I do not believe that this is a prejudice community.

1. used; 2. old-fashioned; 3. supposed; 4. prejudiced; 5. no change; 6. no change; 7. used; 8. supposed; 9. prejudiced.

Exercise 6.6

Add *-d* or *-ed* endings where they are needed. Underline the word that you change and in the blank provided label your reason for the change. Use the labels *past* for past tense verb, *vp* for verb phrase, and *adj* for an adjective derived from a verb.

1. Charlotte Corday murder Jean Paul Marat, a famous eighteenth-century French revolutionary, while he was taking a bath. _____

2. Shredded wheat, the world's first ready-to-eat dry cereal, was introduce in 1893. _____

3. In 1956, a trailer truck that was hauling four hundred crates of eggs slammed into the Rhyne Bridge in Charlotte, North Carolina. The bill for the damage truck and bridge came to six thousand dollars. But guess what? Not one egg was broken. _____

4. *The Fire Next Time* by James Baldwin is a distinguish collection of essays on the hearts and minds of African-Americans. _____

5. In his paintings, Monet capture the colors of the water lilies and other flowers in his famous ponds and gardens at Giverny, France. _____

6. The much admire *Huckleberry Finn* by Mark Twain is often called the greatest novel of American boyhood. _____

7. The first zoo in the history of the world was establish in Egypt around 1500 B.C. _____

8. According to a recent study of hundreds of couples, morning sickness and other pregnancy-related symptoms are experience by one in ten expectant fathers.

9. Yes, the last word in sentence 8 is suppose to be *fathers,* not *mothers.* _____

10. The same study show that one in ten new fathers also suffered from postpartum blues. _____

The Irregular Verbs

The irregular verbs are not as easy to form as those that end in *-d* or *-ed.* To learn these, you have to memorize them. Here is a list of the most frequently used irregular verbs. Underline the verb forms that sound unfamiliar to you; then practice them in your writing as often as you can. We're using *have* as the helping verb here, but you know that other helping verbs are used as well.

Better Sentence-Writing

Present	Past	Past Participle
become	became	have become
begin	began	have begun
break	broke	have broken
bring	brought	have brought
buy	bought	have bought
build	built	have built
choose	chose	have chosen
come	came	have come
do	did	have done
drive	drove	have driven
eat	ate	have eaten
fall	fell	have fallen
feel	felt	have felt
fight	fought	have fought
find	found	have found
forget	forgot	have forgotten
forgive	forgave	have forgiven
get	got	have gotten
give	gave	have given
go	went	have gone
grow	grew	have grown
keep	kept	have kept
know	knew	have known
lead	led	have led
leave	left	have left
lose	lost	have lost
make	made	have made
meet	met	have met
pay	paid	have paid

Present	Past	Past Participle
read	read	have read
ride	rode	have ridden
rise	rose	have risen
run	ran	have run
say	said	have said
see	saw	have seen
sell	sold	have sold
sing	sang	have sung
sleep	slept	have slept
speak	spoke	have spoken
spend	spent	have spent
stand	stood	have stood
take	took	have taken
teach	taught	have taught
tell	told	have told
think	thought	have thought
throw	threw	have thrown
wear	wore	have worn
win	won	have won
write	wrote	have written

6.3 Consistency of Verb Tense

What's wrong with this sentence?

I was driving to work, and my car runs out of gas.

The problem is that the writer started the sentence in the past tense (with *was driving*) and ended it in the present tense (with *runs*). If there is a logical reason for switching into another verb tense, it's fine to do so. But what logical reason could this writer have? The sentence has two possible corrections:

Past tense: I <u>was driving</u> to work, and my car <u>ran</u> out of gas.

Present tense: I <u>am driving</u> to work, and my car <u>runs</u> out of gas.

Correct illogical changes in verb tense in these examples:

1. Archduke Franz Ferdinand of Austria was killed in Sarajevo in June 1914, and his assassination sets off World War I.
2. Marcus Garvey, who was the most influential black leader in the United States in the 1920s, advocates black separatism and leads a "back to Africa" movement.
3. Mars is the fourth planet in order of distance from the sun, and to the naked eye, it appeared to have a reddish tint.

In 1, *sets off* should be *set off*; in 2, *advocates should be* advocated, and *leads* should be *led;* and in 3, *appeared* should be *appears*.

Logical Changes in Verb Tense

What's a good reason for switching verb tenses? Maybe you want to write about something that used to be true and no longer is. For example, you might write, "When I *was* a child, I *wanted* to watch cartoons bright and early every Saturday morning, but now, I *like* to sleep until noon." The first clause describes something that was true in the past, so it's natural to use the past tense; the second clause describes something that is true in the present, so it's natural to use the present tense. This is not an example of illogical tense switching. The sentence would lack logic if the writer *didn't* switch tenses.

But switching verb tenses without a good reason causes a lot of trouble for many students. In fact, if tenses are switched back and forth just a few times, a student's paper can look much less organized than it really is. Any piece of writing that has illogical or inconsistent verb tenses seems incoherent; the writer appears to lack control of his or her material.

Writing About Literature

Sometimes it's natural to write a paper predominantly in the past tense, and sometimes it's natural to write mostly in the present tense. Occasionally, you have a choice. For example, a writer can often talk about literature in either the past or the present tense. The reason for this is that although a piece of literature was written in the past we tend to think of it as something that lives in the present. Therefore, in writing about *The Great Gatsby* by F. Scott Fitzgerald, we can choose to say, "Jay Gatsby *represented* the American dream" or "Jay Gatsby *represents* the American dream." The important thing is to be consistent. If you choose to write about a work of literature in the present tense, stay with the present tense; if you choose to use the past, stay with the past.

The Helping Verb *Had*

The helping verb *had* is used when you are writing in the past tense and you wish to indicate something that happened even earlier. For instance, these are correct examples:

(a) Samantha *started* breakfast at seven o'clock this morning; by that time, she *had read* the morning paper and *washed* two loads of clothes.

(b) Frank *had visited* France three times in the 1970s and 1980s before he *made* his first trip with Catherine last year.

145

Better Sentence-Writing

A Note about *Will/Would* and *Can/Could*

Before beginning the exercises for this unit, it's important for you to realize that the verb *would* is the past tense of *will*, and the verb *could* is the past tense of *can*. For example:

1. (a) He *will* bake a chocolate pecan pie today.
   (b) He *would* have baked a chocolate pecan pie yesterday if he had found the ingredients he needed.

2. (a) Right now I *can* hardly wait for my children to get home.
   (b) Yesterday I *could* hardly wait for my children to get home.

Many students have trouble with the helping verb *would*. It's a mistake to use it when you really mean the simple past tense. For example, it's an error to write, "When I lived in New York, I *would see* at least two plays a week." Why is this wrong? It's wrong because the writer simply means that he or she *saw* at least two plays a week.

The word *would* should be used only when the writer means that something would happen only if a certain condition were fulfilled. The condition is usually found in a clause that begins with the word *if,* but the condition can also be implied rather than stated. Notice in 1 (b) that the writer *would* have baked the pie only *if he had found the ingredients he needed.* First he had to have the ingredients — that's the condition that had to be fulfilled before he would bake the pie.

If you're writing about something that happened often in the past but there's no condition to be fulfilled, no notion of "if" involved, simply use the past tense. Don't add *would*. To check your understanding, mark each sentence below *correct or incorrect:*

1. Marty would have been on time if he had been given the right directions. _____

146

2. Aunt Dana would kiss you if you stood still for a minute. _____

3. During our teens, we would always watch *American Bandstand* after school. _____

4. When Louise and Kim were studying last night, Louise would crack her gum and drive Kim crazy. _____

5. Matthew would have finished college on time, but his mother contracted a serious illness, and his father needed him full-time in the family business for a year.

Items 1, 2, and 5 are correct because each has a condition to be fulfilled. Items 3 and 4 are incorrect because neither one involves any notion of a condition to be fulfilled. Try to correct the problems in verb tense in 3 and 4.

EXERCISE 6.7

Underline all verbs and verb phrases. Then correct any examples of inconsistent or illogical verb tense.

1. Several years ago, experts in preventive medicine announced newly found reasons why fish is such an important element in a healthy diet.

2. It was common knowledge that fish was high in protein and low in fat, and for that reason, fish would always be a favorite with the diet-conscious.

3. But it turned out that fish has other benefits, too.

4. Perhaps surprisingly, the varieties of fish that could have been considered relatively high in calories when compared with other fish were the ones most enthusiastically recommended by nutritionists.

5. The so-called fatty fish varieties contained a very beneficial oil, which is made up of something called omega-3 fatty acids.

6. What can these fatty fish oils do for you? According to scientists, they had the power to lower your risk of heart disease, and they offered a certain amount of protection against the agonies of arthritis and asthma.

7. They would also quite possibly reduce the risk of breast cancer, but that is a benefit that scientists would need to research in more depth and over a longer period of time.

8. The fish that have enough oil to be recommended highly are tuna, herring, salmon, whitefish, and large bluefish.

9. Shad, mackerel, and pompano would also be included.

10. People who are concerned about calories should not avoid these varieties of fish; they are "fatty" only when compared with other types of fish.

11. A serving of Chinook salmon, for instance, at 180 calories per three-and-a-half-ounce portion, had more than twice the calories of a similar serving of sole, but it would have only half the calories that were in three-and-a-half ounces of beefsteak.

12. Fortunately, shrimp and lobster are also high in omega-3 fatty acids, and they are not nearly as high in cholesterol as nutrition experts previously had thought.

13. So fish might not be brain food, but it's a pretty smart thing to eat.

6.4 Apostrophes

Apostrophes (') are used in two ways: to show possession and to make contractions. We'll spend most of this unit working on possession.

Possession

An apostrophe is added to a noun to show that the noun owns something. For example, if a girl has her own room, you might refer to it as *the girl's room.* Notice that two nouns are involved: *girl* and *room.* The apostrophe is added to the noun that possesses (owns) the other.

In the phrase *the girl's room,* the letter *s* is also added to the word *girl.* But if we were referring to a room shared by *two* girls, the correct form would be *the girls' room.* The apostrophe would be placed *after* the *s.* In the latter example, the *s* is already part of the word because we're talking about two girls, not one girl. When a plural word already ends in *s* before it becomes possessive, you add only the apostrophe.

In other words, ask yourself, "Who owns the room?" If the answer is *the girl,* then you have a word that ends in the letter *l,* so you add an apostrophe plus *-s.* But if the answer to the question is *the two girls,* a word that already ends in *-s,* then you add only the apostrophe.

Make these into possessive phrases:

1. the voice of the singer = _____

2. the voices of the four singers = _____

3. the fleas belonging to one dog = _____

4. the fleas belonging to twelve dogs = _____

1. the singer's voice; 2. the four singers' voices; 3. one dog's fleas; 4. twelve dog's fleas.

Plural Words That Do Not End in *-S*

Sometimes the plural words that end in letters other than *s* give students trouble, but they really shouldn't. These words follow the same rule just described. In other words, whether something belongs to one *man* or to two *men,* you'll show possession in the same way—by adding *-'s.* Why? Because neither *man* nor *men* already ends in *-s* before you make it possessive. They both end in *n.* These are correct examples: *the man's*

149

motive, the men's motive, the woman's car, the women's cars.
This rule holds true for all the plural nouns that end in *-men*
and for nouns such as *people, children, mice,* and *geese.*

Exercise 6.8

Write sentences in which you make possessive phrases from
the following. Add an apostrophe or an apostrophe plus *-s* as
needed. Use your own paper, please.

1. the duties of one librarian
   the duties of two librarians

2. the excitement of the child
   the excitement of the children

3. the shoes of the dancer
   the shoes of both dancers

4. the pet chameleon of one boy
   the pet chameleons of three boys

5. the history of the family
   the histories of the two families

6. the schedule of the woman
   the schedules of the women

7. the images of the poet
   the images of many poets

8. the carrots belonging to one rabbit
   the carrots belonging to all the rabbits

9. the performance of one drummer
   the performance of the drummers

10. the trips of the businessman
    the trips of the businessmen

Exercise 6.9

Change these phrases into ones that require an apostrophe or an apostrophe plus *-s*. For example:

The personality of my brother = my brother's personality

1. the priorities of the mayor = _____

2. the training of the pilots = _____

3. the comic talents of Jerry Seinfeld = _____

4. the game plan of the coaches = _____

5. the ice-cream sandwiches of the vendor = _____

6. the toys belonging to the babies = _____

7. the agreement of the friends = _____

8. the voice of Whitney Houston = _____

9. the role of Rob Morrow in *Northern Exposure* = _____

10. the role of the clowns in the circus = _____

Two Important Notes About the Exercises

Some sentences in the next two exercises may contain no words that call for an apostrophe; other sentences may have more than one.

Make sure that you correct each exercise and analyze any errors before you proceed to the next one.

Exercise 6.10

Add apostrophes where they are needed. (If you underline the words to which you add the apostrophes, they'll be easier to find and correct.)

Better Sentence-Writing

1. What do people like to order when they go out to eat? That was the National Restaurant Associations question, and it asked researchers from NPD Research Inc. to find the answer by surveying the members of 12,800 households.

2. The research organizations national survey reached all parts of the United States, and the poilsters discovered that Americans top five restaurant food choices are French fries, hamburgers, salads, breads, and pizza.

3. But all the various regions of the country have their own special favorites when it comes to ordering in the nations cafés and restaurants.

4. In New England, for instance, restaurant diners top menu choices include heroes and subs, doughnuts and sweet rolls, and sandwiches made of egg salad, tuna salad, and chicken salad.

5. A typical New Yorkers order is likely to include—in addition to heroes, subs, and salad-type sandwiches—frozen yogurt, sherbet, and types of pasta other than spaghetti.

6. In the mountain states of Arizona, Colorado, Idaho, Montana, Nevada, New Mexico, Utah, and Wyoming, peoples favorites range from tacos, burritos, and enchiladas to chicken nuggets and ham and cheese sandwiches.

7. It is anyones guess as to why, but North Dakotans restaurant preferences are mostly on the soft side; mashed potatoes, ice cream, doughnuts, sweet rolls, pancakes, and waffles rated the highest.

8. In Alaska, California, Hawaii, Oregon, and Washington, residents first loves are burritos, enchiladas, tacos, taco salads, and Oriental foods.

9. When food lovers in the South Atlantic states eat out, they are most likely to order the following items from a restaurants menu: breakfast sandwiches, shellfish, potato skins, and chicken.

10. In Illinois, Indiana, Michigan, Ohio, and Wisconsin, restaurant customers tastes are likely to run to chili, French toast, cheese, roast beef, and barbecued ribs.

Exercise 6.11

Add apostrophes where they are needed.

1. A parents greatest fear is that some harm will come to his or her child.

2. Grace Hechinger addresses this fear in a book called *How to Raise a Street-Smart Child.*

3. Hechinger, the mother of two boys, is a journalist and an educator who has written extensively on womens concerns and issues of family life. She has collaborated with her husband on a number of projects; the couples list of coauthored books includes *Teenage Tyranny, The New York Times Guide to New York City Private Schools,* and *Growing Up in America.*

4. Hechingers how-to book on keeping children from becoming victims makes some interesting observations and offers a few unusual bits of advice for parents.

5. One problem that concerns the author is that many childrens training at home puts them at risk when they are outside the home.

A Final Note on Possession

What you've learned in this unit is the simplest system for showing possession. But there are variations to the rules. For example, you usually add an -s to a one-syllable name that already ends in -s, such as *James*. (In other words, you write about *James's future*.) By adding the extra -s, you are supplying a guide to pronunciation. Your teacher may discuss this variation or other ones, but the basic rules you've learned in this unit are sufficient to meet the standards of most college teachers.

Contractions

Using apostrophes to make possessives is challenging for some students, but using them for their other purpose—making contractions—is easy.

A *contraction* is a shortened form of two words, and contractions are usually acceptable in informal speech and writing. (We use them freely in this book.) The only thing you have to remember is that the apostrophe is placed at the spot where one or more letters have been omitted. For example, *I am* becomes *I'm*, and *you have* becomes *you've*.

Make contractions of the following pairs of words:

you are = _____   are not = _____

could have = _____   he is = _____

were not = _____   I am = _____

you had = _____   I would = _____

did not = _____   was not = _____

she will = _____   who is = _____

it is = _____   would not = _____

they have = _____   were not = _____

are not = _____   there is = _____

had not = _____   have not = _____

should not = _____   can not = _____

Correct your answers by consulting a dictionary.

• •

6.5 Pronoun Problems

• •

There are a number of problems that pronouns can present for writers, but two are especially common: *agreement* and *case.* We'll take agreement first.

Pronoun-Antecedent Agreement

You know that subjects have to agree with verbs. Well, pronouns have to agree, too. They have to agree with the nouns that they replace and to which they refer. Those nouns are called *antecedents;* they are the words that appear first and are then replaced by pronouns. For example, if you're talking about Patrick, and after a while you start referring to Patrick as *he,* then *Patrick* is the antecedent, and *he* is the pronoun that takes the place of it and refers to it. *Patrick* and *he* agree because they are both singular. You also have agreement when both the noun antecedent and the pronoun that replaces it are plural. You have disagreement only when one is plural and the other singular. Here are examples of the error of pronoun-antecedent disagreement. Correct 1 through 3 to make the antecedents and the pronouns agree in number:

1. The mailman came late, but *they* always do on Mondays.

2. A student is very fortunate if *they* have a job waiting for them after graduation.

3. All the vetoes were in, but *it* didn't add up to a clear picture.

155

It's really very simple. Singular pronouns agree with singular nouns. Plural pronouns agree with plural nouns.

Avoiding *His* or *Her* When Possible

Sometimes it's better to change a noun than a pronoun. This is especially true if not changing the noun antecedent forces you to overuse an expression such as *he or she* or *his or her*. Sometimes it's unavoidable, and you have to use he or she (unless you prefer *he* or *she* alone). But most of the time, this awkward option can be avoided by making the antecedent noun plural. For example, it's acceptable to write, "A *student* should think seriously about *his or her* real interests," but it's preferable to write, "*Students* should think seriously about *their* real interests."

Singular Collective Nouns

When you're working on pronoun-antecedent agreement, it's important to remember that words such as *group, family, team,* and *association* are normally considered singular. Each collective noun refers to one entity even though it may bring to mind a number of people. Therefore, a team, for example, is considered an *it,* not a *they*.

Prepositional Phrases

Here, as elsewhere, you have to be careful about prepositional phrases. Writers sometimes produce mistakes in pronoun-antecedent agreement by making a pronoun agree with a word inside a prepositional phrase when it really agrees with the noun before the prepositional phrase. Look at this correct example:

ante.

The *number* (of people) who are sick with the flu is almost incredible, and medical authorities tell us that it is still rising.

We say *it is still rising*, not *they are still rising,* because the antecedent is the singular word *number.* In other words, the people are not rising; the number is rising.

This does not mean that an antecedent never agrees with a noun inside a prepositional phrase. For example, what is the antecedent of *their* in this correct example?

The location of the boys was not released until their parents had been notified.

You simply have to use your powers of logic to make sure that your pronouns and antecedents agree.

Exercise 6.12

Fill in the blank with the correct pronoun. Also write *ante.* (for antecedent) over the noun or noun phrase that agrees with the pronoun you choose.

1. Everyone has heard of the Medal of Honor; _____ *(it was / they were)* first awarded during the Civil War.

2. Every man, woman, and child in America should say "Thanks!" to the Hurley Machine Company because in 1907 _____ *(it / they)* came out with the very first electric washing machine.

3. Nikon cameras are the cameras that news photographers use most often. _____ *(It was / They were)* also immortalized in Paul Simon's song "Kodachrome."

4. The Salvation Army is ever hopeful. _____ *(It has / They have)* as _____ *(its / their)* slogan, "A man may be down, but he's never out."

5. The Neanderthal man was discovered in 1856; _____ *(he was / they were)* found in Germany.

6. Apparently neither Gary Player nor his son had any major objection to entering into serious competition with a member of _____ *(his/their)* own family. The Players were the first father and son to compete in the same U.S. Open golf tournament.

7. Ostrich eggs are not known for _____ *(its/their)* daintiness; in fact, if you happened to have one, it would take you four hours just to hardboil _____ *(it/them)*.

8. As the ill-fated *Andrea Doria* sank, the orchestra continued to perform; in fact, the last song _____ *(it/they)* played was "Arrivederci Roma."

9. Paper straws were invented in 1886 by Marvin Stone. He made _____ *(it/them)* by rolling paraffin-coated paper by hand.

10. (a) The McDonald's fast-food empire is constantly coming up with something new to promote business and keep customers happy, but one of the smartest things _____ *(it/they)* ever did was to build indoor and outdoor playgrounds at many of _____ *(its/their)* restaurants.
(b) The people at McDonald's are constantly coming up with something new to promote business and keep customers happy, but one of the smartest things _____ *(it/they)* ever did was to build indoor and outdoor playgrounds at many of _____ *(its/their)* restaurants.

Exercise 6.13

Fill in the blank with the correct pronoun. Also write *ante.* over the noun or noun phrase that agrees with the pronoun you choose.

1. The Elvis Presley memorial stamp was issued in 1993; _____ *(it was / they were)* worth twenty-nine cents.

2. The rulers of Great Britain hold a lease on Hong Kong, but _____ *(it will / they will)* lose control there when _____ *(it expires / they expire)* in 1997.

3. Herschel Walker led the U.S. Football League in rushing yardage in 1983, which was _____ *(its / their)* first season.

4. The Fairy Investigation Society has _____ *(its / their)* headquarters in Dublin, Ireland.

5. If kept as pets, tarantulas are supposedly intelligent enough to recognize _____ *(its / their)* masters.

Pronoun Case

The words *I* and *me* are two different cases of the same pronoun—the first-person singular pronoun. *He* and *him* are two cases of the same pronoun, and so are *she* and *her*. When pronouns are used alone, native speakers of English rarely make mistakes with them, but when they are used in combination with a noun, mistakes are common. These are called mistakes in pronoun case. Here's an illustration:

(a) *She* is a frisky little child. (correct)

(b) Christopher and *her* are frisky little children. (incorrect)

In (a), the word *she* is obviously correct; *she* is the right pronoun to use in the subject position. But in (b), the word *her* is used as a subject, along with the word *Christopher*. No native speaker would write, "*Her* is a frisky little child," but many native speakers would make the error that is represented in sentence (b).

Better Sentence-Writing

It's the act of pairing a pronoun with a noun that seems to make writers occasionally lose their bearings. To avoid errors in pronoun case, all you have to do is watch for the pairings and mentally omit the noun. Then see what pronoun sounds right if used alone. That's the case of the pronoun that is also correct when used in combination with a noun.

Sometimes when you perform this test of omitting the noun, you also have to make a slight adjustment in subject-verb agreement or in the general phrasing of the sentence. For example, in (b) when you mentally omit the words *Christopher and*, you move from a plural subject to a singular subject, so you also have to change *are* to *is*. Then you ask yourself if it sounds right to say "Her is" or "She is."

Exercise 6.14

Fill in each blank with the correct case of the pronoun.

1. When did you last write a letter to _____ *(he / him)* and Annie?

2. Cody and _____ *(her / she)* are coming to Milwaukee for a visit in the spring.

3. Why don't you allow the Joneses and _____ *(them / they)* to go ahead and file the suit?

4. My children and _____ *(I / me)* really should write a book together.

5. The Blue Devils and _____ *(us / we)* battled throughout the entire tournament.

6. I'd like to take a trip to Argentina with Grandma Rosie and _____ *(her / she)*.

7. We can't wait until the Sethneys and _____ *(they / them)* finally get here.

8. Is the box that just arrived for Robin and _____ *(I / me)*?

9. Jackie and _____ *(he / him)* met about a year ago at the bank where she worked.

10. The man was rather rude to my brother and _____ *(I / me)*.

● ●
6.6 Easily Confused Words
● ●

This unit is a brief review of some of the common word pairs that often cause trouble for writers. You also might know of others that cause you uncertainty.

It would not be difficult for you to make up your own exercises on pairs that are not found here; if you do so, ask your teacher or a friend to check your work.

Below are the pairs that we'll consider in this unit. You can see that some are homonyms (words that sound alike but have different meanings), and some are not.

1. a/an	11. it's/its
2. accept/except	12. passed/past
3. affect/effect	13. principal/principle
4. amount/number	14. than/then
5. bare/bear	15. their/there/they're
6. coarse/course	16. threw/through
7. conscience/conscious	17. to/too/two
8. finally/finely	18. weather/whether
9. have/of	19. who's/whose
10. hear/here	20. you're/your

___

Troublesome Pairs

1. A/An

A and *An* are both noun markers. A is used before words that begin with consonant sounds, and an is used before words that begin with vowel sounds. You probably remember that the vowels are *a, e, i, o,* and *u.*

There are two more things you should know. One is that the letter *h* is sometimes silent, and when it is, you use *an.* For example, you write, "It is *an* honor to speak before the assembly." On the other hand, when *h* is sounded, you use a. For example, you might say, "I wonder if there is *a* heaven."

The other special concern is the letter *u.* Words that begin with a long *u* are preceded by *a;* words that begin with a short *u* are preceded by *an.* Study these correct examples: *a* united student body; *an* unsung hero.

2. Accept/Except

Accept is the verb form of the noun *acceptance,* and it means to receive something, not to reject it. The word *except* is a preposition that is related to the noun *exception.* Examples: You *accept* praise from your teacher. You might enjoy all dances *except* the polka.

3. Affect/Effect

If you look in a good dictionary, you'll find a complete explanation of the difference between these two words. For our purposes, it's enough to say that *affect* is a verb, and *effect* is usually a noun. Examples: Your moods *affect* your performance. The *effect* of too little sleep is obvious.

4. Amount/Number

Use the word *number* when you're writing about something that can be counted; use *amount* when you're writing about something that can't be counted. Examples: *an amount of peanut butter, a number of peanuts.* Use *number* if something is "countable," even if you don't know the exact count.

Most people don't make errors with *number;* they make errors by overusing *amount.* Here's a typical mistake: "I had a large *amount* of friends when I lived in Houston." Friends can be counted, even if you don't actually recall how many you had; therefore, it should be "I had a large *number* of friends."

The words *fewer* and *less* operate in the same way. *Fewer* is used as *number* is—with things that can be counted. *Less* is used as *amount* is—with things that can't be counted. Is the TV commercial that tells us one type of beer has "less calories" than another type grammatically correct? The answer is no.

The words *many* and *much* also operate similarly. *Many* is used with things that can be counted; *much* modifies things that can't be counted. Study these correct examples:

Can Be Counted	Cannot Be Counted
the number of jokes	the amount of humor
fewer jokes	less humor
many jokes	much humor

5. Bare/Bear

The word *bare* is an adjective that means naked, plain, unadorned. It is also a verb that means to reveal. *Bear* has two basic meanings: It's a noun that refers to a certain animal; it's also a verb that means to carry a burden or to tolerate something. Examples: The room is too *bare;* it needs a few warm touches. He wants to *bare* his soul to you. You may encounter a grizzly *bear* in Glacier National Park. I can't *bear* to think about final exam week.

6. Coarse/Course

The word *course* means an academic subject, such as a mathematics course. It also means a path or route, such as the course of a river or a golf course. *Course* means a duration, as in the expression "throughout the course of history." Its most frequent use is probably in the phrase *of course.*

163

Coarse, on the other hand, is an adjective that means rough; it can describe such things as the texture of fabric or the sound of language.

7. Conscience/Conscious

Conscience is a noun; it's what is supposed to bother you when you do something wrong; we could say it's your sense of right and wrong. The word *conscious* is an adjective that means aware. It's related to the noun *consciousness.* Examples: He had a guilty *conscience* after betraying his friend's trust. She was *conscious* of someone watching her.

8. Finally/Finely

Finally means at last or eventually. *Finely* means delicately or in small pieces.

9. Have/Of

This problem is a little different. Sometimes writers use the preposition *of* when they really mean the verb *have.* The only time this mistake occurs is after helping verbs such as *should, could, will, would, may, might,* and *must.* In the middle of a verb phrase, you don't want a preposition. Here's a typical error: "I should *of* known better." Here's the correction: "I should *have* known better."

10. Hear/Here

Hear is the verb that means listen. *Here* is an adverb that designates a place.

11. It's/Its

It's is the contraction of *it is.* The word *its* is a possessive pronoun. Examples: *It's* a new day. The snake shed *its* skin.

12. Passed/Past

Passed is a form of the verb *pass. Past* can be a noun or an adjective. Examples: They all *passed* the exam. You *passed* me on the street without saying a word. Who ever really forgets the *past?* (noun) Your *past* mistakes are forgiven. (adjective)

13. Principal/Principle

We all remember that the *principal* is our pal. The noun also refers to a sum of money on which we can earn interest. But the problem most students have is that they don't realize the word *principal* is also an adjective that means main, central, most important. The word *principle* is a noun that means a basic truth, a law, a rule, a belief, a standard, or an ideal. Examples: Solving world hunger is the *principal* goal of the organization. Ozzie's *principal* problem is lack of confidence. This experiment demonstrates the *principle* of supply and demand. Charlie has no *principles;* he'll do anything for a price.

14. Than/Then

Than is used to make comparisons. For example, a person can be stronger *than* someone else, and one climate can be warmer *than* another. *Then* is an adverb of time; it describes when an action occurred. For example, we say, "*Then* I woke up" and "If you decide you want to talk it over, *then* call me."

15. Their/There/They're

Their is a possessive pronoun. It modifies a noun by showing that the noun belongs to someone. We speak of *their pencils, their cars, their future. There* is an indicator of location, as in "Let's go *there* now." It is also a sort of meaningless sentence starter, as in "*There* are a few problems we need to discuss." *They're* is the contraction of *they are*, as in "*They're* going to be here for an hour."

16. Threw/Through

Threw is the past tense of the verb *throw. Through* is a preposition.

---

17. To/Too/Two

To can be part of an infinitive verb phrase, as in "She wants *to* ride." *To* is also a preposition, as in "The poem *to* his daughter was never completed." *Two,* of course, is the number between one and three. It's *too* that gives writers the most trouble. *Too* is an "intensifier"; it makes the adjective that follows it more intense. Roughly, it means "excessively." For example, you can say, "You are *too* impatient," which means you are excessively impatient. *Too* has another meaning, which is "also." For example, you can write, "Please clean up this mess, and do the dishes, *too.*"

18. Weather/Whether

Weather, of course, refers to the climate. *Whether* is a conjunction used in sentences such as "I don't know *whether* I should sign up now or wait until tomorrow."

19. Who's/Whose

Who's is the contraction of *who is. Whose* is a possessive pronoun, and you've worked with it as an embedding word.

20. You're/Your

You're is the contraction of *you are. Your* is a possessive pronoun.

Exercise 6.15

Fill in the blanks with the correct choices.

1. Reindeer's milk has three times more protein _____ *(than/then)* cow's milk, and some people prefer the taste, _____ *(to/too/two).*

2. The _____ *(principal/principle)* center of diamond trading in the United States is New York City's 47th Street; in fact, more _____ *(than/then)* 75 percent of the action in the American diamond trade goes on _____ *(their/there/they're).*

3. Richard Nixon was the first person _____ *(to/too/two)* put a telephone call _____ *(threw/through)* to the moon.

4. The _____ *(principal/principle)* of self-service, which of _____ *(coarse/course)* had a negative _____ *(affect/effect)* on the employment of a great _____ *(amount/number)* of waiters and waitresses, goes all the way back _____ *(to/too/two)* 1885 when the first self-service restaurant, the Exchange Buffet, opened _____ *(it's/its)* doors near the New York Stock Exchange.

5. Joe Louis, _____ *(who's/whose)* considered by many to be the greatest fighter who ever lived, held the heavyweight title longer _____ *(than/then)* anyone else; if _____ *(you're/your)* up on _____ *(you're/your)* boxing trivia, you know that he was the champion from 1937 _____ *(to/too/two)* 1949.

6. Each of the precisely etched, _____ *(finally/finely)* carved faces of the presidents at Mt. Rushmore is _____ *(to/too/two)* times higher _____ *(than/then)* the Great Sphinx of Egypt.

7. The Eighteenth Amendment, which prohibited the sale of liquor in the United States, was the only one ever to be repealed. The American people _____ *(finally/finely)* _____ *(threw/through)* the amendment out on December 5, 1933, after almost 14 "dry years" had _____ *(passed/past)*. Apparently, they came to the conclusion that, for adults, drinking alcohol should be considered less a matter of legislation _____ *(than/then)* a matter of individual _____ *(conscience/conscious)*.

8. The first American husband and wife team to _____ *(accept/except)* the Nobel Prize was

Dr. Carl F. Cori and Dr. Gerty T. Cori. _____ *(Their / There / They're)* work in medicine won them a joint prize in 1947.

9. The United States publishes a greater _____ *(amount / number)* of newspapers _____ *(than / then)* any other country.

10. _____ *(It's / Its)* a fact that _____ *(their / there / they're)* are exactly twenty possible first moves in chess.

11. If _____ *(you're / your)* ever watching a television sitcom and the laughter seems just a bit _____ *(to / too / two)* mechanical, it might _____ *(have / of)* been produced by a machine called a "Mackenzie." _____ *(It's / Its)* job is to cough up canned laughter for a considerable _____ *(amount / number)* of television shows.

12. Throughout the entire _____ *(coarse / course)* of American history, _____ *(their / there / they're)* was probably only one president who didn't let his spouse's views _____*(affect / effect)* his political decisions in even the slightest way. That was James Buchanan, who served from 1857 to 1861 and who was the only American president never _____ *(to / too / two)* marry.

13. By the standards of centuries ago, it didn't really take _____ *(to / too / two)* long for the Mayflower to cross the Atlantic; in fact, the ship left Europe and arrived _____ *(hear / here)* in only _____ *(to / too / two)* months.

14. The presidential candidate who received the greatest _____ *(amount / number)* of votes in one election in American history was Richard M. Nixon. But he must _____ *(bare / bear)* the stigma

of being the only president to resign, _____ *(to / too / two)*.

15. During the time of the Civil War, _____ *(their / there / they're)* was no doubt that money could _____ *(affect / effect)* a young man's chances of serving in the military; to put it plainly, _____ *(a / an)* inductee could pay someone else _____ *(to / too / two)* take his place if, of _____ *(coarse / course),* he could do so without disturbing his own _____ *(conscience / conscious)* _____ *(to / too / two)* much.

∙ ∙

6.7 Capitalization
∙ ∙

There are many fine points of capitalization, but these basic guidelines will meet most of the needs of college writers. The following categories of words are capitalized:

1. **Titles of poems, short stories, plays, books, newspapers, magazines, television shows, radio programs, and movies.** Capitalize the first and last word and every other word with the exception of coordinating conjunctions, prepositions, articles (*a, an,* and *the*) and the word *to* in infinitive verb phrases. (Titles of poems, short stories, and individual television and radio programs are also enclosed within double quotation marks; titles of books, newspapers, magazines, films, and television and radio series are normally italicized.)

   Correct examples: "The Love Song of J. Alfred Prufrock," "Air and Angels," "Delight in Disorder," "On the Death of Dr. Robert Levet," *Murphy Brown, Sesame Street, The Valley of Horses, The Milwaukee Journal, Pro Football Digest, One Flew Over the*

Cuckoo's Nest, Butch Cassidy and the Sundance Kid, On the Waterfront.

2. **Brand names.** Brand names are always capitalized.

   Correct examples: Bisquick buttermilk baking mix, Nike running shoes, Clinique cosmetics, Arrow shirts, Sylvania light bulbs, Head & Shoulders shampoo.

3. **Breeds of animals.** Capitalize the name of a breed of animal if it is derived from another proper (capitalized) noun. The names that are capitalized below are derived from the names of nationalities, which are always capitalized. Use your dictionary if you are in doubt.

   Correct examples: alley cat, Persian cat, Old English sheepdog, beagle, French poodle, quarter horse, Arabian horse.

4. **Buildings and institutions.** The names of buildings and institutions are always capitalized.

   Correct examples: the White House, the Taj Mahal, the Superdome, St. Joseph's Hospital, the University of Iowa, the Berkeley Psychic Institute.

5. **Companies and corporations.** The names of companies and corporations are always capitalized.

   Correct examples: Colgate-Palmolive Company, Mobil Oil Corporation, Lockheed Aircraft Corporation.

6. **Days of the week.** The days of the week are always capitalized.

   Correct examples: Monday, Tuesday.

7. **Directions.** The names of directions are normally *not* capitalized. Capitalize them only when they name or modify an entire region—a whole section of a country or a continent.

Correct examples: I live four miles west of the lake. Her study covered the era when the South was at war with the North.

8. **Geographical locations and words derived from them.** All of these are capitalized: the names of cities, counties, states, nations, lakes, rivers, oceans, mountain ranges, parks, continents, and planets.

    Correct examples: Seattle, Washington, Blue Lake, the Atlantic Ocean, the Allegheny Mountains, France, Jupiter, Mars.

    Two special notes: Most words that are derived from these location words are capitalized; for example, *Switzerland* is capitalized, and so is *Swiss* cheese. The word *Mexico* is capitalized, and so is *Mexican* art.

    Normally, the word *earth* is not capitalized, but when it refers to the entire planet, it is. *These are correct examples:* The earth in some parts of the country has a reddish color. The Earth is not the largest planet that revolves around the sun.

9. **Historical periods.** Names of historical periods are usually capitalized. If you are in doubt, consult your dictionary.

    Correct examples: the Renaissance, the Pleistocene Age, the Middle Ages.

10. **Holidays.** The names of holidays and holy days are always capitalized.

    Correct examples: Christmas, Yom Kippur, Thanksgiving.

11. The word *I* is always capitalized.

12. **Months of the year.** The months of the year are always capitalized.

    Correct examples: January, February, March.

171

A special note: Although the months are capitalized, the seasons are usually not. Capitalize the name of a season only if it is part of the formal name of something else, such as a dance or a celebration of some sort. *These are correct examples:* I won't see you again until next winter. Our school's famous Fall Festival was only a modest financial success this year, but the Spring Fling will probably be a bigger money-maker.

13. **Mother and father.** Mistakes are often made in capitalizing or not capitalizing person nouns such as *mother, father, mom,* and *dad.* But the rule is really very simple: Do not capitalize these words when they are preceded by a possessive noun or pronoun. *Study these correct examples:*

    (a) I have always considered *Dad* a perfectionist.
    I have always considered *my dad* a perfectionist.

    (b) I met *Father* at the restaurant.
    I met *my neighbor's father* at the restaurant.

14. **Names of people and pets.** Names of people and pets are always capitalized.

    Correct examples: Maya Angelou, Sarah Zeilman, John Brown, Snoopy, Fluffy, Killer.

15. **One-of-a-kind events.** Large one-of-a-kind or once-a-year events are normally capitalized.

    Correct examples: the Orange Bowl, the World Series, the War of 1812.

16. **Organizations and associations.** The names of organizations and associations are capitalized. Once again, articles, coordinating conjunctions, and prepositions are not capitalized.

Correct examples: American Civil Liberties Union, Children's Literature Association, National Aeronautics and Space Administration, National Council of Teachers of English.

17. **Political parties.** The names of political parties and words derived from them are capitalized. (Note, however, that the word party is not.)

   Correct examples: the Republican party, the Democratic candidate, the Socialist platform, the Communists.

18. **Religions.** The names of religions and words derived from them are capitalized.

   Correct examples: the Jewish people, the Protestants' representative, the Mormons, the Baptist minister.

19. **The first word in a sentence.** The first word of a new sentence is capitalized, and this is also true of quoted sentences that are a part of larger sentences.

   Correct examples: The note said, "Your books have been overdue for a month. Please return them and pay your fine."

20. **Personal titles.** Personal titles are capitalized only when they directly precede a person's name or when they are used as a form of direct address. This is true for words such as president, general, mayor, doctor, king, queen, professor, dean, and pope.

   Correct examples: Do you realize that President Clinton's press conference is on television right now? Do you realize that the president's press conference is on television right now? The reporter asked, "When did you first know of this situation, Mr. President?"

EXERCISE 6.16

Correct the following sentences, applying what you've learned about capitalization.

1. Experts at the new york museum of modern art, after studying french artist henri matisse's le bateau for more than six weeks, discovered that the painting had been hung upside down.

2. Geoffrey chaucer once wrote, "love is blind," and william shakespeare used that line, too.

3. The lincoln memorial in washington, d.c., has 36 columns.

4. Ernest hemingway, the great american novelist who gave us *the sun also rises, a farewell to arms, for whom the bell tolls, the old man and the sea,* and other important works, was supposedly very reluctant to travel on fridays.

5. It was in a movie called *sudden impact* that clint eastwood first said, "make my day."

6. The best selling car in history was the volkswagen beetle.

7. Three of every four russian doctors are women.

8. It was once suggested by president jimmy carter that each president be elected for a single six-year term of office.

9. In the frontier days of the west, cheyenne, wyoming, was nicknamed "hell on wheels."

10. John lindsay, a former mayor of new york city, made his acting debut in the movie *rosebud* in 1975.

Answer Key

Chapter 1 Answer Key

If some of your answers for the exercises in this unit vary a bit from those shown, your answers are not necessarily wrong. When marking clauses, you may have included slightly more or less than is shown here; such differences are inconsequential and to be expected.

Exercise 1.1

1. s = motive; v = was; *sub com* = mysterious
2. s = I; v = bought; *do* = suit
3. s = woman; v = coughed
4. s = Caroline; v = gave; *io* = Steven; *do* = choice
5. s = nectarines; v = feel; *sub com* = ripe

Exercise 1.2

1. s = fans; v = consider; *do* = Nolan Ryan; *ob com* = pitcher
2. s = pitcher; v = shows; *io* = hitters; *do* = best stuff
3. s = season; v = was; *sub com* = twenty-fourth
4. s = fastballs; v = reached; *do* = speeds
5. s = fastball; v = made; *do* = curveball; *ob com* = more effective

Exercise 1.3

1. beginning
2. prediction
3. organization
4. liar
5. gentleness
6. decision

175

7. allowance
8. reliability
9. collection
10. defiance

Exercise 1.4

1. s = To work hard today
2. s = What the world needs now
3. s = Tracking students into so-called ability groups
4. s = Outside that crazy office
5. s = What a racist or sexist joke reveals about its teller

Exercise 1.5

1. s = deprivation; v = can prevent; do = retention
2. s = tongue; v = has given; io = doctors; do = mirror
3. s = Malcolm X; v = had made; do trips; v = had altered; do = position
4. s = *Nintendo Power* magazine; v = is published
5. s = Vincent van Gogh; v = painted; do = suns; $ob\ com$ = yellow
6. s = Competition; v = has been defined
7. s = Chester F. Carlson; v = should have named; do = intervention; $ob\ com$ = after himself
8. s = mannequins; v = wear; do = size 40 regular

9. s = size; v = has been decreasing
10. s = people; v = should blame; do = diet

Exercise 1.6

1. polished, oak
2. biggest, small
3. negative, best
4. deep, raspy
5. persistent, drastic
6. supporting, historical
7. crystal, big
8. tallest, old-fashioned, blackberry
9. final, difficult, challenging
10. dramatic, sunburnt, pale, white

Exercise 1.7

In each answer for this exercise, the words between the commas form the appositive, and the labeled parts of the clause form the kernel.

1. George Washington, the first president of the United States, loved peanut soup. s = George Washington; v = loved; do = peanut soup
2. John Quincy Adams, the sixth president, liked swimming nude in the Potomac River every morning at five o'clock. s = John Quincy Adams; v = liked; do = swimming

3. Zachary Taylor, a career officer in the army for most of his life, voted for the first time at the age of 62.
   s = Zachary Taylor; v = voted

4. James Buchanan, president from 1857 to 1861, was a bachelor throughout his entire life.
   s = James Buchanan; v = was; *sub com* = bachelor

5. Abraham Lincoln, an extremely persistent individual, won the presidency in 1860 after eight election losses in a row.
   s = Abraham Lincoln; v = won; *do* = presidency

Exercise 1.8

After you have crossed out the prepositional phrases and other modifiers, the remaining components that form the kernels are these:

1. s = Robin Burns; v = is; *sub com* = officer; *App.:* the highest paid woman in the United States

2. s = Babe Ruth; v = pitched

3. s = number; v = exceeded; *do* = number

4. s = color; v = has been; *sub com* = blue

5. s = Treasury Department; v = dry-cleaned; *do* = money

6. s = female tree frog; v = recognizes; *do* = connection

7. s = headquarters; v = has; *do* = waterbed

8. s = matter; v = is; *sub com* = duff

9. s = size; v = was; *sub com* = 5 feet and 7 inches and 135 pounds

10. s = record; v = was; *sub com* = I'll Never Get Out of this World Alive"

Chapter 2 Answer Key

Exercise 2.1

1. s = Mexican-Americans; v = have; *do* = families s = they; v = can claim; *do* = rate United States, and they

2. s = gardeners; v = wanted; *do* = melons s = they; v = watered; *do* = them melons, so they

3. s = tissues; v = are; *sub com* = great; s = sheets; v = were invented sufferers, but those

4. s = Wilson and Smith; v = had; *do* = problem; s = they; v = joined; *do* = forces; v = started; *do* = Alcoholics Anonymous problem, so they

5. s = people; v = keep; *do* = resolutions; s = they; v = don't make; *do* = them weeks, or they

Exercise 2.2

1. s = you; v = lick; do = stamp
   s = you; v = consume; do = one-tenth
   Conj. = When
   stamp, you

2. s = birth; v = created; do = sensation
   s = set; v = had survived
   Conj. = because
   no punctuation added

3. s = Pretty Boy Floyd; v = was known
   Conj. = Although
   robberies, he

4. s = people; v = must live s = government; v calls; do = it; $ob com$ = city
   Conj. = before
   no punctuation added

5. s = Fitzgerald; v = had completed; do = *The Last Tycoon*
   s = it; v = might have been; $sub com$ = novel
   Conj. = If
   44, it

Exercise 2.3

1. Thomas Jefferson, who was certainly one of America's most brilliant presidents, was broke when he died.

2. Monrovia, which is the capital of the West African nation of Liberia, was founded in 1822 and named after President James Monroe.

3. Herbert Hoover, who once gave an order that no White House staffers were to pet his dog, was supposedly worried that King Tut was becoming too attached to other people.

4. James Buchanan, whose 23-year-old fiancé broke off their engagement and died mysteriously a short time later, was the only president to remain a bachelor.

5. Grover Cleveland's duties as a sheriff in New York State, which included serving as one county's official hangman, resulted in his participation in the execution of two convicted murderers.

Exercise 2.4

1. *Reduced:* A quetzal, unable to take off into the air like other birds, has to jump off a tree branch backward to avoid snagging its 24-inch tail.

   Moved: Unable to take off into the air like other birds, a quetzal has to jump off a tree branch backward to avoid snagging its 24-inch tail.

2. *Reduced:* Male narwhals, nicknamed "unicorns of the sea," sport a single nine-foot-long tusk.

   Moved: Nicknamed "unicorns of the sea," male narwhals sport a single nine-foot-long tusk.

3. *Reduced:* Some biologists, puzzled by the hump on the back of the thorny devil, speculate that the lizard can push the hump up to create the illusion of a second head when it wants to confuse its enemies.

   Moved: Puzzled by the hump on the back of the thorny devil, some biologists speculate that the lizard can push the hump up to create the illusion of a second head when it wants to confuse its enemies.

4. *Reduced:* A sloth, blessed with three very efficient curved claws on each foot, normally hangs from a tree for its daily 18-hour snooze.

   Moved: Blessed with three very efficient curved claws on each foot, a sloth normally hangs from a tree for its daily 18-hour snooze.

5. *Reduced:* One scientist, curious about the basic color of the zebra, conducted a study and concluded that zebras are actually black with white stripes, not white with black stripes.

   Moved: Curious about the basic color of the zebra, one scientist conducted a study and concluded that zebras are actually black with white stripes, not white with black stripes.

Exercise 2.5

Possible revisions for the run-on sentences are offered here. You may have come up with different revisions.

1. RO; them/this
   For over 2,700 years, diamonds have had a certain mystique.

2. CS; India,/they
   The first diamonds were discovered along riverbeds in south central India in about 800 B.C.

3. CS; years,/then; source,/later South central India was the primary source of diamonds for about two thousand years. Then, South America became the major source; later, South Africa was the major source.

4. OK

5. CS; mines,/most
   There are 19 diamond mines in the United States, most of which are around the border between Colorado and Wyoming.

Exercise 2.6

1. OK

2. CS; three C's,/the
   Diamonds are judged on the basis of the three C's: carats, cut, and clarity.

3. RO; "carob seed"/carob
   The word carat comes from

the Greek word keration, which means "carob seed." Carob seeds were used to measure the weight of diamonds long ago in India.

4. RO; measure/it
In the modern world of diamond dealing, a carat, which represents $\frac{1}{142}$ of an ounce, is a more standard measure.

5. CS; carats,/that
The largest diamond ever found was 3,106 carats, which equals about 1.3 pounds.

Exercise 2.7

1. F
The Statistical Abstract, which is produced annually by the U.S. Commerce Department, fills almost 1,000 pages.

2. OK

3. F
Massachusetts, for example, is the state with the highest number of doctors per 100,000 people.

4. F
New York has more lawyers per person than any other state.

5. OK

Exercise 2.8

1. F
Cross Your Fingers, Spit in Your Hat is a book about superstitions and folklore.

2. F
The most interesting superstitions are the ones about love and marriage.

3. OK

4. OK

5. F
The object of your desire will also love you if you give him or her a bowl of soup that is flavored with three drops of your blood.

Chapter 3 Answer Key

Exercise 3.1

1. Complex
Conj. = When
1919, Handley Page Transport; *s* = it; *v* = introduced; *do* = box lunches
s = Handley Page Transport; *v* = became; *sub com* = airline

2. Complex
Conj. = when
no punctuation added; *s* = no one; *v* = was; *sub com* = surprised; *s* = Wilma P. Mankiller; *v* = became; *sub com* = chief

3. Compound
Conj. = but
cans, but; *s* = drinkers;

v = buy; do = beer; s = beer; v = outsold; do = beer

4. Complex
   Conj. = after
   no punctuation added; s = Queen Victoria; v = wore; do = in black; s = she; v = lost; do = husband or Albert or husband Albert

5. Complex
   Conj. = since
   48, the royalties; s = Gibran; v = died; s = royalties; v = have helped; do = people

Exercise 3.2

1. s = St. Nicholas
   St. Nicholas, **who was a fourth-century bishop in Asia Minor**, is the patron saint of children and sailors.

2. s = The dog who guarded the gates of Hades
   no punctuation should be added

3. s = Janet Reno
   Janet Reno, **who became U.S. Attorney General shortly before the cult-related tragedy in Texas,** was praised … decisions.

4. s = The person who wrote the Oz books
   no punctuation should be added

5. s = The average child who is between two and three years of age

no punctuation should be added

Exercise 3.3

1. s = A person
   no punctuation should be added

2. s = The person
   no punctuation should be added

3. s = The U.S. Senate
   The U.S. Senate, **which has been called "the most exclusive club in the world,"** is never open to more than 100 members.

4. s = The grape
   no punctuation should be added

5. s = The abbreviation *lb.*
   The abbreviation *lb.*, **which means pound,** comes from the Latin word *libra,* meaning "scales."

Exercise 3.4

1. Chubby Checker, whose real name was Ernest Evans, worked as a chicken plucker in a poultry shop before he became famous for doing "The Twist."

2. Neil Sedaka, who had enjoyed a great deal of success as a songwriter and singer in the 1950s, made a comeback in the 1970s with the help of Elton John.

3. Critic Jon Landau, who wrote a rave review after seeing "the Boss" in concert in 1974, is responsible for the line "I saw rock 'n' roll's future, and its name is Bruce Springsteen."

4. Annie Mae Bullock, who married Ike Turner in 1958, changed her name to Tina Turner.

5. The heart attack that left Jackie Wilson in a coma for the rest of his life occurred while the famous soul singer was performing on stage in Cherry Hill, New Jersey, on September 25, 1975.

Exercise 3.5

1. racetrack, a maiden
2. American Revolution, the Purple Heart
3. years, having
4. 1918, followed
5. *khaki,* meaning

Exercise 3.6

1. ducks, swans, geese, eagles, foxes, wolves, and
2. *Fly patterns, flares, bombs, safety blitzes,* and
3. 164 feet high, 148 feet wide, and
4. wisdom, wealth, power, and
5. Ariel, Miranda, Oberon, Titania, and

Exercise 3.7

1. (a) quick little smile
   (b) generous, good-hearted smile
2. (a) serious military affair
   (b) ridiculous, tragic affair
3. (a) perfect tea roses
   (b) delicate, delightful roses
4. (a) creamy, buttery soup
   (b) delicious bean soup
5. (a) skillful, thoughtful sculptor
   (b) thoughtful Italian sculptor

Exercise 3.8

1. Timbuktu, you'll Timbuktu, which ... gold, was settled
2. sundae, now ... treat, was ... parlor, and
3. October 25, 1940, Col. B.O. Davis
4. 1886, John Styth Pemberton, an Atlanta pharmacist, will
5. light up, they experts, male
6. France, who ... old, is credited
7. fused, eroded Desert roses, which ... elements, are
8. Cicero, not George Washington
9. bread, a sweetbread
10. longest, heaviest ... python, a typical

Exercise 3.9

1. track; she
2. structure; it
3. bone; they
4. full-time job; high school girls
5. riflemen; oarsmen

Exercise 3.10

1. Caspian Sea; however, the
2. East; the less
3. *The Gambler;*—in fact, the
4. three inches; consequently, the
5. injury; for example, if
6. copyrighted work; in fact, it
7. hair; the wife
8. *Casablanca;* however, few people
9. bad luck; a talisman
10. amulets; a four-leaf clover

Exercise 3.11

1. (a) no punctuation should be added
   (b) His idea, however, was
   (c) great idea; however, it
2. (a) Ben's; in fact, she
   (b) no punctuation should be added
   (c) She was, in fact, his
3. (a) no punctuation should be added
   (b) is, therefore, going
   (c) engineering; therefore, he

4. (a) no punctuation should be added
   (b) children; for example, some
   (c) youngsters, for example, speak
5. (a) no punctuation should be added
   (b) choice; on the other hand, John is afraid
   (c) John, on the other hand, thinks

Exercise 3.12

Only the parts of each item requiring additional punctuation appear here.

1. Those periods are the following: between three and ten months, between two and four years, between six and eight years, between 10 and 12 years, and between 14 and 16 years. *sub com* = the following
2. Santa's eight tiny reindeer are Dasher, Dancer, Prancer, Vixen, Comet, Cupid, Donner, and Blitzen.
3. These are the seven wonders of the ancient world: the Great Pyramid of Cheops, the Hanging Gardens of Babylon, the Tomb of King Mausolus at Halicarnassus, the Temple of Artemis, the Colossus of Rhodes, the Statue of Zeus at Olympia, and the lighthouse

on the Isle of Pharos.
sub com = wonders

4. But those who want to be more precise might use one of these terms: a bevy of quail, a muster of peacocks, a charm of finches, or an exaltation of larks.
do = one (or one of these terms)

5. Charles Biondin, the French acrobat and tightrope walker, crossed Niagara Falls in 1855, 1859, and 1860.

Exercise 3.13

1. *Sea of Slaughter,* which … Press, was
2. Mowat, who is a Canadian, is
3. seaboard, Mowat
4. area, his conclusions
5. author, human beings … mammals, birds, and fish of North America; in fact, Mowat
6. reasons: economic, recreational, and scientific
7. meat, hides, and fur
8. survived, but … difficulty; for example, the wolf, the Plains buffalo, and
9. animals, such as the passenger pigeon, the sea mink, and the Eastern buffalo, are gone forever, driven into
10. harsh, tragic realities, and … history; animals … for sport,

for fashion, for food, and for experimentation

Exercise 3.14

1. *Sea of Slaughter, a* … 400 pages, points out
2. people, for example, believe
3. bird, which … hour, did exist
4. 100 million, its natural
5. That enemy, of course, was deadly; it was man.
6. whale, once … life forms, is
7. odds: the coyote
8. no additional punctuation necessary
9. predator, Mowat … future, but … individuals, not
10. rare, they … sensitive, aware publication, it

Chapter 4 Answer Key

Exercise 4.1

The sample rewrites given here are not the only possibilities. You may have come up with other good revisions.

1. OK; *s* = beer
2. OK; *s* = hard candies and caramels
3. DM; *s* = U.S. Army
   According to the U.S. Army, an M-1 rifle that is cared for properly should last 10,000 rounds.

4. DM; *s* = scientists
   Scientists believe that the
   sun, which is four to five
   billion years old, has a life
   span of 10 billion years.

5. DM; *s* = plastic surgeons
   Plastic surgeons estimate
   that a successful face lift
   performed upon average skin
   should last from six to 10
   years.

Exercise 4.2

The following sample re-
writes are not the only possibilities. You may have come
up with other good revisions.

1. DM; *s* = Southeast Asia
   Southeast Asia is the home of
   the world's largest bat, which
   can weigh up to 32 ounces
   and which has a wingspan
   that's been measured at five
   feet, seven inches.

2. OK; *s* = basenji dog

3. DM; *s* = it
   Swans, which are extremely
   long-lived, can survive up to
   one hundred years.

4. OK; *s* = goliath beetle

5. DM; *s* = zoos
   Some zoos have black and
   white Bengal tigers that lack
   the tiger's usual reddish
   orange coloring. The Bengals
   are all descendants of a single
   white male tiger named
   Bohan, who was found in a

jungle in India around the
middle of this century.

Exercise 4.3

These sample rewrites are
not the only possible corrections. You may have come up
with other strong revisions.

1. (a) In addition, if the teachers
   of the future are to come from
   the best class of students,
   they will need higher
   salaries, greater professional
   status, and more
   opportunities for
   advancement.

   (b) In addition, if the teachers
   of the future are to come from
   among the best students,
   educators will need to earn
   more money, enjoy greater
   professional status, and have
   more opportunities for
   advancement.

2. (a) Seasoned travelers
   suggest that you take a
   daytime flight, eat as little as
   possible on the plane, and
   nap as much as you can while
   in the air.

   (b) The suggestions of
   seasoned travelers include
   taking a daytime flight,
   eating as little airline food as
   possible, and napping as
   much as you can while you're
   in the air.

3. (a) The child who is ready for
   kindergarten should be able

to name at least three or four colors, draw or copy a square, repeat a series of four numbers without practice, tell the right hand from the left, and identify what things such as cars, chairs, and shoes are made of.

(b) If children can name three or four colors, draw or copy a square, repeat four numbers in a row without practice, tell their right hand from their left, and identify what such items as cars, chairs, and shoes are made of, then they are probably ready to start kindergarten.

Exercise 4.4

Here are possible rewrites; yours may differ.

1. The baby calf of a blue whale gains approximately 200 pounds per day.

2. Goldfish in captivity have reached the age of 80 and over.

3. (a) Storks observe the practice of monogamy.

   (b) Storks are monogamous.

4. When an iguana is threatened, it uses its tail effectively as a whip.

5. Cats eat one-third of all the canned fish in the United States.

Exercise 4.5

Here are some possible rewrites; yours may differ.

1. Human beings can develop their physical senses to a much higher degree than most people realize.

2. Anyone can find enough examples from everyday life to determine that this is true.

3. For example, an experienced vintner can taste the amount of alcohol or acid in a particular wine to within one percent.

4. Expert color technicians can see differences between certain shades of red that are indistinguishable to the layperson.

5. Some professional bakers can measure the moisture content of bread dough to within two percent of accuracy just by its feel when they are kneading it.

Exercise 4.6

1. Zsa Zsa Gabor once said, "I'm a wonderful housekeeper. Every time I get a divorce, I keep the house."

2. In 1787, the United States minted a copper coin with a simple motto: "Mind Your business."

3. *The Outer Limits*, a science fiction TV series, always

opened with the same line: "There is nothing wrong with your set."

4. "Assassination is the extreme form of censorship," claimed George Bernard Shaw, the famous playwright.

5. indirect quote; no change

Chapter 5 Answer Key

Throughout this chapter, the sample combinations offered are not the only possible revisions. You may have come up with other good revisions.

Exercise 5.1

A. 1. Two football teams from King's Island, Alaska, were practicing before the 1938 New Year's Day Ice Bowl game.

2. They had been practicing on a huge flat ice floe near their village.

3. When they went out to practice on December 18, 1937, they couldn't find their practice field; gale-force winds had blown it away.

B. Traditionally, French boxers had kissed each other at the end of each bout, but that practice was officially banned by the French Boxing Federation in 1924.

C. 1. How slow can you go and still win?

2. The slowest time for a winning racehorse was set during a steeplechase in 1945.

3. The horse, which was named Never Mind II, refused a jump, so his jockey gave up and returned the horse to the paddock.

4. When the jockey arrived at the paddock, he learned that all the other horses had either fallen or been disqualified.

5. So he jumped on Never Mind II and rode him back onto the track.

6. Never Mind II won the two-mile race, normally finished in 4 minutes, in 11 minutes and 28 seconds.

D. 1. Here's another odd bit of trivia from the world of horseracing.

2. A jockey named Hayes dropped dead immediately after winning the first race of his career on June 4, 1923.

E. 1. The "New York Nine" and the Knickerbockers played the first official baseball game in the United States on June 19, 1846.

2. During the game, a New York player started a long

187

and rich baseball tradition by swearing at the umpire.

3. The New York player, who was named Davis, was fined six cents for his outburst.

F. 1. Hockey is known for its violence, and most of it seems to be intentional.

2. But one hockey game, which was played on the junior amateur level in Quebec in 1930, was marked by a very unusual incident of unintentional violence.

3. A puck that was lined at the goalie, Able Goldberry, struck a pack of matches in his pocket, and his uniform caught on fire.

4. The fire was put out by players and spectators, but Able Goldberry was badly burned in the bizarre incident.

G. 1. During a basketball game between sophomores and seniors on March 16, 1937, at St. Peter's High School in Fairmount, Virginia, all of the players on one team, with the exception of Pat McGee, fouled out.

2. When all the others fouled out, the game was tied at 32 - 32 with four minutes left to play.

3. It didn't look good for McGee's team.

4. But McGee faced the five players on the opposing team, scored a goal, made a foul shot, defended his team's basket, and prevented his opponents from scoring.

5. The final score was 35 - 32: McGee had won the game for his team single-handedly.

H. 1. In 1958, Robert Legge, a 53-year-old Navy doctor, swam the 28.5-mile-long Panama Canal in 21 hours and 54 minutes.

2. During the swim, he encountered only two living creatures: a boa constrictor and an iguana.

3. At times, swells caused by heavy ship traffic made his progress difficult.

4. When he arrived at Balboa, he was greeted by several hundred well-wishers and a toll collector, who charged Legge 72 cents, the minimum fee for a one-ton vessel in ballast.

I. 1. In 1890, a best-of-seven postseason baseball series was played between New York of the National League and St. Louis of the American Association.

2. New York had won three games and St. Louis had won two when the St. Louis Browns won game

six to tie up the series at three games apiece.

3. After they evened up the series, the Browns stayed out all night celebrating, and the next day they claimed to be "too tuckered out" to take the field; as a consequence, the final game was canceled, and the best-of-seven series stands as "tied 3 - 3" in the record books today.

J. 1. In 1865, Louis Fox was playing pool against John Deery in Rochester, New York, for a $1,000 purse.

2. Louis Fox, a billiard champion, was enjoying a very comfortable lead when a fly suddenly landed on the cue ball.

3. The problem was how to get the fly to move without moving the cue ball.

4. Those who were present tried everything, but the fly would not budge, no matter what anyone did.

5. Fox was more than bugged by the presence of the fly; in fact, he became completely rattled.

6. Angry at miscuing and losing the match to Deery, he rushed out of the pool hall.

7. Several days later, his body was found floating in the river near the pool hall,

and many people assumed that Fox committed suicide after his strange loss.

Exercise 5.2

A. 1. Several years ago, the editors of *Psychology Today* asked their readers if they remembered their dreams.

2. Of the more than 1,000 readers who responded, approximately 95 percent reported that they do remember some of their dreams, and about 68 percent claimed to have a recurring dream.

3. Two themes were represented most frequently in the recurring dreams: the experience of being chased and the sensation of falling.

4. The readers reported other recurring themes, including flying, appearing naked or almost naked in a public place, being unprepared to take a test, and returning to one's childhood home.

5. About 45 percent of the readers said that they sometimes dream about celebrities, usually sex symbols and rock stars.

6. After sex symbols and rock stars, people most often reported dreaming about politicians and historical

figures, such as Abraham Lincoln.

7. Lincoln himself put a lot of stock in dreams; in fact, he believed that one dream had forewarned him that he would be assassinated.

8. Of those who responded to the *Psychology Today* survey, 28 percent had seen themselves die in a dream; that sounds very ominous, but most experts say a dream of one's own death should not be at all frightening.

B. 1. Psychologist Ann Faraday, author of *The Dream Game,* says that a dream about one's death often indicates something far different from what you might expect.

2. She says it usually symbolizes the death of an obsolete self-image and signals an opportunity to move to a higher state of self-definition.

3. The interpretation of dreams in general is a highly controversial area.

4. Those who follow Sigmund Freud believe that dreams are the key to the unconscious.

5. Those who follow the thinking of Nobel laureate Francis Crick believe that

dreams are a garbage disposal for the mind.

6. According to Crick, the function of dreams is to clear out useless information that interferes with rational thought and memory.

7. A third school of thought consists of psychologists who believe that dreams are important not in themselves, but only because people think they are important.

8. These psychologists believe that people give dreams their meaning, influence, and power.

Exercise 5.3

A. 1. *The People's Almanac #3,* by David Wallechinsky and Irving Wallace, includes a cautionary tale for anyone who has ever daydreamed about what it would be like to be a giant.

2. It's not a tall tale; it's the true story of Robert Wadlow, probably the tallest person who ever lived.

3. Wadlow, who was born in Alton, Illinois, on February 22, 1918, was a normal eight-and-a-half-pound baby boy.

4. The medical history of his family, in which there were no unusually tall members, was normal.

5. But he grew rapidly and steadily from his birth until his death.

6. At six months, he weighed 30 pounds, which is about double the weight of a normal baby at that age.

7. When he was weighed again at 18 months, a time when the average toddler weighs 24 or 25 pounds, Wadlow weighed 62 pounds.

8. He was five feet, four inches tall and 105 pounds when he underwent his first thorough examination at the age of 5.

9. Wearing clothes made for 17-year-olds, he started school when he was five and a half.

10. When he was measured again at the age of 8, he had reached a height of six feet, and his father, Robert Wadlow, Sr., started wearing hand-me-downs from his son.

B. 1. After Wadlow was diagnosed at age 12 with excessive pituitary gland secretion, careful records of his growth were kept at Washington University in St. Louis, Missouri.

2. He grew an average of three inches a year throughout his life; at his death on July 15, 1940, his height was eight feet, eleven inches.

3. His early death was not surprising.

4. Pituitary giants usually die before middle age because their organs outgrow the ability to function correctly.

5. Because physical coordination becomes difficult for a giant, he or she usually has many more accidents than a normal-sized person has.

6. A giant's accidents also tend to result in more serious injuries, which is compounded by the fact that a giant's body heals more slowly.

7. Wadlow in particular had more than his share of physical problems, beginning with surgery for a double hernia when he was 2 years old.

8. Everything he encountered in this world was on the wrong scale: school desks were too small, doorways were too low, beds were too short, and chairs were too tiny.

9. He had terrible problems with his feet.

10. Doctors advised Wadlow to walk as much as possible to strengthen his feet, but the walking damaged his arches even more severely.

11. For a while, he attended Shurtieff College with the hope of becoming a lawyer, but he had to drop out because it was too difficult for him to walk from classroom to classroom.

C. 1. Though Robert Wadlow's life was marked by tragedy, it wasn't completely tragic.

2. He was intelligent and charming, and he had good parents who tried to make his life as normal and as full as possible.

3. His boyhood days were filled with typical things: hobbies, sports, Boy Scouts, and books.

4. But his life was also filled with things that were not so typical.

5. The more unusual aspects of Wadlow's story started when he was discovered by the media at age 9.

6. It happened when the Associated Press came across a photograph and circulated it in newspapers all across the nation.

7. That's when Robert Wadlow became a public person.

8. From that time on, he had to deal with a steady stream of people: reporters, medical researchers, curiosity seekers, and entrepreneurs.

9. Theatrical agents who wanted his services made very attractive offers to pressure him to perform.

10. His parents rejected all opportunities to make money from his misfortune.

11. He did, however, make paid appearances for the Peters Shoe Company in St. Louis.

12. This endorsement arrangement was appropriate because Wadlow had to have specially made shoes; unfortunately, he often outgrew new shoes even before they were delivered.

13. Robert Wadlow also worked for a short time in 1937 for the Ringling Brothers Circus in New York and Boston, but there were strict conditions in his contract.

14. The conditions stated that he would make only three-minute appearances in the center ring in ordinary street clothes; he would not appear in the sideshow.

15. Wadlow occasionally made appearances for churches to raise funds for charities; he accepted no pay for these activities.

D 1. In 1936, Robert Wadlow had a visit from a small-town Missouri doctor who was studying giantism.

2. He happened to catch Wadlow on one of his relatively rare bad days.

3. The doctor later wrote an article about Wadlow for the *Journal of the American Medical Association* in which he described Wadlow as dull and surly.

4. According to The *People's Almanac #3*, this characterization is generally true of most pathological giants, but it was not true of Robert Wadlow, who was truly an exceptional human being.

5. The unflattering description in the medical journal hurt and disillusioned Wadlow for two reasons.

6. First, all his life he had put up with medical researchers who had invaded his privacy and taken up his time, and he had done so voluntarily and graciously.

7. Second, the article was based on the quick impressions the doctor had made after a visit of less than an hour.

8. Wadlow and his family wanted his character vindicated, so they took legal action against the doctor and the American Medical Association (AMA).

9. The AMA strongly defended the doctor, so the litigation dragged on and on and was not resolved when Wadlow died at the age of 22.

10. Partly as a result of this episode, Wadlow stipulated that after his death he wanted his body to be kept out of the hands of medical researchers.

11. In accordance with his wishes, there was no examination of his body after his death.

12. He was buried in a custom-built 10-foot-long casket, which was placed in an almost impregnable tomb in his hometown.

13. More than 46,000 people came to the funeral home in Alton, Illinois, to pay their last respects to Robert Wadlow.

Exercise 5.4

A. 1. Judith Rodin, who teaches psychology at Yale University, has been involved in important studies on a number of topics, including bystander intervention, learned helplessness, obesity, and aging.

2. She is interested in relationships in general, but she is especially interested in the relationship between the mind and the body and the relationship between biology and environment.

3. Older people, in particular, have benefitted from Rodin's research.

4. In fact, it's been said that it's not easy for her to find places in Connecticut where she can continue to study the problems of older people in nursing homes because the state's nursing homes have improved so much as a result of her work.

5. At one point in her career, Rodin, along with psychologist Ellen Langer, conducted a fascinating study on perceived choice among residents of nursing homes, and this study was described in *Psychology Today*.

6. Perceived choice is the amount of control that a person believes he or she has over events.

7. On the basis of laboratory studies, Rodin already knew that the degree to which people feel they can exert control in important areas of their lives influences three things: their happiness, their ability to perform, and their sense of well-being.

B. 1. Judith Rodin and Ellen Langer wanted to investigate perceived choice or control in a real-life setting, so they chose a nursing home.

2. They were especially interested in the relationship between the degree of control that the nursing home residents thought they had and the residents' health and happiness.

3. Rodin and Langer believed that improvements in well-being would be quite obvious among the sick and frail residents of a nursing home once they were given increased control.

4. It would be difficult to show the positive benefits of an increased sense of control in people who were younger and healthier

because, in that group, any benefits would more likely be in the form of prevention rather than improvement.

5. The results of the study were indeed dramatic.

6. Nursing home residents in the study were given new choices, many of which seemed quite trivial, in areas in which they previously had no choice.

7. For example, residents were allowed to choose when they could see a movie and how to arrange their rooms.

C. 1. The choices may have been trivial, but the results were not.

2. Using a variety of methods of measurement, the researchers discovered that the residents' new sense of control had a number of effects: the residents' health and overall mental state improved, and dropped the death rate at the nursing home.

3. Why would having new choices in trivial areas of life produce such profound effects?

4. Rodin explains that the choices seem trivial only to people who have a broad range of choices in their lives; to those who have

little or no choice, any choice at all has a great impact.

5. A sense of control or perceived choice created a profound psychological state in which the residents felt better about themselves.

6. They felt a sense of power, which caused them to respond more positively to family members, other residents, and nurses and doctors. In turn, everyone in their lives responded more positively toward them.

7. Choosing when to see a movie or where to put a picture on a wall might seem trivial, but Rodin says that small bit of control can have an energizing effect on every aspect of an older person's life.

Exercise 5.5

A. 1. Mabel Keaton Staupers, a fast-talking, energetic black woman, was one of the outstanding women of the twentieth century.

2. Almost single-handedly, she broke a link in a chain, a chain that had kept many black women from using their talents and skills and had denied them

their full rights as American citizens.

3. A classic David and Goliath tale, her fascinating and inspiring story is told in *Black Leaders of the Twentieth Century*.

4. It is the story of a battle between one woman, the executive secretary of the National Association of Colored Graduate Nurses (NACGN), and two branches of the military, the U.S. Army and the Navy.

5. Mabel K. Staupers's accomplishment must be viewed within the context of a certain period in American history if it is to be fully appreciated.

6. It was around the time that the United States entered into World War II, and for many reasons, including the anti-Nazi mood of the nation, American blacks recently had become much less accepting of the racial status quo.

7. For many blacks, their unequal treatment in their own country was highlighted in an ironic way by America's opposition to Nazi Germany.

8. In opposing the philosophy and actions of Germany's Nazis, the U.S. government, many members of the press, and the public in general did a lot of talking about the ideals upon which America had been founded.

9. They contrasted Germany to an America that was pure in the realization of its democratic ideals and just in its treatment of people of different religious, ethnic, and racial backgrounds.

10. Such statements about this country struck some Americans, both blacks and whites, as hypocritical and ironic.

11. Summing up the situation, Walter White wrote, "World War II has immeasurably magnified the Negro's awareness of the disparity between the American profession and practice of democracy."

B. 1. It was during this time that Mabel K. Staupers used patience, persistence, and a great deal of political savvy to begin her long fight for the rights of black nurses.

2. Staupers, who was born in Barbados, West Indies, in 1890, came to New York with her parents in 1903.

3. After graduating from Freedmen's Hospital School

of Nursing in Washington, D.C., in 1917, she began her career as a private nurse in New York City.

4. She played an important role in establishing the Booker T. Washington Sanatorium in Harlem, which was the first facility in the area where black doctors could treat patients.

5. Then she worked for 12 years as the executive secretary for the Harlem Committee of the New York Tuberculosis and Health Association.

6. Finally in 1934, Staupers was appointed executive secretary of the NACGN, and in this position, she had one goal: to help black nurses become fully integrated into the mainstream of American health care.

7. Then the United States entered World War II in 1941.

8. Because the war created a great demand for nurses to care for the wounded, Mabel K. Staupers had a perfect opportunity to realize her goal.

9. That demand could result in the acceptance of black nurses into the Army and Navy Nurse Corps, which would be the vehicle for the full inclusion of blacks into the profession of nursing in America.

C. 1. Staupers knew that black nurses had suffered great discrimination in World War I, and she vowed that would not happen again.

2. So Staupers fought her own battle on various fronts throughout the years of the American war effort.

3. First, she fought the exclusion of black women from the Army and Navy Nurse Corps.

4. Later, when the Army established a quota system for black nurses, she fought the quota system because it implied that black nurses were inferior to other nurses.

5. At one point, she also fought the military's policy of having black nurses care for black soldiers and no others.

6. The Army finally assigned black nurses to care for white soldiers, but only white soldiers who were German prisoners of war, not American, so she fought that practice, too.

D. 1. These were tough battles, but Staupers eventually found a powerful ally in First Lady Eleanor Roosevelt.

2. Eleanor Roosevelt began lobbying for black nurses.

3. She talked to Norman T. Kirk, surgeon general of the U.S. Army, W.J.C. Agnew, a rear admiral in the U.S. Navy, and Franklin D. Roosevelt, her husband.

4. Meanwhile, Staupers staged a public confrontation with Norman T. Kirk that received a good deal of press coverage.

5. In a speech at the Hotel Pierre in New York, Kirk described the dire shortage of nurses in the Army and predicted that a draft for nurses might be necessary.

6. Staupers was in Kirk's audience of about 300 people, which included nurses, politicians, and private citizens.

7. She rose to her feet and asked the surgeon general, "If nurses are needed so desperately, why isn't the Army using colored nurses?"

8. She explained to the audience that, while there were 9,000 black registered nurses in the United States, the Army had taken 247 and the Navy had taken none.

9. According to newspaper reports, Kirk was visibly uncomfortable and didn't have much of an answer for Staupers.

E. 1. At about the same time, President Roosevelt announced in a radio address on January 6, 1945, that he wanted to amend the Selective Service Act of 1940 so that nurses could be drafted.

2. The public reaction was tremendous; the irony of calling for a general draft while at the same time discriminating against black nurses was obvious to almost everyone.

3. Staupers showed a lot of political savvy in the way she handled the public's dissatisfaction with the plans of the top brass.

4. She gave speeches, issued press releases, and urged people to send telegrams to President Roosevelt.

5. The groups that sent messages of protest to the White House included the National Association for the Advancement of Colored People (NAACP), the Congress of Industrial Organizations, the American Federation of Labor, the United Council of Church Women, the

Catholic Interracial Council, the Alpha Kappa Alpha Sorority, and the New York Citizens' Committee of the Upper West Side.

6. The great wave of public protest caused the Army, the Navy, and the War Department to drop the policies of exclusion, segregation, and quota systems for black nurses.

7. A few weeks later, Phyllis Dailey was the first black woman to break the color barrier in the U.S. Navy Nurse Corps.

8. The Army also began to accept black nurses with no restrictions.

9. Most of the credit goes to one woman alone: Mabel K. Staupers.

Chapter 6 Answer Key

Exercise 6.1

1. a carpenter builds
   carpenters build

2. one star shines
   all the stars shine

3. the golfer putts
   golfers putt

4. roses grow
   a rose grows

5. the chimneys smoke
   the chimney smokes

6. a pitcher pitches
   pitchers pitch

7. one loaf rises
   the loaves rise

8. bombs explode
   a bomb explodes

9. the popsicle melts
   popsicles melt

10. last-minute shoppers rush
    a last-minute shopper rushes

Exercise 6.2

1. the article explains
   the articles explain

2. one baby cries
   all the babies cry

3. one player wins
   four players win

4. the team performs
   the teams perform

5. the ink spots dry
   the ink spot dries

6. the soldiers march
   a soldier marches

7. the telephone rings
   telephones ring

8. ideas form
   an idea forms

9. chickens hatch
   a chicken hatches

10. a peacemaker pacifies
    peacemakers pacify

Exercise 6.3

1. movie has
   movies have

2. attitude is
   attitudes are
3. carriers were
   carrier was
4. pretzels are
   pretzel is
5. fingernail was
   fingernails were

Exercise 6.4

Note: The subject of each clause is itaticized here.

1. *pounds* are; *intake* was; *Forecasters* say; *increases* are; *Meat and fruit* appear
2. *term* is
3. *fan* cares; *names* were
4. *habits* begin
5. *Final Payments and The Company of Women* are; *Men and Angels* is

Exercise 6.5

Note: The subject of each clause is italicized here.

1. *One* ends; *This* happens; *owner* plunks ... forces; *one* shares
2. *nuts* stay; *they* remain; *pecans and Brazil nuts* keep; *you* store
3. *Moonbeams* are ... take
4. *life span* depends; *moisture* is; *moisture and oil* affect; *cards* are; *condition* is; *deck* lasts;

pack has; *cards* show; *they* slow; *they* are
5. *series* is; *length* is; *earthquakes* have; *one* was

Exercise 6.6

1. murdered; *past*
2. was introduced; vp
3. damaged; adj
4. distinguished; adj
5. captured; *past*
6. admired; adj
7. was established; vp
8. are experienced; vp
9. is supposed; vp
10. showed; *past*

Exercise 6.7

1. no change
2. change *would always be* to *has always been* or *was always*
3. no change
4. change *could have been* to *had been* or *were*
5. change *contained* to *contain*
6. change *had* to *have;* change *offered* to *offer*
7. omit *would* or change *would* to *can;* change *would need* to *need* or *will need*
8. no change
9. change *would also be* to *are also*
10. no change

11. change *had* to *has;* change
    would have to *has;* change
    were to *are*
12. no change
13. no change

Exercise 6.8

1. one librarian's duties
   two librarians' duties
2. the child's excitement
   the children's excitement
3. the dancer's shoes
   both dancers' shoes
4. one boy's pet chameleon
   three boys' pet chameleons
5. the family's history
   the two families' histories
6. the woman's schedule
   the women's schedules
7. the poet's images
   many poets' images
8. one rabbit's carrots
   all the rabbits' carrots
9. one drummer's performance
   the drummers' performance
10. the businessman's trips
    the businessmen's trips

Exercise 6.9

1. the mayor's priorities
2. the pilots' training
3. Jerry Seinfeld's comic talents
4. the coaches' game plan
5. the vendor's ice-cream
   sandwiches

6. the babies' toys
7. the friends' agreement
8. Whitney Houston's voice
9. Rob Morrow's role in
   Northern Exposure
10. the clowns' role in the circus

Exercise 6.10

1. the National Restaurant
   Association's question
2. The research organization's
   national survey; Americans'
   top five restaurant food
   choices
3. the nation's cafes and
   restaurants
4. restaurant diners' top menu
   choices
5. A typical New Yorker's order
6. people's favorites
7. anyone's guess; North
   Dakotans' restaurant
   preferences
8. residents' first loves
9. a restaurant's menu
10. restaurant customers' tastes

Exercise 6.11

1. A parent's greatest fear
2. no apostrophe needed
3. women's concerns; the
   couple's list
4. Hechinger's how-to book
5. many children's training

Exercise 6.12

1. it was; *ante.* = Medal of Honor
2. it; *ante.* = the Hurley Machine Company
3. They were; *ante.* = Nikon cameras
4. It has, its; *ante.* = Salvation Army
5. he was; *ante.* = Neanderthal man
6. his; *ante.* = neither Gary Player nor his son
7. their; *ante.* = Ostrich eggs it; *ante.* = one
8. it; *ante.* = the orchestra
9. them; *ante.* = Paper straws
10. (a) its, its; *ante.* = empire
    (b) they, their; *ante.* = people

Exercise 6.13

1. it was; *ante.* = stamp
2. they will; *ante.* rulers it expires; *ante.* = a lease
3. its; *ante.* = U.S. Football League
4. its; *ante.* = Fairy Investigation Society
5. their; *ante.* = tarantulas

Exercise 6.14

1. him
2. she
3. them
4. I
5. we
6. her
7. they
8. me
9. he
10. me

Exercise 6.15

1. than; too
2. principal; than; there
3. to; through
4. principle; course; effect; number; to; its
5. who's; than; you're; your; to
6. finely; two; than
7. finally; threw; passed; than; conscience
8. accept; Their
9. number; than
10. It's; there
11. you're; too; have; Its; number
12. course; there; affect; to
13. too; here; two
14. number; bear; too
15. there; affect; an; to; course; conscience; too

Exercise 6.16

1. New York Museum of Modern Art; French artist Henri Matisse's *Le Bateau*
2. Chaucer; "Love is blind,"; William Shakespeare

3. Lincoln Memorial; Washington, D.C.

4. Hemingway; American; *The Sun Also Rises; A Farewell to Arms; For Whom the Bell Tolls; The Old Man and the Sea;* Fridays

5. *Sudden Impact*; Clint Eastwood; "Make my day."

6. Volkswagen Beetle

7. Russian

8. President Jimmy Carter

9. West; Cheyenne, Wyoming; "Hell on Wheels."

10. John Lindsay; New York City; *Rosebud*

Sources

The examples and exercises in *Better Sentence-Writing In 30 Minutes a Day* were drawn from the following sources. Books are arranged alphabetically by title; magazine and newspaper articles are arranged alphabetically by article title.

Books

The American Heritage Dictionary of the English Language, ed. William Morris, American Heritage Publishing Co., Inc., and Houghton Mifflin Company, New York, 1975.

The Best by Peter Passell and Leonard Ross, Farrar, Straus and Giroux, New York, 1974.

Black Leaders of the Twentieth Century, University of Illinois Press, Urbana, Illinois, 1982.

The Book of Firsts by Patrick Robertson, Bramhall House, Crown Publishers, Inc., New York, 1982.

The Book of Lists #3 by Amy Wallace, David Wallechinsky, and Irving Wallace, William Morrow and Company, Inc., New York, 1983.

Can Elephants Swim? by Robert M. Jones, Time-Life Books, New York, 1969.

Cross Your Fingers, Spit in Your Hat by Alvin Schwartz and Glen Rounds, J.B. Lippincott Company, Philadelphia and New York, 1974.

The Dance Encyclopedia by Anatole Chujoy and P.W. Manchester, Simon and Schuster, New York, 1967.

Deep Song: The Dance Story of Martha Graham by Ernestine Stodelle, Schirmer Books, New York, 1984.

Better Sentence-Writing

Dick Clark's The First 25 Years of Rock & Roll by Michael Uslan and Bruce Solomon, Delacorte Press, New York, 1981.

Encyclopaedia Britannica, Volumes 7 and 22, Encyclopaedia Britannica, Inc., William Benton, Publisher, Chicago, 1963.

The Encyclopedia of Sports by Frank G. Menke, A. S. Barnes and Company, New York, 1960.

From Slavery to Freedom: A History of Negro Americans, 4th ed., by John Hope Franklin, Alfred A. Knopf, New York, 1974.

The Great American Sports Book by George Gipe, A Dolphin Book, Doubleday & Company, Inc., Garden City, New York, 1978.

The Healing Heart by Norman Cousins, W. W. Norton & Company, New York, 1983.

The Heart of Hollywood by Bob Thomas, Price/Stern/Sloan Publishers, Inc., Los Angeles, California, 1971.

How to Raise a Street-Smart Child by Grace Hechinger, Facts On File Publications, New York, 1984.

Incredible Animals, A to Z, National Wildlife Federation, 1985.

Joan Embery's Collection of Amazing Animal Facts by Joan Embery with Ed Lucaire, Delacorte Press, New York, 1983.

Knock on Wood: An Encyclopedia of Talismans, Charms, Superstitions & Symbols, Carole Potter, Beaufort Books, Inc., New York, 1983.

Life-spans, Or, How Long Things Last by Frank Kendig and Richard Hutton, Holt, Rinehart and Winston, New York, 1979.

Linden Hills by Gloria Naylor, Ticknor & Fields, New York, 1985.

The Misunderstood Child by Larry B. Silver, McGraw-Hill Book Company, New York, 1984.

More FYI, For Your Information, ed. Nat Brandt, M. Evans and Company, Inc., New York, 1983.

The People's Almanac #2 by David Wallechinsky and Irving Wallace, Bantam Books, New York, 1978.

The People's Almanac #3 by David Wallechinsky and Irving Wallace, Bantam Books, New York, 1981

Pictorial History of American Sports by John Durant and Otto Bettmann, A. S. Barnes and Company, New York, 1952.

The Presidents, Tidbits & Trivia by Sid Frank and Arden Davis Melick, Greenwich House, a division of Arlington House, Inc., distributed by Crown Publishers, Inc., New York, 1984.

The Quintessential Quiz Book by Norman G. Hickman, St. Martin's Press, New York, 1979.

Race Matters by Cornel West, Beacon Press, Boston, 1993.

The Rolling Stone Encyclopedia of Rock & Roll, eds. Jon Pareles and Patricia Romanowski, Rolling Stone Press/Summit Books, New York, 1983.

The Rule Book by Stephen M. Kirschner, Barry J. Pavelec, and Jeffrey Feinman, A Dolphin Book, Doubleday & Company, Inc., Garden City, New York, 1979.

Speaker's Treasury of Anecdotes About the Famous by James C. Humes, Harper & Row, Publishers, Inc., New York, 1978.

Sources

Stay Tuned, A Concise History of American Broadcasting by Christopher H. Sterling and John M. Kittros, Wadsworth Publishing Co., Belmont, California, 1978.

This Day in Sports by John G. Fetros, Newton K. Gregg, Publisher, Novato, California, 1974.

Van Gogh by Gerald E. Finley, Tudor Publishing Company, New York, 1966.

The Westerners by Dee Brown, Holt, Rinehart and Winston, New York, 1974.

Your Five-Year-Old, Sunny, and Serene by Louise Bates Ames and Frances L. Ilg, A Delta Book, Dell Publishing Co., Inc., 1979.

Magazine and Newspaper Articles

"A Cutthroat Business," by Philip Jacobson, *Connoisseur,* December 1994.

"A Sense of Control," by Elizabeth Hall, *Psychology Today*, December 1984.

"A very special crystal: Mystique of diamonds still endures," by Dennis R. Getto, *The Milwaukee Journal*, April 24, 1985.

"After 73 Years, a Titanic Find," *Time*, September 16, 1985.

"An aching America," UPI, *The Milwaukee Journal*, October 22, 1985.

"An Ancient 'Nuclear Winter,'" by Sharon Begley, *Newsweek,* October 14, 1985.

"Bakelite Envy, Depression-Era Plastic Costume Jewelry Has Become a Hot Item," by Andrea DiNoto, *Connoisseur,* July 1985.

"Coffee trivia," *The Milwaukee Journal*, April 24, 1985.

"Death of an American Icon," by Jack Kroll, *Newsweek,* August 23, 1982.

"Facing up to feelings: Your expressions may trigger physical reactions," Los Angeles Times service, *The Milwaukee Journal*, June 18, 1985.

"Ferrets fancied by city dwellers," by Caroline Nichols, *Milwaukee Sentinel,* October 7, 1985.

"Fish—For Health," *Vogue,* July 1985.

"Following in the footsteps of Rachel Carson," by Robert W. Smith, *USA Today*, April 5, 1985.

"For every region, a special food," by Dan Sperling, *USA Today,* October 8, 1985.

"Getting there without motion sickness," by Cynthia Dennis, *The Milwaukee Journal*, April 29, 1985.

"Houses from Sears," by Nelson Groffman, *Country Living,* June 1984.

"Little Swamis," by Claire Warga, *Psychology Today*, January 1985.

"Looking for Mr. Good Bear," *Newsweek,* December 24, 1984.

"Mabel K. Staupers and the Integration of Black Nurses into the Armed Forces," by Darlene Clark Hine, in *Black Leaders of the Twentieth Century,* eds. John Hope Franklin and August Meier, University of Illinois Press, Urbana, Illinois, 1982.

Better Sentence-Writing

"Manhattan Serenade," by David Ansen, *Newsweek,* February 3, 1986.

"Name Calling," by Harris Dienstfrey, *Psychology Today,* January 1983.

"New Bodies For Sale," *Newsweek,* May 27, 1985.

"Nuclear Winter and Carbon Dioxide," by John Maddox, *Nature,* December 13, 1984.

"Nutty pets often the owner's fault." UPI. *The Milwaukee Sentinel,* April 26, 1985.

"Overachievers—When Toil Gets Them in Trouble," *Vogue,* May 1985.

"Pets can pose problems." UPI, *The Milwaukee Journal,* June 9, 1985.

"Pulitzer winner tapped as U.S. poet laureate," AP, *The Ann Arbor News,* May 19, 1993.

"Rah, rah, rah: As spirit grows, so do souvenir sales," UPI, *The Milwaukee Journal*, April 11, 1985.

"Remember Them?" Jacquelyn Mitchard, *The Milwaukee Journal*, March 17, 1985.

"Ruth Gordon: her life and work had 'this zing,'" by Michael Gordon, Washington Post Service, *The Milwaukee Journal*, August 31, 1985.

"The Secret Payoff of Hypochondria," *Vogue,* August 1983.

"So THAT'S what it was!" by Michael Bauman, *The Milwaukee Journal*, October 2, 1985.

"Strong, special bond sustains sisters through life," by Barbara Bisantz Raymond, *USA Today,* August 8, 1983.

"They're still making 501 jeans the old-fashioned way," *The Milwaukee Journal*, April 17, 1985.

"Thieves like popular cars, too," *The Milwaukee Journal*, May 4, 1985.

"Titanic: The questions remain," Duane Valentry, copyright 1985 Duane Valentry, News America Syndicate, *The Milwaukee Journal*, April 15, 1985.

"To Sleep, Perchance to Dream," by Elizabeth Stark, *Psychology Today,* October 1984.

"The US trivia team has a quiz for you," by Gary C. Rummler, *The Milwaukee Journal*, June 12, 1985.

"Washington married into money," AP, *The Milwaukee Journal*, April 29, 1985.

"What Makes a Top Executive?" by Morgan W. McCall, Jr., and Michael M. Lombardo, *Psychology Today*, February 1983.

"What's black and orange and scary?" by Tony Staffieri, *The Milwaukee Journal,* October 17, 1985.

"Will the Real Impostor Please Stand Up?" by Jeff Meer, *Psychology Today,* April 1985.

Index